Cook Smart
for a
Healthy
Heart

Cook Smart
for a
Healthy
Heart

PUBLISHED BY THE READER'S DIGEST ASSOCIATION LIMITED
LONDON • NEW YORK • SYDNEY • MONTREAL

COOK SMART FOR A HEALTHY HEART includes material from the Illustrated Series, Eat Well, Live Well, published by The Reader's Digest Association Limited, and Cooking Smart for a Healthy Heart, published by The Reader's Digest, Inc., USA. It is adapted from Cook Smart for a Healthy Heart, designed and published by Reader's Digest (Australia) Pty Limited.

This edition was published by
The Reader's Digest Association Limited
11 Westferry Circus, Canary Wharf, London E14 4HE
www.readersdigest.co.uk
© 2006 Reader's Digest Association

We are committed both to the quality of our products and the service we provide to our customers. We value your comments so please feel free to contact us on 08705 113366 or via our web site at **www.readersdigest.co.uk**.

If you have any comments or suggestions about the content of our books you can contact us at **gbeditorial@readersdigest.co.uk**

Origination Colour Systems Ltd
Printed in China

Front cover Turkey and spinach roulades, p. 159
Back cover Blueberry cheesecake, p. 302
Title Stir-fried beef with fine noodles, p. 95
Foreword Rice with prawns and dill dressing, p. 102
Contents (left) Leek and prosciutto pizza muffins, p. 48; (right) Spanish orange and almond cake, p. 301

Book code 400-278-01
ISBN (10) 0 276 44083 8
ISBN (13) 978 0 276 44083 0
Oracle code 250007888H.00.24

Contributors

Chief Nutritionist Catherine Saxelby

Writers Catherine Atkinson, Shirley Bond, Anna Brandenburger, Sara Buenfeld, Carole Clements, Linda Collister, Gail Duff, Christine France, Anne Gains, Carole Handslip, Beverly LeBlanc, Sara Lewis, Sally Mansfield, Janette Marshall, Maggie Mayhew, Kate Moseley, Jenni Muir, Angela Nilsen, Maggie Pannell, Anne Sheasby, Marlena Spieler, Susanna Tee, Judith Wills

Recipe Testers Pat Alburey, Catherine Atkinson, Juliet Barker, Valerie Barrett, Anna Brandenburger, Bridget Colvin, Christine France, Emma-Lee Gow, Bridget Jones, Clare Lewis, Jane Middleton, Heather Owen, Maggie Pannell, Anne Sheasby, Gina Steer, Susanna Tee

Photographers Sue Atkinson, Martin Brigdale, Gerry Colley, Gus Filgate, Amanda Heywood, Graham Kirk, William Lingwood, Sean Myers, Simon Smith

Stylists LJ Crompton, Michelle Lucia, Penny Markham, Helen Payne, Sue Russell, Helen Trent, Jody Vassallo

Home Economists Caroline Barty, Jules Beresford, Maxine Clark, Joanna Farrow, Nicola Fowler, Lisa Heathcote, Joss Herd, Justine Kiggen, Lucy McKelvie, Lucy Miller, Louise Pickford, Bridget Sargeson, Joy Skipper, Linda Tubby, Sunil Vijayakar

For Reader's Digest, UK

Project Editor Lisa Thomas
Designer Louise Turpin
Book Editor Norma MacMillan
Nutritionist Fiona Hunter
Indexer Marie Lorimer

READER'S DIGEST GENERAL BOOKS

Editorial Director Julian Browne
Art Director Nick Clark
Managing Editor Alastair Holmes
Picture Resource Manager Martin Smith
Pre-press Account Manager
Penny Grose
Product Production Manager
Claudette Bramble
Senior Production Controller
Deborah Trott

foreword

More people in the UK die from Cardiovascular Disease than any other condition, including cancer. This alarming fact can by attributed largely to our unhealthy eating habits and lifestyles. Diets high in saturated fat, lack of exercise and smoking all contribute towards heart disease. Every minute two people in the UK suffer a heart attack. The majority of these could be prevented.

As a nation we have been seduced by advertising and convenience. We take less time to prepare and cook nutritious meals and eat pre-packaged foods with a high saturated fat and salt content and then when things go wrong, we rely on doctors to put them right.

Great progress has been made in the fight against heart disease with Heart Research UK at the forefront of research into pioneering methods in the treatment, prevention and cure of the condition. Many lives have been saved because of technological advances in surgery and breakthroughs in the treatment of heart disease; however, we know that more can be done to prevent the disease in the first place. Following a healthy lifestyle can significantly reduce your risk of developing heart disease and the easiest place to start is with diet.

Eating the wrong types of food results in higher levels of blood cholesterol, which is one of the major risk factors of heart disease. The solution is not to go on a 'low cholesterol diet' since recent research suggests that the cholesterol content in food has little to do with the amount of cholesterol in the blood. It is the high saturated fat content of the western diet that causes high cholesterol levels and the only way to reduce this is to follow a healthy, balanced diet low in saturated fat. Salt is another big problem. In this country many people eat almost twice the recommended 6g of salt per day, contributing to the many thousands of deaths caused each year from hypertension, or high blood pressure. Cutting right down on salt has a dramatic and swift effect on the problem.

Eating healthily does not mean compromising on taste or spending hours in the kitchen. **Cook Smart for a Healthy Heart** contains delicious and appealing heart friendly recipes that are beautifully illustrated and carefully explained. They cover a wide range of ingredients and incorporate flavours from around the world. Preparation and cooking times are given for each dish and the nutritional content is clearly displayed in an easy to read panel. Eating a balanced diet has never been easier.

The importance of eating a healthy balanced diet, low in saturated fat and salt cannot be stressed enough in the battle against heart disease. Furthermore, the inclusion of a wide range of foods from different food groups, including at least five portions of fruit and vegetables every day will provide everything you need to keep your heart healthy. This book demonstrates how it can be done. Once you have sampled some of the superb recipes and realise how easy it is to keep a check on your intake of nutrients you will find that eating for a healthy heart becomes an absolute pleasure.

Barbara Harpham
National Director,
Heart Research UK
www.heartresearch.org.uk

contents

foreword   5

you & your heart   9

breakfast & brunch   27

soups, starters & snacks   53

pasta, rice & grains   79

fish & seafood   109

poultry   141

meat dishes 179

vegetable dishes & salads 221

breads & pizzas 253

desserts, cakes & biscuits 273

index 312

you &
your heart

heart health

Coronary heart disease (CHD) is one of the major causes of death in the UK. Here are the statistics:

- Every year, nearly 114,000 people in the UK die from CHD: approximately one in five deaths in men and one in six deaths in women. That's three and a half times as many deaths as those caused by lung cancer.
- While the death rates from CHD have been falling rapidly since the 1970s, the rates in the UK are still amongst the highest in western Europe. There are a huge number of people living with heart disease – currently just under 2.7 million people in the UK have CHD.
- The cost of heart disease is high – it imposes a huge annual burden on the UK economy. The costs of health care alone are in excess of £1.7 billion every year.

How heart disease develops

Heart disease develops slowly over many years. Fatty deposits gradually build up on the inner walls of arteries, which thicken and stiffen, losing their elasticity and ability to 'flex'. Eventually, the artery narrows or stops the flow of blood. This process is called 'atherosclerosis'.

Blood clots can lodge in the narrowed artery and cut the blood supply – and therefore the oxygen supply – to the heart muscles. When this happens, a heart attack can occur. Which artery is affected, and how severe the blockage is, will determine how serious this is, or even whether it's fatal. If the blockage is in the brain, it can trigger a stroke.

Preventing heart disease

However, the good news is that in many cases heart disease is preventable – the key causes, such as smoking, high blood pressure, high cholesterol, obesity and lack of exercise, are all factors that you can reduce or eliminate from your life with a healthy lifestyle, involving regular exercise and a heart-healthy eating plan.

The importance of diet

Heart-healthy eating doesn't mean an end to delicious food. You'll discover that you can still cook your favourites, but enjoy them in a heart-healthy form. The recipes in this book are low in saturated fat and salt, and include plenty of fibre and whole grains. And these days you have a lot more choice at the supermarket with the ever-growing range of heart-healthy products.

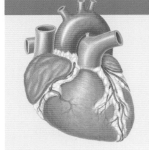

YOUR CARDIOVASCULAR SYSTEM

Blood provides your body's cells with the vital nutrition they need to survive and function. Your heart is the powerful 'pump' that drives the blood through your blood vessels – a vast plumbing network that stretches into every nook and cranny of your body. Together, the pump and plumbing make up your cardiovascular system.

By following the nutrition guidelines outlined in this book, you'll find that:

- Losing weight is easier.
- You will slow the progression of heart disease, so you are less likely to suffer a second heart attack (or need a second by-pass).
- Your blood pressure will be easier to keep in control (if it's too high).
- You will build strong bones.
- Your meals will be healthy and balanced, ensuring you get all the important vitamins, minerals, fibre and antioxidants.
- And, if you suffer from diabetes, you will find this condition is better managed.

risk factors

Don't leave your heart health to chance. Brush up on your knowledge of risk factors, then take measures to avoid them. Work with your GP and make sure you have regular screening tests, such as blood pressure and cholesterol checks.

Are you at risk of heart disease?

Here are the 11 top risk factors, listed in order of importance. If you have one of them, your risk of having a heart attack or angina is increased. If you have two or more, your risk rises sharply.

1 Cigarette smoking Smoking contributes to the narrowing of blood vessels and loss of lung function. It also lowers your overall fitness. The link between smoking and heart disease is too well proven to ignore. If you smoke, take steps today to quit. Speak to your GP for help via nicotine patches, nicotine lozenges or medication to stop cravings. Enlist support from family and friends. Try to quit with a friend.

2 High blood pressure High blood pressure puts extra strain on the heart and blood vessels. Talk to your doctor about managing this via changes to your lifestyle, such as healthy eating, less salt, less alcohol and weight loss.

3 High blood cholesterol High levels of total cholesterol and the 'bad' LDL cholesterol put you at risk of heart disease. Have a blood test and discuss the results with your doctor.

4 Diabetes Having diabetes increases your risk of heart disease by two to four times. Many of the problems of heart disease overlap with those of diabetes, such as obesity, high blood pressure, high triglycerides and circulation problems, so their treatment is similar. If you have diabetes, follow the guidelines in this book and they will help manage both conditions. A consultation with a dietitian is a must to plan a suitable diet.

5 Older age group (over 50) Advancing years make it more likely you'll run into heart problems.

6 Being overweight Carrying too much weight, especially around your abdomen, increases your chance of heart troubles as your heart has to pump harder. And you're more likely to have high blood pressure, high cholesterol and diabetes. Therefore, aim for the healthy weight range by eating right and keeping fit. Following the healthy eating principles in this book will help.

7 Being inactive Our sedentary lifestyle and technology, such as computers and remote controls, cause us to move about less. But physical activity is essential for a healthy heart. It can raise the 'good' HDL cholesterol, lower blood pressure and burn off calories. Therefore, try to incorporate some regular exercise into your schedule. Find ways to be active – try taking the stairs rather than the lift and walking rather than driving.

8 Family history If a close relative of yours has died from heart disease or had heart problems before the age of 60, you're at higher risk of heart problems too.

9 Gender The risk of heart disease is greater for men than for women up until menopause, when women 'catch up' to men.

10 High blood triglycerides Another type of blood fat, triglycerides are often elevated if you have diabetes or are overweight, or consume too much alcohol. Like cholesterol, if triglycerides are too high, they point to a higher chance of heart disease in the future.

11 High homocysteine levels A high level of homocysteine in the blood is now considered another risk factor. Like cholesterol, when it's high, it means you are more likely to succumb to heart troubles. Eating plenty of B vitamins – especially folate and vitamins B_6 and B_{12} – can reduce the homocysteine and keep you safe.

DID YOU KNOW?

The total length of all the thousands of blood vessels (arteries, veins and capillaries) in your body is around 96,000 km – which is long enough to encircle the Earth more than twice.

know your fats

It's critical to look at the types and amounts of the fats you eat if you have high cholesterol, or need to eat for a healthy heart. There are four different types of fatty acids – saturated, trans, monounsaturated and polyunsaturated.

Saturated fats

Saturated fats raise both the total cholesterol and the LDL cholesterol. Eating less saturated fat is one of the most important things you can do for your heart, but knowing where these fats are found requires a little homework. Saturated fats predominate in animal fats such as butter, cream, cheese, fat on meat, and deli meats (salami, bacon, sausages and so on) as well as in commercial shortenings used to make cakes, biscuits, pastries, confectionery and fried take-away food. Coconut and palm oil, although vegetable in origin, are also high in saturated fatty acids. Dietary guidelines recommend that we reduce saturated fats to less than 10 per cent of the total calories consumed.

Trans fats

Trans fats behave in a similar way to saturated fats and also raise LDL cholesterol and lower HDL cholesterol. A natural component of animal fat, trans fatty acids are found in very small amounts in all meat and dairy products.

A type of trans fats may also be created synthetically during hydrogenation (see the 'Hydrogenated Fats' box, right). Some evidence suggests that this type of trans fats may have worse effects on the body than saturated fats, increasing the risk of coronary heart disease.

Some margarines have high levels of trans fats; however, many manufacturers of margarines and spreads in the UK have reduced trans fats in their products to extremely low levels.

Monounsaturated fats

Monounsaturated fats lower the total and the 'bad' LDL cholesterol when they displace saturated fats in the diet – although not as effectively as polyunsaturates. Monounsaturates are found in all fats but are particularly high in olive, canola/rapeseed and groundnut oils, most nuts and avocados. The abundance of the mono-unsaturated olive oil in the Mediterranean diet is thought to be one of the factors responsible for the low rate of heart disease in Italy and Greece.

Polyunsaturated fats

Polyunsaturated fats lower both total cholesterol and the LDL cholesterol in the blood and reduce the risk of heart disease. They are found in all fats and exist as two distinct types:

Omega-3 fats such as alpha-linolenic acid and its derivatives eicosapentaenoic acid (EPA) and docosahexaenoic acid (DHA) are primarily found in the fats of fish, particularly deep sea oily fish. These are important for your heart.

Omega-6 fats such as linoleic acid are the main polyunsaturated fatty acids of common vegetable oils (sunflower, safflower, corn, cottonseed and grapeseed), some nuts (walnuts, brazil nuts and pine nuts) and polyunsaturated margarines. Aim to eat a little of these, but concentrate more on the omega-3 fats.

CALORIES AND FAT

All types of fat contain the same amount of calories – 9 kilocalories (37 kilojoules) per gram, which is twice as many calories as from the same weight of protein or carbohydrate. So if you have a weight problem, aim to cut down on ALL fats but especially the saturates.

HYDROGENATED FATS – WHAT ARE THEY?

Hydrogenation is a process used to solidify vegetable oils for commercial use. It turns liquid oils into a semi-solid fat, which is more suited to frying and baking. Hydrogenated fats are most commonly found in margarines and spreads, and used to make commercially produced biscuits, cakes, pastries, snack foods, meat pies, crackers and take-away fried foods. If a food label lists hydrogenated vegetable oil or hydrogenated fat, there may also be trans fats in the product.

DO YOU EAT TOO MUCH FAT?

Take our quick test to see whether you are cutting back enough on saturated fat for your heart. Simply answer Yes or No to each question and add up your score at the end.

Do you trim all visible fat from your meat?	Yes	No
Do you use margarine instead of butter?	Yes	No
Are cream and soured cream items you buy only rarely?	Yes	No
Do you limit fast food (pizza, burgers, chips, fried chicken) to no more than once a week?	Yes	No
Have you swapped your milk for a lower fat variety?	Yes	No
Do you buy yoghurt and cheese in a reduced-fat or low-fat form?	Yes	No
Do you have a non-stick pan for cooking or frying?	Yes	No
Do you roast your meat on a rack to allow the fats to drip away?	Yes	No
Are you careful with coconut milk or cream in curries?	Yes	No
Do you avoid cooking with lard and suet?	Yes	No
Do you limit pastries and cakes?	Yes	No
Do you say 'no' to potato crisps, tortilla chips and other salty snack foods?	Yes	No

How did you score?

Add up all your Yes answers.

If you scored 8 or more: You're doing well and reducing the main sources of saturated fat from foods. Keep going.

If you scored 4 to 7: You've made a good start but you need to be a little more vigilant if you want to protect your heart.

If you scored 0 to 3: You're not doing enough. Start today to rethink your food choices and use the suggestions in this book to cut back on saturated fats.

MAKE THE FAT SWITCH

Replace your saturated fat with the healthier unsaturated types. Here's how:

- Dip your bread in olive oil instead of using butter.
- Cook with oils instead of butter.
- Add nuts or seeds to stir-fries and salads.
- Spread avocado on sandwiches instead of cheese.
- Make salad dressing with olive oil.
- Bake your own cakes and biscuits, using margarine high in unsaturated fats rather than butter.
- Snack on nuts instead of crisps.

All about cholesterol

Cholesterol finds its way into the body from your diet, but it is also made by the liver, where it is used by the body to maintain cell structure. While cholesterol is important for body function, it can be unhealthy due to its role in the development of heart disease. Cholesterol is one of the major materials that build up on the walls of blood vessels. This build-up, known as atherosclerosis, causes blood vessels to narrow, making it harder for blood to pass through. Atherosclerosis can result in heart attack or stroke because the blood supply eventually becomes blocked completely.

There are two types of cholesterol important to heart health: HDL and LDL. LDL (low-density lipoprotein) is known as 'bad' cholesterol since it increases the deposit of cholesterol in the blood vessel wall. HDL (high-density lipoprotein) picks up the cholesterol from around your body and takes it to the liver for disposal. Raised levels of HDL cholesterol counteract some of the detrimental effects of high LDL. The object of a healthy diet is to lower your LDL levels and raise your HDL levels.

the glycaemic index (GI) and how it can help your heart

What is the glycaemic index?

The glycaemic index (or GI) is a ranking of foods, from 0 to 100, that measures whether a carbohydrate food raises blood sugar (glucose) levels dramatically, moderately or a little. Carbohydrate foods that are digested and absorbed slowly, such as pasta or chickpeas, release glucose into the blood gradually. These are low-GI carbohydrate foods. They have a GI value of 55 or less. Carbohydrate foods that are digested and absorbed quickly, such as mashed potato and white bread, cause a fast release of glucose – these carbohydrate foods are high GI, with a value of 70 or over.

How low GI helps your heart

Most people know about GI due to its benefits in diabetes and blood sugar control. What many do not realise is that the GI of their diet can also influence the health of their heart, just like the type of fat. Recent research shows that a diet based on slowly digested carbohydates can lower total and LDL cholesterol, raise HDL cholesterol and help to lower body weight.

What to aim for

Not every carbohydrate you eat needs to be a 'slow carb'. Just aim for one low-GI food at each meal and you will significantly lower the GI of your total diet and improve heart health. For example, at dinner add some beans or lentils to your lamb curry or cook pasta in place of potato.

Making the change

Read the following information to see how easy it is to make your diet lower in GI, or refer to the table opposite to see the figures. Look for the 'low GI' symbol in the recipes of this book – these recipes have had particular ingredients included to ensure a low GI result.

Seven key foods to change

Certain high-GI foods may feature prominently in your diet but can easily be substituted with a low-GI option. Do you base your meals around potato? Are you a big bread eater? Do you love rice? You don't have to look up a table of figures each time. Just follow the food swaps outlined here for the key carbohydrate foods you eat and that will influence the final GI of your diet.

Bread White bread and fine wholemeal loaves are typically high in GI, meaning they are rapidly absorbed. Swap these for grainy varieties with visible grains or 'heavier' breads. Fruit loaf (raisin bread) is also a good choice.

Cereal Switch to less processed wholegrain cereals, such as rolled oats or muesli or high-fibre bran types. Or sprinkle some oat bran over your usual breakfast cereal.

Rice Long-grain rices, particularly basmati, are the best options. Other low-GI choices are pearl barley, wheat noodles or bulghur wheat.

Potatoes Most potatoes are rapidly absorbed (high GI). Improve your GI rating by making mash with semi-skimmed milk, or by choosing new potatoes with skins on or sweet potato instead.

Pulses All pulses (lentils, chickpeas, dried peas and beans) have a small effect on blood sugar and insulin. Use them in soups, casseroles and salads to lower the GI of your favourite dish. In addition, they are rich in fibre and an excellent protein source if you are a vegetarian.

Fruit With the exception of some of the tropical fruits, fruit is low in GI. Eat at least two pieces each day. Fruit juices are nutritious but have a higher GI than fresh fruit, as well as lacking fibre – it is better to eat whole fruit and quench your thirst with water.

Pasta All pasta and noodles are low in GI. Enjoy them as an alternative to rice and potatoes.

GLUCOSE LOAD

Not only is the nature of the carbohydrate important (whether it is slow or fast), but so is the actual amount of carbohydrate you eat. Even if a food is low GI, if you consume large quantities, your blood sugars will rise.

FOODS AND THEIR GI FACTORS

The following table lists a variety of common food items, both fresh and commercially prepared, together with their GI factor. Remember, foods with a low GI are the ones to include more of, and foods with a higher GI are the ones to reduce. Use this table as a guide to help you switch to a low GI diet.

FOOD	GI

LOW – 55 AND LESS

Peanuts*	14
Rice bran	19
Cherries	22
Grapefruit	25
Lentils, red, boiled	26
Chickpeas, boiled	28
All Bran™ breakfast cereal	30
Apricots, dried	30
Milk, full-fat	31
Fettuccine, egg	32
Milk, skimmed	32
Yoghurt, low-fat flavoured	33
Custard (home-made with powder)	35
Apple, raw	38
Pear, raw	38
Spaghetti	38
Tomato soup	38
Apple juice, unsweetened	40
Pumpernickel bread	41

Chocolate, milk	42
Corn chips*	42
Orange	42
Peach	42
Porridge	42
Apple muffin	44
Sweet potato	44
Grapes	46
Noodles, 2-minute	46
Sweetcorn kernels, canned	46
Fruit loaf	47
Baked beans	48
Peas, boiled	48
Bürgen® mixed grain bread	49
Carrots, boiled	49
Banana	52
Kidney beans, canned	52
Honey	55

MODERATE – 56 TO 69

Muesli, untoasted	56
Papaya	58
Rice, basmati, boiled	58
Ice-cream, regular fat	61
Muesli bar	61
Biscuits, shredded wheatmeal	62
Mars Bar*	62
Beetroot, canned	64
Shortbread biscuits*	64
Couscous	65

Cordial, diluted	66
Pineapple	66
Croissant*	67
Fanta®	68
Sugar (sucrose)	68
Sustain cereal™	68
Vita Brits™	68
Crumpet	69
Weetabix™	69

HIGH – 70 AND OVER

Bread, white	70
Popcorn	72
Bagel, white	72
Watermelon	72
Sultana Bran™	73
Pumpkin	75
Bread, wholemeal	77
Coco Pops™	77
Water biscuits	78
Jelly beans	78
Pretzels	83
Rice, calrose	83
Potato, baked	85
Rice Krispies™	87
Parsnip	97

* These are foods high in fat. Use them only occasionally and count them as part of your fat allowance.

If you want to know more about the GI rating of foods, visit the website of the University of Sydney at www.glycemicindex.com.

Reprinted with permission from The New Glucose Revolution by J Brand-Miller, K Foster-Powell and S Colagiuri (Hodder Headline Australia, 2002)

eat less salt

Except for some of the breads, our recipes do not call for any added salt and, where we can, we've substituted reduced-salt products. It is important to cut down on the amount of salt you eat, as too much salt can contribute to high blood pressure (hypertension), which in turn increases your risk of heart disease, stroke and kidney failure. A diet high in salt may also raise your chances of suffering osteoporosis, fluid retention and kidney stones.

Five easy steps to cut back on salt

1 Do not cook with salt. You can reduce salt gradually so that you get used to the natural taste of the food. And instead of salt, you can boost flavour by adding onions, garlic, curry paste, chilli, lemon juice, aromatic herbs such as basil and coriander and full-flavoured spices such as cinnamon and cumin.

2 Buy reduced-salt, reduced-sodium and no-added-salt products whenever you can. Those commonly available include canned vegetables and beans, soy sauce, stock, gravy powder, crispbreads, canned fish and breakfast cereals. Note though that if a product is labelled 'reduced salt', which means it should have at least 25 per cent less salt than the standard version, this does not necessarily mean it is actually low in salt. It is important to check food labels for sodium content and then to work out the amount of salt (see right).

3 Use fresh or frozen vegetables, or choose those vegetables and beans that are canned without salt. If you cannot find these, drain the can's contents and rinse well.

4 Try to avoid heavily salted ingredients, such as anchovies and stock cubes (see the panel right), as well as salty snacks, ready meals and other convenience foods.

5 At the table, stop sprinkling salt over the food on your plate. If necessary, use a salt substitute, although it is much better to train your taste buds to enjoy foods with less salt.

Sodium or salt?

Chemically, salt is sodium chloride. It is actually the sodium part that causes high blood pressure and other problems of fluid balance. For adults, the recommended maximum sodium intake per day is 2.4g, which is equivalent to 6g of salt or slightly more than a teaspoon.

If all our sodium came just from the salt you add, then you could limit it to a teaspoon a day. But because most of it is 'hidden' in bought foods, it's impossible to tell how much you're eating. Most foods contains some salt. If you eat a lot of foods that are high in salt it is easy to exceed the daily recommended limit, which is why it makes sense to avoid adding salt in cooking or at the table and to buy reduced-salt/reduced-sodium foods if possible.

On food labels you will not always find mention of salt. Instead the sodium content is usually listed. As 1 gram of sodium equals 2.5 grams of salt, you need to multiply the sodium by roughly 2.5 to work out the amount of salt a product contains. For example, if a portion or 100g of the food contains 1.2g sodium, that means the salt content is 3g.

SEA SALT AND ROCK SALT

Sea salt is made by evaporating sea water. Rock salt has a more intense salty flavour than sea salt because the salt occurs in large coarse chunks rather than as a fine powder. However, neither sea salt nor rock salt is a healthier substitute for table salt, as they are both high in sodium and will not lower your salt intake.

FOODS HIGH IN SALT

Anchovies

Crisps

Pretzels and other salty snack foods

Salted nuts

Pickled vegetables

Yeast spreads (Marmite, Bovril)

Salami

Bacon

Corned beef

Cheese

Canned soups

Stock cubes

Soya is a heart-health superfood. In fact, scientists think that the significantly lower rate of heart disease among the Japanese may be related to the soya protein in their diet.

and can keep your heart in good shape – which is a similar action to that of soya. Crush seeds and sprinkle over cereal, toss them in salads and add them to bread dough. Also look for the soya-linseed breads. One or two tablespoons a day is all it takes to boost your intake.

Nuts

Munching on a handful of nuts (around 25g) a day is now one of the strategies nutritionists recommend for your heart. Are you surprised? Most of us will be, as for years we've been told that nuts are too high in fat and will make us put on weight, and are certainly not part of a heart-smart diet.

However, a wave of studies over the past few years has changed the thinking on nuts. One of these – a 14-year study of 85,000 British nurses – showed that regularly eating any kind of nut can significantly reduce the likelihood of CHD. Nuts are now considered a healthy, energy-packed snack that will out-perform potato crisps any way you look at it!

Despite having more than 50 per cent total fat content, the fat in nuts is heart-friendly. It is either predominantly monounsaturated or polyunsaturated, both of which will keep your cholesterol in check. Nuts also boast a good dose of vitamin E (a well-established antioxidant), lots of fibre and arginine (an amino acid) – all key factors that lower the harmful LDL cholesterol or prevent oxygen damaging it.

Walnuts appear to be the top nut in terms of health, because they contain a high level of linolenic acid, which helps to keep the heart's rhythm normal.

The best way to eat nuts is lightly roasted but not salted. Toss them into salads and stir-fries or use them in baking or as a crunchy topping.

Soya beans

Soya protein lowers the harmful LDL cholesterol and prevents artery 'clogging', according to more than 38 soya trials spanning 20 years. In fact, the evidence is so strong that in the United States, soya foods are now permitted to carry a health claim on their label saying soya, as part of a low-fat diet, can reduce the risk of heart disease.

Researchers think that the protein in soya binds cholesterol in the intestine and therefore prevents its absorption. But don't forget that its isoflavones work as antioxidants and 'artery flexors' and, like oat bran, it contains a high level of fibre and is low in saturated fat.

To achieve heart benefits, you need to eat around 25g of soya protein a day, which you can get in 700ml soya milk or 250g tofu. Tofu is a handy ingredient – you can use soft tofu as a cream substitute or to make mayonnaise-like dressings, or toss firm diced tofu into stir-fries and noodle soups. Some foods, such as cereal bars and breakfast cereals, are now fortified with soya protein.

Tea

People who regularly drink tea (green or black) are reported to have significantly lower risks of heart troubles than those who don't. Tea's powerful protective effects are believed to be due to flavonoids, substances shown to be strong antioxidants, even more so than beta carotene and vitamin E. It seems that tea flavonoids

an effect similar to aspirin. Red wine, made with the skins and seeds of grapes, has nine to ten times more of these natural chemicals than white wine. One phenolic, resveratrol, has been intensively studied, but others, such as epicatechin and quercetin, are emerging as important.

But all things in moderation – a glass of red wine a day is fine, but any more can put you at risk of other illnesses, such as breast cancer or liver disease.

Olive oil

Believed to be one of the reasons for the low rate of heart disease and general good health of those from the Mediterranean, olive oil is a rich source of monounsaturated fat and contains vitamin E. Extra virgin olive oil will also be rich in antioxidants.

Cholesterol-lowering spreads and other foods

Look out for spreads (margarines), mayonnaise, drinks and yoghurts that are functional foods designed specifically for lowering cholesterol (brand names Benecol and Flora Pro-activ). If you already use margarine, it's worth swapping to a cholesterol-lowering spread. To see a drop in your total cholesterol and LDL cholesterol levels, the spreads usually need to be used three times a day and the drinks taken once a day. Check the labels for specific advice.

Plant sterols (also known as phytosterols) are natural compounds found in vegetables, seeds, nuts and pulses but in low concentrations. They have a similar chemical structure to cholesterol yet have the ability to block its absorption from the digestive tract into the body. They are extracted from soya beans or wood pulp and then added as a concentrate to a spread – at a much higher concentration than we normally get from food.

help maintain heart health by decreasing inflammation, lowering the tendency for clotting (an early factor in heart attacks) and by keeping the arteries more 'elastic'. These effects are obtained regardless of whether you add milk or sugar. Best of all, if you take it black with no milk or sugar, tea has no calories and has the ability to both relax and revive you.

Alcohol

All alcohol has a cardio-protective effect, but red wine seems to be particularly efficacious. Red wine has proved to be the answer to the so-called 'French paradox' – why the French have one of the lowest rates of heart disease in the world, despite their love of rich, cholesterol-laden fare such as pâté, croissants and high-fat cheeses.

Wine's secret is more than 50 phenolic compounds known as polyphenols. These act as antioxidants, reduce thickening of the arteries and keep the blood 'thin' and smooth-flowing –

eating lighter and healthier

Eating for a healthy heart needn't be hard work. Make simple food changes to tip the scales in favour of a diet that's low in saturated fat and your heart will reap the benefits. Put into practice these healthy tips for eating less saturated fat.

Out shopping

- Choose lean cuts of meat, such as skinless chicken and trimmed pork.
- Opt for skimmed or semi-skimmed milk, reduced-fat cheeses and low-fat yoghurt.
- Stock up on low-fat snacks such as yoghurt, muesli or cereal bars and dried fruit instead of crisps, chocolate and biscuits.
- Choose cholesterol-lowering spreads or margarines high in unsaturated fats.
- Read labels and check for the amount of fat per serving, especially on products claiming to be 'light', 'low-fat' and 'cholesterol-free'.

- Look for ingredients to make your cooking interesting without too much fat and salt, such as fresh herbs, mustards, chutneys, balsamic vinegar, salad dressings, spices (nutmeg, ginger, chilli and cumin) and heart-friendly garlic.

Label watch

No cholesterol or cholesterol-free Even though the food may have no cholesterol, it can still be high in saturated fat and should be avoided – this applies to foods such as potato crisps and other salty snack foods, pies, pastries, biscuits, sauces and doughnuts. Remember no cholesterol does not mean NO FAT.

Lite or light Can apply to a food's texture, flavour, salt or alcohol content, and doesn't necessarily mean light in fat. Always check the nutrition information panel. Generally if a food has less than 10g of fat per 100g, it's suitable.

Reduced fat Seen on labelling for cheeses, ice-creams, mayonnaise and desserts. Contains less fat than a comparable product, but may not necessarily be low in fat (three per cent or less). Such foods have at least 25 per cent less fat than the normal counterpart, so they still taste good and help you save on fat. But you can't eat them as if they were 'free' foods.

Vegetable oil Don't be fooled into thinking this means an unsaturated vegetable oil such as canola/rapeseed, olive, soya, corn or sunflower oil. The words 'vegetable oil' may mean palm oil, a tropical oil with 50 per cent saturated fat, which is widely used by the food industry to fry fast foods and snack foods. Like all oils, it has no cholesterol but is high in saturated fat and therefore not recommended.

Baked not fried This often appears on snack foods and implies that the food is low in fat. For some snacks, such as pretzels, this is true but for

CHECK OUT THE FAT CONTENT

Learn to read the figures on the nutrition information panel when food shopping, so you know exactly how much fat is present and how much of the total fat is saturated. Compare brands to see which has the lowest fat percentage (grams of fat per 100g). Low-fat foods must have less than 3g fat per serving, but if not labelled as 'low fat', then buy those products with less than 10g of fat per 100g.

The nutrition information here is for a muesli bar. Each bar contains 4g of fat. Of this, only 1g is saturated fat, which is low. However, if you compared it to other bars at the supermarket, you would use the 'per 100g' column – it has 9g of fat per 100g, which may be higher than other muesli bars.

	Per portion	Per 100g
Energy	650 kJ	1625 kJ
	155 kcal	385 kcal
Protein	2g	5g
Fat	4g	9g
of which saturates	1g	3g
Fibre	2g	5g
Sodium	5mg	12mg

others, such as biscuit snacks, it means they are *lower* in fat (around 25 per cent) but not necessarily *low* in fat. Check the nutrition information panel for the grams of fat per 100g.

In the kitchen

- Always trim off any visible fat from meat *before* cooking; do not eat poultry skin.
- Grill, steam, poach, microwave, stir-fry, boil or bake in preference to frying or deep-frying.
- Avoid adding or cooking in unnecessary fat – for example, spray a thin film of oil into the pan when cooking, don't pour it in.
- Dry-roast meats on a roasting rack to allow the fat to drain away.
- Skim fat from meat juices before making gravy.
- Use unsaturated cooking oils such as canola/rapeseed, olive, groundnut or soya.
- Replace some of the meat and chicken in curries and casseroles with a handful of chickpeas, lentils or other pulses.
- Let home-made soups and casseroles cool before serving so that any fat can solidify on top. Remove this fat layer before reheating.
- Substitute low-fat plain or Greek-style yoghurt for soured cream in dips or to finish soups.
- In place of a melted cheese topping on baked pasta dishes, use a little shaved Parmesan, or mix together wholemeal breadcrumbs with reduced-fat Cheddar.
- Use light evaporated milk or soft tofu as a replacement for cream and coconut cream.

Eating out

- Order fish and seafood as often as you can – restaurants cook them well, and it saves you having to cook them at home if you find fish difficult to handle.

- Avoid high-fat starters such as pâté or anything deep-fried – opt for soup, salad, prawns, scallops or smoked salmon.
- When you order at a restaurant, don't be afraid to ask for vegetables served without butter, or meat and fish with sauce on the side.
- Avoid creamy sauces, pastry and fried foods.
- Vegetarian options are not always lower in saturated fat – avoid vegetable dishes with lots of cheese.
- You don't have to miss out on dessert if you choose wisely. Fruit-based puddings, sorbets and meringues are delicious, heart-healthy choices. Or, if you want a richer offering, share the dessert with a friend.
- Eat small. Order two starters or share a starter and then enjoy your main course. Ask for a 'doggie bag' if you can't finish everything at one sitting.
- Eat slowly and enjoy the conversation with others. This will help you to not overeat.
- Watch your alcohol intake. Enjoy a drink or two but sip slowly and intersperse with mineral water or a diet soft drink.

Stir-frying is a healthy cooking method as the ingredients cook quickly while being stirred rapidly in a hot wok or non-stick pan, thereby needing only a spray of oil.

FAT ON THE LABEL

Here is a quick guide to what is a lot of fat and what is a little fat per 100g of food:

- 20g or more fat is a lot of fat
- 5g or more saturates is a lot of fat
- 3g or less fat is a little fat
- 1g or less saturates is a little fat

how to use the recipes

Next to each recipe is a panel with at-a-glance icons to help you select quick recipes, low-calorie recipes, high-fibre recipes and recipes with a low glycaemic index. Also provided are full nutritional statistics per serving. These analyses are based on the ingredients listed in each recipe. They do not include the serving suggestions.

STATISTICS PANEL

30 Kc Fb GI

preparation time **10 mins**
cooking time **15 mins**
serves **4**

PER SERVING

1429 kcal
11 g protein
6 g total fat
1 g saturated fat
2 mg cholesterol
60 g total carbohydrate
8 g sugars
7 g fibre
204 mg sodium

 Quick recipes

Recipes that have this icon at the top of the nutritional statistics panel can be both prepared and cooked in 30 minutes or less.

 Calories

Calories is the shortcut term used when referring to kilocalories (kcal), which are a measure of food energy. We've highlighted those recipes that are 'lighter' or lower in calories for those who are trying to lose weight.

Main courses 400 kcal per serving or less
Light meals/lunches 300 kcal per serving or less

Recipes such as these will fit within a standard weight-loss diet of 1200 kcal per day for most women and 1800 kcal per day for most men.

 Fibre

We've highlighted those recipes with 3g or more of fibre per serving. These are usually recipes that contain beans, lentils, wholemeal flour, brown rice, oats, high-fibre vegetables such as sweetcorn, peas or cabbage, and fruit. Aim to eat as much fibre as you can. At least 18g a day is suggested for good health,

more if you want to lose weight or stay regular. High-fibre foods are nutritious and filling. For fewer calories, you get to eat more volume.

GI **GI (glycaemic index)**

Recipes with a low glycaemic index (GI) are marked with this icon. It indicates that the overall GI of all the ingredients is low so the carbohydrates from them will be slowly digested and absorbed. Low-GI recipes are ideal for anyone with diabetes or wanting to lose weight. They will cause only a small rise in blood sugar levels and fill you up for longer so you're less inclined to snack between meals.

Fat

Both the total fat and the saturated fat are listed. The total fat is handy to check if you're counting fat grams or trying to lose weight. Some recipes are higher in fat than others because they contain avocado, olive oil or nuts. However, these are okay as they're high in the 'healthy' fats (monounsaturated and polyunsaturated) and yet low in unhealthy saturated fat. Just eat smaller portions of these if you're trying to lose weight.

How much fat you should eat will depend on how active you are. No more than 30 per cent of the calories you eat should come from fat, which means around 50 to 70g fat a day for a moderately active person.

Cholesterol

Cholesterol has been listed for those people who need to watch their levels. Recipes with eggs or prawns will have a higher cholesterol content but are lower in saturated fat.

Sodium

Except for some of the bread recipes, none of the recipes contains any added salt (sodium chloride), and salt-reduced products have been used wherever possible to minimise the final sodium content of the recipes. Remember to use only small quantities of salty ingredients such as cheese, stock cubes and bottled sauces.

breakfast
& brunch

citrus wake-up

What an invigorating drink this is, made with fresh citrus, lightly sweetened and flavoured with a little lime zest and mint.

4 juicy oranges, about 500g in total
1 pink grapefruit
1 lemon
1 lime
grated zest of 1 lime
1 tablespoon caster sugar
2 tablespoons finely shredded fresh mint leaves

1 Cut the oranges, grapefruit, lemon and lime across in half. Juice them using either an electric juicer or a simple citrus squeezer, preferably one that strains out the seeds but leaves in a generous quantity of pulp. If you have no squeezer at all, poke a fork into the flesh several times, then squeeze the juice from the fruit by hand, prodding with the fork now and again.

2 Combine the citrus juices in a jug with the lime zest, sugar, 4 tablespoons water and shreds of mint. Stir to mix, then pour into glasses over a few ice cubes and, if you like, some slices of lime and lemon.

preparation time **15-20 mins**
serves **4**

PER SERVING
60 kcal
1g protein
0g total fat
0g saturated fat
0mg cholesterol
14g total carbohydrate
14g sugars
2g fibre
7mg sodium

red pepper pick-me-up

Drinking fresh vegetable and fruit juices is one of the easiest ways to add vitamins and minerals to your diet.

1 large red pepper
200ml tomato juice
4 celery sticks, coarsely chopped
dash of Tabasco sauce

TO SERVE
ice cubes
paprika
celery leaves to garnish (optional)

1 Preheat the grill to the hottest setting. Grill the pepper for about 10 minutes, turning often, until the skin is charred on all sides. Place the pepper in a polythene bag and leave for 15 minutes or until it is cool enough to handle.

2 Peel off the skin, then cut the pepper in half and discard the seeds, the white ribs of pith and the stalk. Cut the flesh into chunks.

3 Put the pepper, tomato juice and celery in a blender or food processor and purée until smooth. For a very smooth result, press the drink through a sieve. Stir in the Tabasco.

4 Pour the drink into two large glasses and add a few ice cubes. Sprinkle the top of each with a pinch of paprika and garnish with celery leaves, if you wish. Serve immediately.

preparation time **20 mins**
plus 20 mins standing
serves **2**

PER SERVING
45 kcal
2g protein
0.5g total fat
0.1g saturated fat
0mg cholesterol
9g total carbohydrate
8g sugars
3g fibre
269mg sodium

exotic fruit salad

This simple but very special fruit salad is just bursting with the wonderful colours and fragrance of exotic fruits – papaya, mango, kiwi fruit and passion fruit. It's rich in vitamins too, making a refreshing and nutritious breakfast.

1 Peel and halve the papaya and scoop out the seeds. Slice the fruit crossways and arrange the slices in two rows on a serving platter, or cut into chunks and put into a large serving bowl.

2 Stone and peel the mango and cut lengthways into wedges. Arrange the wedges in a row between the papaya slices. Or cut into chunks and add to the serving bowl.

3 Peel the kiwi fruit and cut lengthways into wedges or chunks. Scatter them over the slices of mango and papaya.

4 Mix the orange juice with the lime juice. Halve the passion fruit and scoop out the seeds and pulp into the juice mixture. Spoon over the salad and serve immediately.

1 large papaya
1 large mango
2 kiwi fruit
6 tablespoons freshly squeezed orange juice
2 tablespoons freshly squeezed lime juice
2 passion fruit

preparation time **15 mins**
serves **4**

PER SERVING

120 kcal
2g protein
0.5g total fat
0g saturated fat
0mg cholesterol
27g total carbohydrate
19g sugars
5g fibre
11mg sodium

HEALTH HINT

Mango, papaya, kiwi and passion fruit are all excellent sources of vitamin C. An average slice of papaya provides more than double the recommended daily requirement of vitamin C, and the mango provides six times the daily requirement of vitamin C.

eggs Benedict

This dish traditionally uses ham or bacon and a rich butter sauce. Here, a yoghurt and chive hollandaise sauce contrasts with the richness of poached eggs and lean Parma ham, to make a lighter, but equally special version.

1 teaspoon vinegar

4 eggs

4 wholemeal English muffins, halved

4 slices of Parma ham, about 50g in total, trimmed of all visible fat

pepper to taste

YOGHURT AND CHIVE HOLLANDAISE SAUCE

2 egg yolks

1 teaspoon Dijon mustard

150g plain Greek-style yoghurt

1 tablespoon snipped fresh chives

pepper to taste

TO GARNISH

paprika

1 tablespoon snipped fresh chives

1 To make the hollandaise sauce, whisk together the egg yolks, mustard and yoghurt in a heatproof bowl. Set over a saucepan of barely simmering water and cook for about 12–15 minutes, stirring constantly, until thick – the sauce will become thinner at first, but will then start to thicken. Stir in the chives, and season with pepper. Remove from the heat and keep the sauce warm over the pan of hot water.

2 Half-fill a frying pan with water. Bring to the boil, then add the vinegar. Reduce the heat so the water is just simmering gently, then carefully break the eggs into the water, one at a time. Poach for 3–4 minutes, spooning the hot water over the yolks towards the end of cooking.

3 Meanwhile, preheat the grill to high. Lightly toast the muffin halves for about 1 minute on each side. Place one half on each of four warmed plates and top each with a slice of Parma ham, crumpled slightly to fit. Season with pepper.

4 Using a slotted spoon, remove the poached eggs from the pan, one at a time. Drain on kitchen paper and, if liked, trim off any ragged edges of egg white with scissors. Place an egg on each ham-topped muffin half.

5 Spoon the warm hollandaise sauce over the eggs, and sprinkle each serving with a pinch of paprika and the chives. Serve immediately with the remaining toasted muffin halves.

Variations Instead of chives, add 1 tablespoon chopped fresh tarragon to the hollandaise, and garnish with sprigs of tarragon. • You can also use thin slices of lean cooked ham instead of Parma ham.

30 **Fb**

preparation and cooking time **25 mins**

serves **4**

PER SERVING

341 kcal

21g protein

16g total fat
6g saturated fat

345mg cholesterol

30g total carbohydrate
3g sugars

3g fibre

490mg sodium

HEALTH HINT

Like other animal foods, eggs provide useful amounts of vitamin B_{12}. Free-range eggs tend to contain more than eggs from battery hens. All the fat in eggs is found in the yolk (around 6g per average-sized egg) and is predominantly unsaturated fat.

eggs Florentine

The term 'florentine' in a recipe title indicates that the dish uses spinach. This updated version of the classic eggs florentine uses a sauce thickened with cornflour rather than a butter and flour roux. Serve with wholemeal toast.

30 Kc Fb

preparation and cooking time **30 mins**
serves **4**

PER SERVING

309 kcal
20g protein
20g total fat
7g saturated fat
249mg cholesterol
13g total carbohydrate
7g sugars
5g fibre
511mg sodium

HEALTH HINTS

Spinach is a good source of nutrients with antioxidant properties, including vitamins C and E and carotenoid compounds.

Leeks belong to the onion family. They provide useful amounts of fibre, and the green part of the leek is a good source of beta carotene.

1 To make the cheese sauce, mix the cornflour to a paste with a little milk. Pour the remaining milk into a non-stick saucepan and bring to the boil. Stir the boiling milk into the cornflour mixture, then pour back into the pan. Bring to the boil, stirring. Once it has thickened, simmer for 2 minutes. Remove from the heat, stir in the Gruyère cheese, and season with nutmeg and pepper. Cover the surface of the sauce with greaseproof paper to prevent a skin from forming and set aside in a warm place.

2 Heat the margarine with the oil in a saucepan. Add the leeks and cook for about 3 minutes or until beginning to soften. Add the spinach and stir. Cover the pan and cook over moderate heat for 2–3 minutes or until the spinach has wilted and the leeks are tender. Drain the vegetables in a sieve, pressing down with the back of a spoon to remove any excess moisture. Return to the pan and season with pepper. Cover and keep warm.

3 While the vegetables are cooking, half-fill a large frying pan with water and bring to simmering point. Add the vinegar. Break in the eggs, one at a time, and cook them gently for 3–4 minutes, spooning the hot water over the yolks. Lift out the eggs with a slotted spoon and drain on kitchen paper.

4 Preheat the grill to high. Spread the leek and spinach mixture in an even layer in a large flameproof dish. Make four hollows in the vegetables using the back of a spoon and place a poached egg in each hollow. Spoon the cheese sauce over the eggs. Lightly dust with paprika, then place the dish under the grill. Cook for 3–4 minutes until lightly browned. Serve at once.

15g margarine
1 tablespoon extra virgin olive oil
200g small leeks, thinly sliced
800g baby spinach leaves
pepper to taste
1 teaspoon vinegar
4 eggs
paprika to garnish

CHEESE SAUCE
20g cornflour
300ml semi-skimmed milk
50g Gruyère cheese, finely grated
pinch of grated nutmeg
pepper to taste

egg white omelette with spinach, tomato and Cheddar

A delicious basic omelette minus the fat and cholesterol – that's the kind of recipe every health-conscious cook needs. To make it even more delicious, you can embellish the dish in creative, savoury ways with simple fillings.

3 egg whites
2 teaspoons chopped fresh dill
pepper to taste
30g fresh spinach leaves, finely shredded
1 large plum tomato, chopped
2 tablespoons grated reduced-fat Cheddar cheese

1 Whisk the egg whites with 1 teaspoon water, the dill and pepper in a medium bowl until soft peaks form.

2 Toss the spinach, tomato and Cheddar in a small bowl.

3 Lightly coat a small non-stick frying pan with cooking spray and set over moderate heat. When the pan is hot, pour in the egg mixture and cook until it begins to set on the base. Lift up the edge of the setting eggs with a spatula and push the cooked part towards the centre of the pan to let the uncooked egg run underneath. Cook until the omelette is almost set and the base is just lightly browned.

4 Reserve 1 tablespoon of the spinach filling for garnish, and spoon the rest over half the omelette, leaving a 1cm border. Lift up the omelette at the edge nearest the handle of the pan and fold in half, slightly off-centre, so the filling just peeks out. Cook for a further 2 minutes, then slide the omelette onto a plate. Garnish with the reserved filling and serve at once.

 30 Kc

preparation time **5 mins**
cooking time **5 mins**
serves **1**

PER SERVING

141 kcal

20g protein

5g total fat
3g saturated fat

13mg cholesterol

4g total carbohydrate
3.5g sugars

1.5g fibre

434mg sodium

COOK'S TIP

The fat in this omelette is kept to a minimum by cooking in a non-stick frying pan or omelette pan coated with cooking spray, instead of using butter or margarine for the cooking, and by filling with vegetables and reduced-fat cheese.

American buttermilk pancakes

American-style pancakes, which are thick like a drop scone, are perfect for breakfast, providing the energy boost the body needs to start the day. This recipe includes fruit, which makes the pancakes even more nutritious.

1 Sift the white and wholemeal flours into a large bowl, and tip in the bran left in the sieve. Stir in the sugar. Mix the egg yolks with the buttermilk and 1 tablespoon cold water. Gradually beat the yolks into the flour mixture to make a very thick batter.

2 Whisk the egg whites in a separate bowl until light and fluffy. Fold into the batter, then fold in the banana.

3 Heat a griddle or a large, heavy-based, non-stick frying pan over a moderate heat, then lightly grease with a little of the oil. Spoon large, heaped spoonfuls of the batter onto the hot griddle or pan, spacing them well apart. You'll probably be able to cook three or four pancakes at a time, depending on the size of the griddle or pan.

4 Cook for 1–2 minutes or until golden and firm on the underside and bubbles appear on the surface. Flip the pancakes over using a large palette knife, and cook on the other side for 1–2 minutes. Remove them from the pan and keep warm while cooking the rest of the pancakes, lightly greasing the griddle or pan with more oil between each batch.

5 Mix the yoghurt with the cinnamon. Place two warm pancakes on each serving plate, add 1 tablespoon of spiced yoghurt and drizzle over 1 teaspoon honey. Serve immediately.

115g self-raising white flour
115g self-raising wholemeal flour
30g caster sugar
2 large eggs, separated
300ml buttermilk
1 large banana, thinly sliced
1½ teaspoons sunflower oil

TO SERVE

6 tablespoons plain Greek-style yoghurt
¼ teaspoon ground cinnamon
6 teaspoons clear honey

---

preparation time **20 mins**
cooking time **15–20 mins**
serves **6** (makes 12)

PER SERVING

340 kcal

11g protein

10g total fat
3g saturated fat

81mg cholesterol

57g total carbohydrate
30g sugars

2.5g fibre

205mg sodium

HEALTH HINT

Buttermilk is traditionally the liquid left over after the creamy part of milk has been turned into butter by churning. Nowadays, though, buttermilk is usually made by adding a culture to skimmed milk. Whichever way it is made, buttermilk is extremely low in fat (0.2–0.5g fat per 100ml).

blackberry and lemon scones

Make these scones in the autumn when firm, sweet blackberries are in season.
The addition of buttermilk to the mixture ensures the result is light and flaky.
Serve fresh from the oven for a deliciously different brunch scone.

115g self-raising white flour, plus extra
    to sprinkle
115g self-raising wholemeal flour
1 teaspoon baking powder
55g caster sugar
55g margarine, cut into small pieces
finely grated zest of 1 lemon
85g small, firm, fresh blackberries
120ml buttermilk, or more as needed

1 Preheat the oven to 200°C (gas mark 6). Sift the white and wholemeal flours and the baking powder into a large bowl, tipping in any bran left in the sieve. Stir in the sugar. Add the margarine and rub it in with your fingertips until the mixture resembles fine breadcrumbs.

2 Stir in the grated lemon zest, then very gently stir in the blackberries. Do not overmix, as the blackberries can easily become crushed.

3 Lightly stir in the buttermilk using a round-bladed knife, again being careful not to crush the blackberries. If there are any dry bits of dough in the bottom of the bowl, add a little more buttermilk. As soon as the mixture comes together into a soft dough, lift it from the bowl onto a floured surface and knead gently two or three times only, to form a rough ball.

4 Pat out the dough carefully with your hands to make an 18cm round. Transfer it to a greased baking sheet. Mark into eight wedges with the back of a knife and sprinkle with a little extra white flour. Bake for 20–25 minutes or until pale golden and risen. Serve warm, broken into the marked wedges. These scones are best eaten freshly baked, or on the day they are made, but will still be good to eat the next day; store them in an airtight tin.

preparation time **15 mins**
cooking time **20–25 mins**
makes **8 scones**

PER SCONE

182 kcal	
3g protein	
6g total fat	
1g saturated fat	
0.5mg cholesterol	
30g total carbohydrate	
9g sugars	
1g fibre	
218mg sodium	

HEALTH HINT

Blackberries are high in fibre and vitamin C, and are one of the richest fruit sources of vitamin E. This vitamin is an important antioxidant that helps to protect cell membranes from damage by free radicals, thus helping to protect against heart disease.

fruity vegetable muffins

 Not only do grated vegetables and dried fruit add food value and flavour to these muffins, but they also make them deliciously moist. Unlike many muffins, these are not too sweet, so they are as good in a packed lunch or as a snack.

preparation time **15 mins**
cooking time **20–25 mins**
makes **12 muffins**

PER MUFFIN

260 kcal

5g protein

13g total fat
2g saturated fat

59mg cholesterol

34g total carbohydrate
19g sugars

2g fibre

102mg sodium

HEALTH HINT

Combining wholemeal flour with white flour increases the fibre content of baked goods without making them too heavy.

1 Preheat the oven to 180°C (gas mark 4). Put paper muffin cases in a 12-cup muffin tin (each cup should be 3–3.5cm deep) or grease the cups with cooking spray.

2 Sift the flours and cinnamon into a mixing bowl. Add the sugar and any bran left in the sieve. Stir in the dried mixed fruit or raisins and make a well in the centre.

3 In another bowl, beat together the carrots, courgettes, oil and eggs. Pour this mixture into the well in the dry ingredients and stir until almost blended, but with a small amount of dry flour still visible in places.

4 Divide the mixture among the muffin cups, filling them about two-thirds full. Bake for 20–25 minutes or until the muffins are well risen, peaked in the centre and springy to the touch. Transfer the muffins to a wire rack to cool.

5 Serve the muffins warm or at room temperature. They are best eaten on the day they are made, but they can be stored in an airtight container for up to 2 days. Alternatively, you can freeze them for up to 3 months.

125g self-raising white flour
125g self-raising wholemeal flour
2 teaspoons ground cinnamon
170g caster sugar
55g dried mixed fruit or raisins
125g carrots, finely grated
125g courgettes, finely grated
125ml sunflower oil
3 eggs

waffles with glazed nectarines

Waffles aren't just for weekends any more! You can dig into this hot breakfast any weekday morning. Light and simple ingredients and plenty of juicy nectarines make these wonderful waffles a heart-healthy way to start the day.

3 medium nectarines, about 500g in total, thinly sliced
50g dark soft brown sugar
125ml freshly squeezed orange juice
1½ tablespoons cornflour
4 waffles

1 Lightly coat a large non-stick frying pan with cooking spray and set over moderate heat. Add the nectarines and sauté for about 5 minutes or until they are lightly browned. Stir in the brown sugar and cook for 2 minutes or until the sugar dissolves and becomes syrupy. Transfer the nectarines to a bowl using a slotted spoon.

2 Whisk the orange juice and cornflour in a small bowl until smooth, then add 240ml cold water. Whisk this mixture into the frying pan. Bring to the boil over moderately high heat and cook, whisking constantly, for about 2 minutes or until the sauce boils and thickens. Return the nectarines to the frying pan and allow to heat through.

3 Toast the waffles in a toaster. Serve two waffles per person, topped with about six slices of nectarine. Serve hot.

preparation and cooking time **35 mins**

serves **4**

PER SERVING

329 kcal

7g protein

10g total fat
2g saturated fat

2mg cholesterol

55g total carbohydrate
29g sugars

2g fibre

356mg sodium

HEALTH HINT

Nectarine skins are high in pectin, a soluble fibre that aids in controlling your blood cholesterol level and keeping your heart healthy.

tomato and ham bruschettas

Capture the flavour of the Mediterranean with these bite-sized toasts topped with pesto sauce, thinly sliced Parma ham and tomatoes, a combination popular all along the Med in France and Italy.

preparation and cooking time **about 15 mins**

serves **4** (makes 12)

PER SERVING

228 kcal

11g protein

9.5g total fat
1.5g saturated fat

5mg cholesterol

27g total carbohydrate
3g sugars

2g fibre

306mg sodium

HEART SUPERFOOD

Raw tomatoes are an excellent source of vitamin C and a significant source of vitamin A from beta carotene.

1 Preheat the grill to high. Slice the baguette into 12 equal slices. Place the slices on the rack in the grill pan and grill until toasted on the top side.

2 Turn the toasts over and spread with the pesto sauce. Top each with Parma ham, cut and folded to fit on the bread. Divide the tomato slices among the toasts, then drizzle with the olive oil. Season to taste with pepper.

3 Return the bruschettas to the grill and cook for 1–2 minutes or until the tomato slices begin to soften and char at the edges. Garnish each bruschetta with a few rocket leaves and serve hot or at room temperature.

Variations Replace the Parma ham with 100g crumbled feta cheese, and use ciabatta instead of a baguette. Toast the slices of bread on one side, turn them over and brush with 2 tablespoons extra virgin olive oil instead of the pesto sauce. Divide the feta cheese among the toasts and season with pepper. Grill until the cheese melts and bubbles, then garnish with fresh basil sprigs instead of rocket. • Leftover grilled red, yellow or orange peppers, or grilled peppers in jars, are ideal to add to the bruschettas. Alternatively, if you have time, place fresh peppers under a preheated grill and grill until they are blistered and blackened all over. Put them in a polythene bag and leave until cool enough to handle, then peel off the skins and cut the flesh into slices.

1 thin baguette, about 170g

2 tablespoons pesto sauce

85g Parma ham, sliced wafer-thin and trimmed of all fat

3 vine-ripened tomatoes, about 85g each, sliced

1 tablespoon extra virgin olive oil

pepper to taste

rocket leaves to garnish

caramelised banana crumpets

Forget about smothering toasted crumpets in butter; this yummy low-fat topping is much healthier. Mashed bananas are mixed with fromage frais and spices and piled onto crumpet fingers, then drizzled with honey and grilled.

8 crumpet fingers, about 30g each
2 bananas
4 tablespoons fromage frais
seeds from 4 cardamom pods, crushed
½ teaspoon ground cinnamon, plus
    extra to sprinkle
1 teaspoon finely grated orange zest
8 teaspoons clear honey

1 Preheat the grill to high. Arrange the crumpet fingers on the rack of the grill pan and toast for 2–3 minutes on each side or until browned and crisp.

2 Meanwhile, mash the bananas with a fork, keeping them a little textured. Add the fromage frais, crushed cardamom, cinnamon and orange zest, and mix well together.

3 Spread the banana mixture over the toasted crumpets, levelling the surface, then drizzle each with 1 teaspoon honey.

4 Return to the grill and cook for 2–3 minutes or until the tops are lightly browned and the honey is bubbling. Leave the crumpets to cool slightly, then sprinkle over a little extra cinnamon and serve at once.

Variations Use wholemeal crumpets for added fibre. If you cannot find crumpet fingers, you can simply cut round crumpets in half. • Instead of cardamom seeds, use ¼–½ teaspoon ground cardamom.

30

preparation and cooking
time **15 mins**
serves **4**

PER SERVING

262 kcal

7g protein

4g total fat
2g saturated fat

1.5mg cholesterol

53g total carbohydrate
29g sugars

2g fibre

440mg sodium

HEALTH HINT

Bananas are a concentrated source of carbohydrates and one of the best fruit sources of potassium, which is vital for muscle and nerve function – this is why bananas are so popular with athletes.

herbed French toast with mushrooms

Give breakfast or brunch a new twist with this savoury version of French toast. Triangles of bread are dipped into a fresh herb and egg mixture, then fried until crisp and golden. Serve with grilled mushrooms and lean bacon.

1 Combine the eggs, milk, most of the parsley, the chives, thyme and paprika in a shallow dish. Season with pepper and set the mixture aside.

2 Preheat the grill to moderately high. Remove the stalks from the mushrooms. Using 1 tablespoon of the oil, lightly brush the gill sides of the mushroom caps. Place them gill-side up on the grill rack. Add the bacon to the grill rack too. Grill the bacon for 10 minutes, turning the rashers over halfway through; grill the mushrooms for 6–7 minutes. When the bacon and mushrooms are cooked, remove from the grill and keep warm.

3 Meanwhile, cut each slice of bread into four triangles. Heat a large non-stick frying pan over moderate heat and add 1 tablespoon of the remaining oil. Dip about one-third of the bread triangles into the egg mixture to moisten on both sides, then place in the hot pan. Cook for 1–2 minutes or until golden brown. Remove from the pan and keep warm while you cook the rest of the bread, adding the remaining oil as needed.

4 To serve, arrange five triangles of French toast on each plate. Cut the mushrooms into thick slices and add to the plates, together with the bacon. Sprinkle with the remaining parsley.

4 large eggs

4 tablespoons semi-skimmed milk

1 tablespoon finely chopped parsley

1 tablespoon finely chopped fresh chives

½ tablespoon chopped fresh thyme or ½ teaspoon dried thyme

pinch of paprika

pepper to taste

4 large portobello mushrooms or large flat mushrooms, about 250g in total

3 tablespoons sunflower oil

4 rashers lean back bacon, trimmed of visible fat

5 thick slices of wholemeal bread

30 · Fb

preparation and cooking time **about 25 mins**

serves **4**

PER SERVING

390 kcal

20g protein

25g total fat
6g saturated fat

271mg cholesterol

22g total carbohydrate
2g sugars

3g fibre

1135mg sodium

HEALTH HINT

This hearty breakfast dish contains fewer calories than the traditional version of French toast, which is often served with melted butter and maple or golden syrup.

butter beans and bacon on toast with red leaf salad

Here's a new version of beans on toast, combining creamy butter beans with crisp bacon, cottage cheese and mustard. Accompanied by a fresh salad, this makes a fabulous meal that is ready to serve in about 15 minutes.

15g margarine

4 rashers lean back bacon, trimmed of visible fat and chopped

1 bunch of spring onions, sliced

85g watercress, tough stalks removed, roughly chopped

2 cans (about 400g each) butter beans, drained and rinsed

55g low-fat cottage cheese

1 teaspoon Dijon mustard

pepper to taste

8 thick slices of wholemeal bread

RED LEAF SALAD

2 tablespoons extra virgin olive oil

2 teaspoons freshly squeezed lemon juice

1 teaspoon clear honey

pepper to taste

1 small head radicchio, cut into thin wedges

1 small Lollo Rosso lettuce, leaves separated

1 To make the salad, put the oil, lemon juice, honey and pepper to taste in a salad bowl. Whisk together, then add the radicchio and lettuce. Set aside (do not toss yet).

2 Preheat the grill to high. Melt the margarine in a large non-stick frying pan until it begins to sizzle. Add the bacon and spring onions, and cook over moderate heat for about 3 minutes, stirring frequently, until the bacon begins to colour and the spring onions are just tender.

3 Add the watercress and cook for a few seconds, stirring, then add the butter beans, cottage cheese, mustard and pepper. Lower the heat and cook for 2 minutes, stirring constantly, until the mixture is hot.

4 While the bean and bacon mixture is cooking, toast the slices of bread under the grill or in a toaster. Spoon the bean and bacon mixture onto the hot toast. Quickly toss the salad, and serve while the lettuce is still crisp.

Variation Drain and rinse 2 cans (about 400g each) borlotti beans and put in a saucepan with 85g crumbled Gorgonzola cheese, 2 tablespoons plain low-fat yoghurt and 2 tablespoons quark. Heat very gently, stirring frequently, until the Gorgonzola melts and the beans are hot. Stir in 1 tablespoon red pesto. Spoon into ciabatta rolls, split in half and lightly toasted. You can serve with the red leaf salad above or a fennel and rocket salad. For the dressing, whisk 2 tablespoons extra virgin olive oil with 1 teaspoon balsamic vinegar, 2 tablespoons freshly squeezed orange juice and pepper to taste. Add 1 thinly sliced fennel bulb, 85g rocket leaves, 1 thinly sliced small red onion and 30g stoned black olives, and toss just before serving with the rolls.

30 **Fb** **GI**

preparation and cooking time **15 mins**

serves **4**

PER SERVING

494 kcal

26g protein

13g total fat
2g saturated fat

14mg cholesterol

70g total carbohydrate
9g sugars

15g fibre

933mg sodium

HEALTH HINTS

As their name suggests, butter beans have a buttery flavour. They offer plenty of dietary fibre, essential for a healthy digestive system.

Trimmed of fat, lean bacon is a high-protein, low-fat ingredient that provides particularly useful amounts of vitamin B_1, which is essential for maintaining a healthy nervous system.

potato cakes with baked tomatoes

Potato and leek cakes, flavoured with tasty cheese and fresh herbs, make a satisfying vegetarian meal served with baked tomatoes and accompanied by a simple leaf salad. Use floury potatoes, such as King Edward or Maris Piper.

1kg floury potatoes, scrubbed

1 large leek, about 225g, sliced

2 tablespoons semi-skimmed milk

2 teaspoons wholegrain mustard

85g reduced-fat Cheddar cheese, grated

5 tablespoons chopped parsley

1 tablespoon chopped fresh thyme

plain flour for shaping

1 egg, beaten

85g fresh wholemeal breadcrumbs

4 large beefsteak tomatoes, halved

2 tablespoons ready-made garlic-flavoured olive oil

1 Cut large potatoes into halves or quarters. Bring a large saucepan of water to the boil and add the potatoes. Bring back to the boil, then turn down the heat and simmer for 15 minutes or until tender. Add the leek to the pan for the last 5 minutes of cooking. Drain the vegetables, spread them out on a tray and cool. Preheat the oven to 220°C (gas mark 7).

2 When the potatoes are cool, peel them. Place in a bowl with the leek and mash together. Add the milk, mustard, cheese, parsley and thyme, and mix well. Divide the mixture into eight portions. Shape each into a ball, then press on a floured surface into a cake about 10cm across and 3cm thick.

3 Set the cakes on a clean tray. Brush with the beaten egg and sprinkle over half the breadcrumbs. Turn the cakes and coat the other side with egg and breadcrumbs. Transfer them to a non-stick baking tray and bake for 15 minutes.

4 Meanwhile, place the tomatoes in an ovenproof dish, cut-side up. Brush them with the garlic oil and sprinkle over any remaining breadcrumbs.

5 Turn the potato cakes over carefully with a fish slice. Place the tomatoes in the oven Continue baking for 10 minutes or until the potato cakes are golden. Serve hot.

 Fb

preparation time **35 mins** plus cooling

cooking time **25 mins**

serves **4** (makes 8)

PER SERVING

452 kcal

19g protein

13g total fat
4g saturated fat

69mg cholesterol

68g total carbohydrate
8g sugars

7g fibre

480mg sodium

HEALTH HINT

Potato cakes are often fried in oil or butter. Here they are oven-baked to produce cakes that are equally tasty but with a lower fat content.

potato and courgette tortilla

30 **Kj**

preparation time **15 mins**
cooking time **15 mins**
serves **8**

PER SERVING

165 kcal
9g protein
8g total fat
2g saturated fat
179mg cholesterol
14g total carbohydrate
1g sugars
1g fibre
187mg sodium

HEALTH HINT

Courgettes are a good source of vitamin B$_6$ and niacin. The skin contains the greatest concentration of these vitamins.

Tortilla is made from the simplest of ingredients – eggs, onions and potatoes – cooked like a flat omelette and served warm or cold, cut into wedges. All kinds of extra ingredients can be added, such as asparagus, peas and mushrooms.

1 Add the potato dice to a saucepan of boiling water. Bring back to the boil, then lower the heat slightly and cook for 3 minutes. Drain thoroughly.

2 Heat the oil in a heavy-based non-stick frying pan that is about 25cm in diameter. Add the potatoes, onion, courgettes and bacon, and cook over moderate heat for 10 minutes, turning and stirring from time to time, until the potatoes are tender and lightly golden.

3 Preheat the grill to high. In a bowl, beat the eggs with 1 tablespoon cold water. Add the parsley and pepper. Pour the egg mixture over the vegetables in the pan and cook for 3–4 minutes or until the egg has set on the bottom, lifting the edges to allow the uncooked egg mixture to run onto the pan.

4 When there is just a little uncooked egg on the top, place the pan under the hot grill and cook for a further 2 minutes to set the top. Slide the tortilla out onto a plate or board and allow to cool for 2–3 minutes. Cut into small wedges or other shapes and serve warm, or leave to cool completely before cutting and serving.

600g waxy potatoes, peeled and cut into 1cm dice

2 tablespoons extra virgin olive oil

1 red onion, finely chopped

1 courgette, about 150g, diced

2 rashers lean back bacon, trimmed of visible fat and chopped

6 eggs

2 tablespoons chopped parsley

pepper to taste

leek and Parma ham pizza muffins

Leeks, basil and Parma ham combine with mozzarella to make a sophisticated pizza-style topping for wholemeal muffins. Serve with a simple salad of rocket and grated carrot tossed with extra virgin olive oil and lemon juice.

1 tablespoon extra virgin olive oil

2 leeks, about 250g in total, thinly sliced

pepper to taste

4 wholemeal English muffins, halved

4 tablespoons shredded fresh basil leaves

4 slices of Parma ham, about 50g in total, trimmed of visible fat and halved crossways

100g mozzarella cheese, cut into thin strips

4 tablespoons coarsely chopped rocket

1 Heat the oil in a saucepan, add the leeks and cook over moderately high heat, stirring frequently, for about 5 minutes or until the leeks are tender and the juices have evaporated. Season with pepper.

2 Preheat the grill to high. Place the muffins, cut-side down, in the grill pan without the rack. Grill to toast the bases, then turn the muffins over. Divide the leeks equally among the muffins. Top with the basil, then place a piece of Parma ham on each muffin half. Gently pinch the ham up into loose folds. Scatter the strips of mozzarella over the top.

3 Cook the muffin pizzas under the hot grill for 4–5 minutes or until the mozzarella has melted and is bubbling. The ham and cheese should be lightly browned in places. Sprinkle with the chopped rocket and serve.

Variation Use 75g lean cooked ham, cut into fine strips, instead of the Parma ham, and a handful of small watercress sprigs instead of the basil.

30 Fb

preparation time **15 mins**
cooking time **4–5 mins**
serves **4** (makes 8)

PER SERVING

310 kcal

17g protein

14g total fat
4g saturated fat

14mg cholesterol

32g total carbohydrate
3g sugars

3g fibre

393mg sodium

ham and celeriac pittas

This refreshing salad sandwich is packed with a mixture of crunchy vegetables, smoked ham, dried fruit and green olives, giving lovely contrasting flavours and textures. The tangy mustard dressing is based on yoghurt and mayonnaise.

1 Preheat the grill to high. Mix together all the dressing ingredients in a medium-sized bowl.

2 Peel and coarsely grate the celeriac and carrots. Add to the bowl of dressing and mix well. Add the ham, onion, olives, currants and chopped parsley and mix everything together.

3 Warm the pitta breads under the grill for about 1 minute on each side. Cut each pitta bread across in half to make two pockets of bread.

4 Divide the lettuce among the pitta pockets, then add the ham and celeriac salad. Garnish with parsley and serve.

Variation For chicken, apple and celery pittas, cut 375g cooked chicken breast fillets into thin slices. Toss 1 green apple, diced, 3 celery sticks, thinly sliced, and 4 spring onions, sliced, with the mustard dressing. Fold in the chicken. Put some shredded lettuce and a small handful of rocket or watercress leaves into each pitta pocket, then add the chicken salad.

125g piece of celeriac

2 carrots, about 150g in total

170g thickly sliced lean smoked ham, cut into 1cm dice

1 small red onion, thinly sliced

8 stoned green olives, pimiento-stuffed if wished, halved

50g currants

2 tablespoons chopped parsley

6 garlic pitta breads

1 heart of romaine or cos lettuce, finely shredded

parsley to garnish

MUSTARD DRESSING

3 tablespoons plain Greek-style yoghurt

½ teaspoon wholegrain mustard

2 tablespoons mayonnaise

preparation time **15 mins**
serves **6**

PER SERVING

320 kcal

13g protein

6g total fat
1g saturated fat

7mg cholesterol

54g total carbohydrate
11g sugars

3g fibre

677mg sodium

HEALTH HINTS

Celeriac is related to celery and, like celery, it provides potassium. When eaten raw, as in these sandwiches, it also offers vitamin C.

Currants provide a useful amount of fibre and some magnesium, which is important for healthy bones, the release of energy from food, and nerve and muscle function.

avocado and chicken club sandwich

This club sandwich packs in lots of interesting flavours and textures. Crisped Parma ham replaces the usual bacon, and mashed avocado the butter. Adding a few leaves to a sandwich is a cunning way to get children to eat their greens.

12 slices of mixed grain bread

4 tablespoons reduced-fat mayonnaise

115g iceberg lettuce, finely shredded

115g cooked chicken breast meat, skin removed, sliced

4 slices of Parma ham, cut into strips

pepper to taste

1 avocado

1 tablespoon freshly squeezed lime juice

1 orange, peeled and chopped

1 bunch of watercress, tough stalks discarded

20g alfalfa sprouts

2 teaspoons pumpkin seeds, toasted in a frying pan for 2 minutes without oil

1 Spread four slices of bread with half of the mayonnaise. Divide the shredded lettuce among the slices, then add the sliced chicken breast meat.

2 Heat a non-stick frying pan and dry-fry the strips of Parma ham for 1–2 minutes or until crisp and curly. Pile on top of the chicken and season with pepper. Spread the remaining mayonnaise on another four slices of bread and put these, mayonnaise-side down, on the chicken and ham.

3 Mash the avocado flesh with the lime juice. Divide among the sandwiches, spooning onto the uppermost layer of bread and spreading out roughly. Top with the chopped orange, watercress, alfalfa sprouts and pumpkin seeds. Place the final slices of bread on top. Press down gently, then cut each sandwich in half or into quarters for serving.

Variation For fruity chicken club sandwiches, replace the top deck of avocado, orange, watercress, alfalfa sprouts and pumpkin seeds on each sandwich with 1 tablespoon crunchy peanut butter, ½ sliced banana sprinkled with a little lemon juice, 2 fresh dates, skinned and chopped, and 1 teaspoon chopped parsley.

30 — Fb

preparation and cooking time **25 mins**

serves **4**

PER SERVING

481 kcal
26g protein
17g total fat
4g saturated fat
30mg cholesterol
59g total carbohydrate
7g sugars
6g fibre
813mg sodium

HEALTH HINT

Avocados have a reputation for being a 'fatty' fruit, but most of their fat is of the good, unsaturated type, making them a valuable source of essential fatty acids as well as vitamin E.

roasted vegetable baguettines

These Mediterranean-style 'sandwiches' are generously filled with char-grilled peppers, courgettes and red onion, spiked with garlic and rosemary, and topped with a sprinkling of feta cheese. They make a satisfying brunch.

1 Preheat the grill to high and grill the red peppers, skin-side up, for 10 minutes or until the skins are blackened. Place the peppers in a polythene bag and set aside for 15 minutes.

2 Meanwhile, lightly toast the cut sides of the baguettines under the grill. Remove from the grill and set aside on a board.

3 Remove the grill rack and discard any crumbs from the grill pan. Place the onion, courgettes and garlic in the pan. Sprinkle with rosemary and pepper to taste and drizzle with oil. Grill for 8–10 minutes, turning the vegetables once, until browned.

4 Peel the skin off the peppers using a small sharp knife and cut them into thick slices. Arrange the peppers and courgette mixture over the bottom halves of the toasted bread, spooning all the pan juices from the courgettes over the top. Arrange side by side in the grill pan.

5 Crumble the feta cheese over the vegetables and grill for 3–4 minutes or until the cheese is slightly browned. Top with the remaining bread halves. Cut the baguettines in half at an angle and serve immediately.

2 red peppers, quartered lengthways and deseeded

4 short French sticks or baguettines, about 125g each, halved horizontally

1 red onion, cut into small wedges

2 large courgettes, about 340g in total, sliced diagonally

2 garlic cloves, chopped

3 sprigs of fresh rosemary

1 tablespoon extra virgin olive oil

pepper to taste

100g feta cheese

Fb

preparation and cooking time **45 mins**

serves **4**

PER SERVING

464 kcal

18g protein

11g total fat
4g saturated fat

17mg cholesterol

79g total carbohydrate
11g sugars

5g fibre

1135mg sodium

HEALTH HINT

Feta cheese is quite high in fat and salt, but because it has such a strong flavour, a little goes a long way.

soups,
starters
& snacks

country vegetable soup with pesto

Fragrant basil pesto adds a taste of summer to this healthier version of a classic French soup. Aromatic vegetables add flavour and plenty of vitamins while keeping the fat in check. What a wonderful way to eat your vegetables!

500g ripe plum tomatoes

1 onion, chopped

1 carrot, chopped

1 celery stick, sliced

2 garlic cloves, finely chopped

2 courgettes (1 yellow and 1 green), about 300g in total, sliced

450ml reduced-sodium chicken stock or stock made without salt

450ml reduced-sodium vegetable stock or stock made without salt

45g fresh basil leaves

2½ tablespoons prepared basil pesto

1 Skin, deseed and chop the tomatoes.

2 Grease a large saucepan with cooking spray and set over moderately high heat. Add the onion, carrot, celery and garlic and sauté for about 5 minutes or until soft. Add the tomatoes and courgettes and continue to sauté for about 8 minutes or until the courgettes are soft.

3 Stir in the chicken and vegetable stocks and bring to the boil. Reduce the heat and simmer, uncovered, for 20 minutes.

4 Place the basil and pesto in a food processor and pulse until the basil is chopped, then process until the mixture is thick and creamy.

5 Ladle the soup into bowls, top with the pesto and serve.

preparation time **25 mins**

cooking time **35 mins**

serves **4**

PER SERVING

144 kcal

12g protein

7g total fat
0.7g saturated fat

0mg cholesterol

11g total carbohydrate
8g sugars

3g fibre

470mg sodium

COOK'S TIP

For a vegetarian soup, use 900ml vegetable stock (omit the chicken stock). You can also vary the vegetables. Always start with sautéed onion, carrot, celery and garlic. In spring, add a handful of podded fresh peas for the last 10 minutes of cooking. During summer, team the tomatoes with sweetcorn kernels and chopped green beans.

preparation time **10 mins**

cooking time **20 mins**

serves **4**

PER SERVING

330 kcal

15g protein

14g total fat

4g saturated fat

38mg cholesterol

40g total carbohydrate

7g sugars

4g fibre

602mg sodium

HEART SUPERFOOD

Canned fish such as kippers are an excellent source of calcium – the fish bones disintegrate in the canning process so they are eaten as well as the fish. Kippers are also full of omega-3 fatty acids, which help to lower blood cholesterol.

kipper and sweetcorn chowder

With a few fresh ingredients, storecupboard standbys can be transformed into a great quick dish. Canned kippers and sweetcorn make a delicious chowder combined with leeks, potatoes and herbs. Serve with crusty rolls.

1 Heat the oil in a large saucepan. Add the leek and cook over a moderate heat for 2 minutes or until it is just softened. Stir in the potatoes and cook for a further 2 minutes. Stir in the fish stock and bay leaf, and bring to the boil. Reduce the heat, cover and simmer for 15 minutes.

2 Remove and discard the bay leaf. Stir in the milk, creamed sweetcorn and half the chives and parsley. Use a fork to break the kippers into chunky pieces and add them to the soup. Taste the soup and add pepper to taste. Bring the soup to the boil, then immediately remove the pan from the heat to prevent the kippers from overcooking.

3 Ladle the soup into bowls and garnish each portion with a sprinkling of the remaining chives and parsley. Serve at once.

Variation To make a tuna chowder, add 2 crushed garlic cloves and the grated zest of 1 large lemon with the leek, and replace the kippers with 1 can (about 180g) tuna in water, well drained. Add 1 deseeded and finely chopped mild green chilli with the chives and parsley for the garnish.

1 tablespoon extra virgin olive oil

1 leek, thinly sliced

300g small new potatoes, quartered

600ml reduced-sodium fish stock or stock made without salt

1 bay leaf

300ml full-fat milk

1 can (about 418g) creamed sweetcorn

2 tablespoons snipped fresh chives

2 tablespoons chopped parsley

1 can (about 190g) kippers in oil, thoroughly drained and skinned

pepper to taste

chunky gazpacho with garlic croutons

 This chilled soup is a delicious concoction of tomatoes, peppers and cucumbers with a hint of garlic – all high in what's good for you and low in fat and calories. Ladle into cups as a starter or into bowls for a light supper.

2 garlic cloves, peeled
4 slices of crusty French bread
  (wholemeal if possible), about
  2cm thick
1 teaspoon pepper
85g coarsely chopped red onion
2 cans (about 400g each) tomatoes
25g dried breadcrumbs
4 tablespoons chopped parsley
3 tablespoons red wine vinegar
1 tablespoon olive oil
2 cucumbers, peeled and chopped
2 green peppers, deseeded and
  chopped
2 red peppers, deseeded and chopped

1 Preheat the oven to 180°C (gas mark 4). Cut one garlic clove in half and rub the cut sides on the inside of a large bowl and on both sides of the bread slices. Tear the bread into 2cm pieces. Place the bread in the bowl and lightly coat with cooking spray. Sprinkle with ½ teaspoon pepper. Toss to coat, then transfer to a baking tray. Bake the croutons for about 15 minutes or until golden brown. Allow to cool.

2 Pulse the onion and remaining garlic in a food processor or blender until finely chopped. Add half the tomatoes with all their juice, and purée. Add the breadcrumbs, parsley, vinegar, oil and remaining pepper. Process just until blended. Pour into a large non-metallic bowl.

3 Chop the remaining tomatoes. Stir them into the tomato mixture with half the chopped cucumbers and half the green and red peppers. Chill for about 1 hour. Ladle the soup into bowls and top with the remaining cucumber and green and red peppers and the croutons. Serve chilled.

preparation and cooking
time **35 mins**
plus 1 hour chilling
serves **4**

PER SERVING

241 kcal

9g protein

5g total fat
0.5g saturated fat

0mg cholesterol

43g total carbohydrate
18g sugars

6g fibre

350mg sodium

COOK'S TIP

Acids in foods like tomatoes, citrus fruit, vinegar and even buttermilk can react with some metals, resulting in an undesirable metallic taste. Prepare acidic dishes such as this soup in glass or pottery bowls.

spinach and onion soup with crostini

A colourful vegetarian version of classic French onion soup, this makes a filling lunch or supper. The secret of the rich flavour lies in frying the onions very slowly until they are well browned, caramelised and sweet.

1 Melt the margarine with the oil in a large saucepan. Add the onions and fry gently for 10 minutes, stirring occasionally, until softened and pale golden. Stir in the sugar and garlic, then continue to fry for 10 minutes, stirring occasionally, until the onions are browned and caramelised.

2 Stir in the stock and pepper to taste, and bring to the boil. Reduce the heat, cover the pan and simmer for 30 minutes. Add the broccoli and simmer for a further 3 minutes. Take the pan off the heat and stir in the spinach, then cover and leave to stand while making the tomato crostini.

3 Preheat the grill to high, and lightly toast the slices of bread on both sides. Rub one side of each slice with the cut garlic clove and spread lightly with tomato purée. Add two tomato wedges to each slice, season with pepper and sprinkle the Parmesan cheese over the top. Grill for about 2 minutes or until the cheese melts and is just bubbling.

4 While the crostini are grilling, reheat the soup, if necessary. Ladle into four warm bowls. Float two tomato crostini in each bowl of soup and serve immediately.

30g margarine

1 tablespoon extra virgin olive oil

500g large onions, thinly sliced

1 teaspoon caster sugar

2 garlic cloves, chopped

1 litre low-sodium vegetable stock or stock made without salt

pepper to taste

115g broccoli, finely chopped

115g spinach leaves, torn

TOMATO CROSTINI

8 thick slices of French bread

1 garlic clove, halved

2 teaspoons tomato purée

2 tomatoes, each cut into 8 wedges

30g Parmesan cheese, freshly grated

 Fb

preparation time **30 mins**

cooking time **1 hour**

serves **4**

PER SERVING

460 kcal

17g protein

14g total fat
6g saturated fat

24mg cholesterol

73g total carbohydrate
15g sugars

7g fibre

923mg sodium

HEALTH HINT

Spinach is a good source of several antioxidants including vitamins C and E, and carotenoid compounds. It also provides useful amounts of niacin and vitamin B$_6$, and is a good source of folate.

Oriental meatball broth

Aromatic rice and pork meatballs and lots of interesting vegetables bring Oriental flavours to this satisfying main-meal soup. Serve it at the table in a warmed tureen or straight from the pan.

225g red chard leaves

1.4 litres low-sodium chicken stock or stock made without salt

2.5cm piece fresh root ginger, peeled and cut into thin strips

3 tablespoons dry sherry

2 tablespoons reduced-sodium soy sauce, or to taste

200g baby corn, each sliced diagonally into 2–3 pieces

115g shiitake mushrooms, thinly sliced

200g mange-tout, each cut diagonally into 2–3 pieces

1 can (about 220g) sliced bamboo shoots, drained

6 spring onions, thinly sliced diagonally

RICE AND PORK MEATBALLS

170g long-grain rice

340g lean minced pork

2.5cm piece fresh root ginger, peeled and grated

6 spring onions, chopped

1 garlic clove, finely chopped

2 tablespoons reduced-sodium soy sauce

½ teaspoon toasted sesame oil

½ teaspoon five-spice powder

pinch of chilli powder

225g pak choy

1 First prepare the meatballs. Place the rice in a saucepan, pour in plenty of water to cover and bring to the boil. Boil for 1 minute, then drain the rice in a sieve and leave to cool.

2 Mix the pork with the ginger, spring onions, garlic, soy sauce, sesame oil, five-spice powder and chilli powder. Strip the green leaves of the pak choy off the thick white stalks. Finely chop the leaves and add them to the pork. Reserve the stalks for the broth. Pound the mixture with a spoon until thoroughly combined.

3 Turn the drained rice into a large shallow bowl and separate the grains with a fork. Rinse your hands, then take a small lump of pork mixture, squeeze it together and roll it into a small ball about the size of a walnut. Roll the meatball in the rice, pressing it into the grains to coat it thickly. Press the rice firmly onto the meatball and set aside on a plate or dish. Shape the remaining pork mixture to make about 20 rice meatballs in all.

4 Cover the bottom of a steamer rack with a single layer of red chard, leaving gaps between the leaves. (If you are using stacking bamboo steamer baskets, you will need two.) Add the meatballs in one layer, leaving space between them for the rice to swell. Bring the stock and ginger to the boil in the steamer base. Set the steamer on top and cover. Steam the meatballs for 35 minutes.

5 While the meatballs are cooking, cut the stalks of the pak choy across into 1cm pieces. Remove the steamer from the pan and set it aside on a plate. Add the sherry, soy sauce, baby corn, shiitake mushrooms, mange-tout, remaining red chard leaves, bamboo shoots and spring onions to the stock. Bring back to the boil, then replace the steamer rack and steam for a further 5 minutes.

6 Carefully transfer the rice and pork balls to a warm serving bowl. Add the chard leaves from the steamer to the broth. Taste the broth and add more soy sauce, if liked, then transfer it to a warm tureen. To serve, ladle some broth and vegetables into four warm bowls and add a few rice and pork meatballs to each. Ladle in more broth and add meatballs during the meal as required.

 Fb

preparation time **20 mins**

cooking time **40 mins**

serves **4**

PER SERVING

430 kcal

32g protein

10g total fat
3g saturated fat

53mg cholesterol

51g total carbohydrate
7g sugars

6g fibre

1499mg sodium

HEALTH HINT

Shiitake mushrooms contain lentinan, which is believed to help strengthen the immune system. These tasty mushrooms are also thought to help protect against cancer.

Tuscan mixed bean soup

 Tuscan cuisine focuses on fresh, healthy ingredients and uncomplicated cooking techniques to make traditionally delicious fare. These are dishes – like this colourful bean soup – that you can easily duplicate in your own kitchen.

1 tablespoon olive oil

2 onions, coarsely chopped

2 carrots, coarsely chopped

2 celery sticks, chopped

450ml reduced-sodium chicken stock or stock made without salt

2 cans (about 400g each) chopped tomatoes

30g fresh basil leaves, chopped

2 tablespoons chopped fresh oregano or 1 teaspoon dried oregano

1 can (about 420g) red kidney beans, drained

1 can (about 400g) borlotti beans, drained

1 can (about 400g) chickpeas, drained

50g Parmesan cheese, freshly grated

1 Heat the oil in a large non-stick saucepan over moderately high heat. Add the onions, carrots and celery and sauté for about 5 minutes or until soft. Add the chicken stock, tomatoes with their juice, the basil and oregano. Bring to the boil. Reduce the heat to moderately low, partly cover and cook for 10 minutes.

2 Place the kidney and borlotti beans and the chickpeas in a colander and rinse well under running cold water. Stir the beans and chickpeas into the soup and cook, covered, for a further 10 minutes. Remove from the heat.

3 Very coarsely purée about one-quarter of the soup using a hand-held blender. Or transfer about half of the soup to a blender or food processor, very coarsely purée and return to the pan; reheat the soup if necessary. Serve hot, topped with the Parmesan cheese.

preparation time **25 mins**

cooking time **30 mins**

serves **6**

PER SERVING

400 kcal

28g protein

11g total fat
3g saturated fat

16mg cholesterol

53g total carbohydrate
17g sugars

15g fibre

432mg sodium

HEALTH HINTS

Chunks of vegetables and plenty of beans make this soup rich in fibre. Beans are high in soluble fibre – the type that seems to control blood cholesterol in certain people by lowering LDL (the 'bad' cholesterol). Carrots, celery and other vegetables contribute mostly insoluble fibre, which helps the intestines maintain regularity.

Remember that canned beans often have salt added, so be sure to drain and rinse them well before use.

herbed cheese bagels

A little parsley adds a hint of freshness and colour to dishes, but when used in quantity its unique flavour can really be appreciated. It also makes a healthy contribution along with the vegetables to this delicious filling for bagels.

30 **Kc**

preparation time **10 mins**
serves **4**

PER SERVING

170 kcal

8g protein

5g total fat
2g saturated fat

10mg cholesterol

25g total carbohydrate
5g sugars

2g fibre

339mg sodium

HEALTH HINT

Parsley has long been appreciated as a breath freshener, particularly when eaten raw with or after a dish containing garlic. Parsley is a useful source of folate, iron and vitamin C.

1 Put the cheese, spring onions, parsley, dill and tarragon in a bowl. Mix well together using a fork, then add pepper to taste.

2 Slice the bagels in half horizontally. Spread the cheese mixture on the bagel bases. Layer the cucumber, tomato and onion slices on the cheese and cover with the tops of the bagels. Serve immediately.

Variations After splitting the bagels in half, you can toast them lightly under the grill before adding the filling. • For a mild herb flavour, reduce the quantity of parsley to 2 tablespoons. Alternatively, for a peppery flavour, finely chop 1 bunch of watercress, tough stalks discarded, and use instead of parsley. • Use 8 thick slices of Granary bread instead of the split bagels to make chunky sandwiches. • For hearty open sandwiches, spread the herbed soft cheese on 4 individual or 2 large naan breads, cut across in half. Top with diced cucumber and sliced tomatoes (omit the red onion). Add a small handful of rocket or fresh mint leaves to each naan.

100g reduced-fat soft cheese
2 spring onions, thinly sliced
30g parsley, finely chopped
2 tablespoons chopped fresh dill
1 tablespoons chopped fresh tarragon
pepper to taste
4 bagels
½ cucumber, thinly sliced
3 tomatoes, thinly sliced
1 red onion, thinly sliced

66

vegetable crisps with peanut dip

Oven-baked crisps are not only healthier than those that are fried, their flavour is fresher and more concentrated, too. Here, thin slices of beetroot and potato are baked in a hot oven to make dippers for a spicy Asian peanut dip.

2 medium potatoes, about
    350g in total, scrubbed
3 medium beetroot, about
    350g in total, scrubbed
2 tablespoons sunflower oil

SPICY PEANUT DIP
2 teaspoons sunflower oil
1 large shallot, finely chopped
1 garlic clove, crushed
½ teaspoon ground cumin
½ teaspoon ground coriander
55g crunchy peanut butter
1 tablepoon reduced-sodium
    soy sauce
1 tablespoon clear honey
1 tablespoon freshly squeezed
    lemon juice

1 To make the dip, heat the oil in a small pan over moderate heat and fry the shallot and garlic for 3–4 minutes.

2 Stir in the cumin and coriander and cook for a few more seconds, then add the peanut butter, soy sauce, honey and 4 tablespoons water. Stir over low heat until the ingredients are combined. Remove from the heat and mix in the lemon juice. Spoon into a small bowl, cover and set aside.

3 Preheat the oven to 220°C (gas mark 7). Cut the potatoes and beetroot into very thin slices (about 2mm), using the fine slicing blade in a food processor or a sharp knife.

4 Place the potato and beetroot slices in two separate bowls and add 1 tablespoon oil to each bowl. Toss the vegetable slices until they are coated lightly with oil, then spread them out in a single layer on three large non-stick baking trays. Bake for 35 minutes, turning the vegetables frequently and swapping round the position of the baking trays each time you turn the vegetables, until the potatoes are crisp and golden and the beetroot is firm but slightly moist. Keep a close eye on the vegetable crisps to make sure they do not burn. Transfer to a wire rack to cool.

5 To serve, place the bowl of peanut dip on a large serving platter and pile the cooled vegetable crisps around it.

 Fb

preparation and cooking
time **about 1 hour**
plus cooling

serves **4**

PER SERVING

260 kcal

7g protein

14g total fat
3g saturated fat

0mg cholesterol

27g total carbohydrate
11g sugars

4g fibre

328mg sodium

HEALTH HINT

Beetroot, which was originally grown for its spinach-like leaves rather than the now more familiar dark red, swollen root, is related to the sugar beet. It has a sugar content similar to an apple. Beetroot is a good source of folate, a B vitamin essential for healthy blood.

puttanesca pizzinis

Home-made mini pizzas topped with a rich tomato, chilli, olive, caper and artichoke mixture will spoil you for anything less. Some crumbled Gorgonzola cheese melted over the top makes a change from the usual mozzarella.

1 First make the pizza dough. Sift the flour into a large mixing bowl and stir in the oregano and yeast. Make a well in the centre and pour in the water. Gradually work the flour into the water to make a soft dough. If it feels too dry, work in a little more water; if the dough sticks to your hand, add more flour.

2 Turn out the dough onto a lightly floured work surface and knead for about 10 minutes or until smooth and elastic. Return to the bowl, cover with a damp tea towel or cling film and leave to rise in a warm place for 1 hour or until doubled in size.

3 Meanwhile, make the topping. Heat the oil in a saucepan and add the onion and garlic. Cook over a low heat for about 10 minutes or until softened. Stir in the tomatoes and chilli, and cook over a moderate heat for about 25 minutes, stirring occasionally, until very thick. Remove the pan from the heat. Add the olives and capers, and season with pepper to taste. Leave to cool while shaping the pizza bases.

4 Turn out the risen dough onto the lightly floured surface and knead lightly, then divide into six equal portions. Pat or roll out each one to a neat disc about 12.5cm across. Arrange the discs, spaced slightly apart, on two lightly greased baking trays.

5 Spread the tomato topping over the discs, leaving a 5mm border. Top with the artichokes, then scatter over the Gorgonzola. Leave to rise in a warm place for 15 minutes.

6 Preheat the oven to 230°C (gas mark 8). Bake the pizzinis for 15 minutes or until the edges of the crust are golden brown.

OREGANO PIZZA DOUGH

450g white bread flour

1 teaspoon dried oregano

1 sachet easy-blend dried yeast, about 7g

250ml tepid water, or as needed

PUTTANESCA TOPPING

1 tablespoon extra virgin olive oil

1 red onion, finely chopped

4 garlic cloves, crushed

500g ripe tomatoes, diced

1 fresh red chilli, deseeded and finely chopped

50g stoned black and green olives, roughly chopped

1 tablespoon capers

pepper to taste

1 can (about 400g) artichoke hearts, drained and quartered

100g Gorgonzola cheese, crumbled

Fb GI

preparation time **1¾ hours** including rising
cooking time **15 mins**

serves **6**

PER SERVING

388 kcal

14g protein

9.5g total fat

4g saturated fat

65mg cholesterol

66g total carbohydrate

6g sugars

5g fibre

300mg sodium

HEALTH HINT

Artichokes contain a type of dietary fibre called fructoligosaccarides, which encourages the growth of friendly bacteria in the gut.

sesame prawn and crab toasts

These crisp toasts can be served as a starter or as a good savoury snack to hand around with drinks. Traditionally the toasts are deep-fried in oil, but in this healthy version they are baked in a hot oven until crisp and golden.

1 Preheat the oven to 200°C (gas mark 6). For the topping, combine the prawns, crab meat, spring onions, garlic, red pepper, lemon zest, cayenne pepper and cream in a bowl. Add pepper to taste. Mix all the ingredients together well to make a spreadable paste, then set aside until ready to cook. (If you want to prepare the mixture ahead, it can be kept in the refrigerator for 4 hours.)

2 Beat together the cream and egg until smooth. Dip the slices of bread in the mixture to coat both sides well, then place the bread on a greased baking tray. Spread the prawn and crab topping evenly over the bread, spreading right up to the edges.

3 Lightly brush the remaining egg and cream mixture over the surface of the prawn and crab topping and sprinkle evenly with the sesame seeds.

4 Bake the toasts for 20–25 minutes or until they are crisp and golden brown. Cut each slice of toast into eight small triangles and serve immediately, while still hot, garnished with shredded spring onions.

Variation For five-spice prawn and water chestnut toasts, omit the crab meat and use 170g prawns instead of 85g. Season the mixture with ¼ teaspoon five-spice powder instead of the cayenne pepper and lemon zest. Instead of the red pepper, stir in 6 water chestnuts, very finely chopped, and 4 teaspoons chopped fresh coriander.

2 tablespoons whipping cream
1 large egg
2 large slices of oatmeal or soft grain bread
2 teaspoons sesame seeds
shredded spring onions to garnish

PRAWN AND CRAB TOPPING
85g peeled raw prawns, very finely chopped
85g fresh white crab meat, flaked
2 spring onions, thinly sliced
1 large garlic clove, crushed
½ small red pepper, deseeded and diced
½ teaspoon finely grated lemon zest
pinch of cayenne pepper
1 tablespoon whipping cream
pepper to taste

Kc GI

preparation time **15 mins**
cooking time **20–25 mins**
serves **4**

PER SERVING

183 kcal	
14g protein	
10g total fat	
4g saturated fat	
87mg cholesterol	
11g total carbohydrate	
2g sugars	
1g fibre	
352mg sodium	

HEALTH HINT

Crab meat is low in saturated fat and in calories, and has many nutrition benefits for heart-conscious people. It gives you B vitamins and many minerals, in particular potassium, zinc, iodine and phosphorus.

rice croquettes with mozzarella

These rice croquettes are moulded around nuggets of mozzarella and rolled in breadcrumbs before cooking. Traditionally croquettes are deep-fried, but these are oven-baked for a modern streamlined version that is much healthier.

1 tablespoon extra virgin olive oil

1 small onion, finely chopped

200g risotto rice

3 tablespoons dry vermouth

600ml hot reduced-sodium vegetable
stock or stock made without salt

pepper to taste

1 egg, beaten

30g Parmesan cheese, freshly grated

55g fine white breadcrumbs, made
from bread 1–2 days old

55g mozzarella cheese, cut into
8 cubes

TO SERVE

100g baby spinach leaves

lemon wedges

1 Heat the olive oil in a saucepan, add the onion and cook for 5 minutes or until soft. Add the rice and stir. Stir in the vermouth and boil until it has almost evaporated. Add the stock, a ladleful at a time, allowing each one to be almost absorbed before adding the next, stirring frequently. Total cooking time will be 15–20 minutes. The risotto is ready when the rice is tender but still firm and the overall texture is creamy. Remove from heat and season with pepper. Stir in the egg and Parmesan cheese, then leave to cool.

2 Preheat the oven to 200°C (gas mark 6). Heat a lightly oiled baking dish in the oven. Mix the breadcrumbs with some pepper on a large plate.

3 Spoon the risotto into eight mounds on a board. Press a cube of mozzarella into the centre of each mound, then press the risotto over the cheese to enclose it and mould into a neat egg-shaped croquette. Roll the croquettes in the seasoned breadcrumbs until completely coated. Place in the hot baking dish and bake for 30–40 minutes, turning halfway through, until golden brown and crisp.

4 Make a heap of spinach leaves on four plates and top each with two croquettes. Serve immediately, with lemon wedges.

preparation time **35 mins**
plus cooling

cooking time **30–40 mins**

serves **4** (makes 8)

PER SERVING

352 kcal

15g protein

11g total fat
4g saturated fat

74mg cholesterol

46g total carbohydrate
2g sugars

1g fibre

316mg sodium

HEALTH HINT

Raw spinach is a good source of beta carotene and provides vitamins C and E, all of which are antioxidants that help to protect against heart disease, strokes and cancer.

Oriental prawn tartlets

These pretty little filo tartlets, filled with stir-fried prawns and colourful vegetables, make an unusual light snack or a starter. The cases can be made ahead, but they are best filled just before serving, so the pastry remains crisp.

1 Preheat the oven to 200°C (gas mark 6). Mix together the sunflower and sesame oils. Lay the filo pastry sheets out flat, one on top of the other. Trim the stacked pastry to make a 30 x 40cm rectangle (discard the excess pastry). Cut the pastry lengthways into three and then across into four, making 10cm squares. You will have 36 squares of filo.

2 Place one filo square in each of the 12 hollows in a non-stick bun tin. Brush very lightly with a little of the oil mixture. Place another square of filo on top, arranging it so the corners are not directly on top of those beneath. Brush with a little more oil, then place a third filo square on top, again with the corners offset. Bake the pastry cases for 5-7 minutes or until they are golden brown and crisp.

3 Meanwhile, heat the remaining oil mixture in a wok or large frying pan. Add the garlic, spring onions and ginger, and stir-fry over a moderate heat for about 30 seconds. Add the carrot and stir-fry for 2 minutes, then add the prawns and stir-fry for a further 2 minutes or until they turn pink.

4 Add the mange-tout, pak choy and bean sprouts. Stir-fry over a high heat for 2–3 minutes or until all the vegetables are just tender and the mixture is piping hot. Sprinkle with the soy sauce and toss to mix.

5 Spoon the prawn and vegetable mixture into the filo pastry cases and serve immediately, garnished with sprigs of coriander.

1 tablespoon sunflower oil
1 teaspoon toasted sesame oil
3 sheets filo pastry, 30 x 50cm each, about 90g in total
1 garlic clove, crushed
3 spring onions, thinly sliced
1 tablespoon finely chopped fresh root ginger
1 carrot, cut into fine julienne strips
300g peeled raw tiger prawns
75g mange-tout, sliced diagonally
1 small head pak choy, about 85g, sliced
75g bean sprouts
1 tablespoon reduced-sodium soy sauce
sprigs of fresh coriander to garnish

Kc

preparation and cooking time **35–45 mins**

serves **4** (makes 12)

PER SERVING

183 kcal

18g protein

5g total fat
1g saturated fat

210mg cholesterol

18g total carbohydrate
3g sugars

2g fibre

645mg sodium

HEALTH HINTS

Prawns are a good source of low-fat protein and the antioxidant mineral selenium as well as an excellent source of vitamin B$_{12}$.

Mange-tout contain more vitamin C than ordinary garden peas. This is because the pods, which as the name implies are eaten too ('mange-tout' means 'eat all'), make an additional contribution.

goat's cheese and cranberry tartlets

Adding rolled oats to shortcrust pastry not only makes it more nutritious, it also gives it more texture. The little pastry cases have a delectable tart-sweet filling of cranberry sauce, goat's cheese and a yoghurt custard.

150g plain flour
50g rolled oats
85g margarine suitable for baking, well chilled

FILLING
3 large eggs
120ml plain low-fat yoghurt
300ml semi-skimmed milk
4 tablespoons cranberry sauce
3 tablespoons snipped fresh chives
85g goat's cheese, crumbled
pepper to taste

1 Put the flour and oats in a bowl and rub in the margarine. Fork in enough water – about 3 tablespoons – to make the mixture clump together. Gather into a ball, wrap in cling film and chill for at least 30 minutes.

2 Preheat the oven to 190°C (gas mark 5). Cut the dough into six pieces. Roll out thinly and use to line six 12.5cm loose-bottomed, non-stick tartlet tins that are 2.5cm deep.

3 Prick the tartlet cases and line with greaseproof paper and dried beans. Bake for 12 minutes, then remove the paper and beans. Bake for a further 8–10 minutes or until light golden. Remove from the oven. Lower the heat to 180°C (gas mark 4).

4 Mix the eggs with the yoghurt, milk and pepper to taste. Spread 2 teaspoons of the cranberry sauce in the bottom of each pastry case, then scatter over the chives and goat's cheese. Pour in the egg mixture.

5 Bake for 25–30 minutes or until the filling is slightly puffed up and golden brown. Serve warm.

 GI

preparation time **45 mins** plus 30 mins chilling
cooking time **25–30 mins**
serves **6**

PER SERVING

371 kcal

13g protein

21g total fat
7g saturated fat

150mg cholesterol

33g total carbohydrate
7g sugars

1g fibre

270mg sodium

HEALTH HINTS

Cranberries are not only a rich source of vitamin C, they also contain a natural antibiotic that helps to control some urinary tract infections, mostly notably cystitis.

Rolled oats are made from the whole oat grain with only the husk removed before they are rolled flat. The nutritional value of the whole grain is therefore retained.

In common with all cheeses, goat's cheese provides protein, calcium and phosphorus, as well as several B vitamins.

spicy chicken satay

Moist, gingery cubes of chicken and crunchy vegetables are grilled on skewers and served with a peanut sauce. Wedges of lime are included so the hot juice can be squeezed over the cooked chicken just before eating.

1 To make the marinade, mix the ginger, soy sauce, lime juice and oil together in a bowl. Add the chicken and toss to coat. Cover with cling film and leave to marinate in the refrigerator for at least 2 hours, turning once or twice.

2 Soak eight wooden skewers in cold water for 30 minutes.

3 Meanwhile, to make the peanut sauce, heat the oil in a small saucepan, add the onion and cook over moderate heat, stirring, for 3 minutes. Add the peanuts and cook for 3–5 minutes or until both the nuts and onion are lightly browned, stirring occasionally. Add the garlic, curry paste, soy sauce, sugar and 150ml water. Bring to the boil. Stir in the creamed coconut. Simmer gently for 5 minutes or until thickened, stirring occasionally. Purée the sauce in a blender or food processor to make a thick cream. Return to the saucepan and set aside.

4 Preheat the grill to high. Lift the chicken out of the marinade; reserve the marinade. Thread the chicken, lime wedges and vegetables onto the soaked skewers. Arrange the skewers on the grill rack and brush with the marinade. Place under the grill, close to the heat, and cook for 10–15 minutes, turning once or twice, until the ingredients are browned and the chicken is cooked thoroughly – test by cutting one of the chicken pieces in half with a knife; there should be no hint of pink.

5 While the satay is cooking, reheat the sauce. Arrange the satay on four serving plates, garnish with sprigs of coriander and serve with the sauce.

350g chicken breast fillets, cut into 2cm cubes

1 lime, cut into 8 wedges

8 cherry tomatoes

1 yellow pepper, deseeded and cut into chunks

1 courgette, about 150g, thickly sliced

sprigs of fresh coriander to garnish

MARINADE

2cm piece of fresh root ginger, peeled and finely chopped

2 tablespoons reduced-sodium soy sauce

juice of $\frac{1}{2}$ lime

1 tablespoon sunflower oil

PEANUT SAUCE

2 teaspoons sunflower oil

1 small onion, finely chopped

50g unsalted peanuts, finely chopped

1 garlic clove, chopped

1 teaspoon Thai green curry paste

1 tablespoon reduced-sodium soy sauce

$\frac{1}{2}$ teaspoon caster sugar

25g creamed coconut

Kc

preparation time **30 mins** plus 2 hours marinating

cooking time **20–25 mins**

serves **4**

PER SERVING

272 kcal

27g protein

14g total fat
6g saturated fat

61mg cholesterol

12g total carbohydrate
8g sugars

2g fibre

563mg sodium

HEART SUPERFOOD

Like most other nuts, peanuts are high in fat, although much of the fat they contain is of the unsaturated variety. Research suggests that diets that contain a daily intake of peanuts, peanut butter or groundnut oil may help to lower total cholesterol, particularly LDL cholesterol, and thus help to protect against heart disease.

dim sum with dipping sauce

These Chinese dumplings have a chicken filling, which is lighter than the traditional pork mixture, and use wonton wrappers, which are sold in Oriental food shops. Serve the dim sum as the starter for a multi-course Chinese meal.

1 can (about 200g) water chestnuts, drained and chopped

4 spring onions, thinly sliced

2 tablespoons chopped fresh coriander

1 tablespoon reduced-sodium soy sauce

1 tablespoon toasted sesame oil

350g minced chicken

1 teaspoon caster sugar

1 tablespoon finely chopped fresh root ginger

5 garlic cloves, finely chopped

30g fresh shiitake mushrooms, chopped

1 tablespoon cornflour, plus extra for dusting

cayenne pepper to taste

48 wonton wrappers

150g kale, Swiss chard or spring greens

DIPPING SAUCE

hoisin sauce, chopped spring onions, chopped fresh coriander and reduced-sodium soy sauce

1 Mix together the water chestnuts, spring onions, coriander, soy sauce and sesame oil. Add the chicken, sugar, ginger, garlic and mushrooms. Stir in the cornflour and the cayenne pepper and mix well. Cook a small spoonful of the chicken mixture in a frying pan, then taste it to check the seasoning.

2 Dust a plate with cornflour. Place about 1 teaspoon of filling on the middle of a wonton wrapper. Dampen the wrapper slightly just around the filling. Gather up the wrapper, pinching it around the filling to form a cup, open at the top and with 'frilly' edges. Set aside on the plate, and fill the remaining wrappers.

3 Line a multi-layered steamer with the kale, Swiss chard or spring greens. Stand the dim sum on the leaves and steam over rapidly boiling water for 8–10 minutes. Serve the dumplings hot, with the ingredients for the dipping sauce in individual bowls so that diners can mix them together to make a sauce to their own taste.

preparation time **45 mins**

cooking time **8–10 mins**

per batch

serves **6** (makes 48)

PER SERVING

152 kcal

16g protein

4g total fat
0.8g saturated fat

41mg cholesterol

13.5g total carbohydrate
2.5g sugars

1g fibre

177mg sodium

HEALTH HINT

Garlic, onions, leeks and chives contain allicin, which has antifungal and antibiotic properties. Garlic also contains other compounds that have been shown in animal studies to inactivate carcinogens and suppress the growth of tumours.

pork pot-sticker dumplings with crisp and spicy peanut salad

These fragrant Chinese-style pasta purses are made with wonton wrappers. They are part fried, then simmered in stock and served on a bed of green leaves with a spicy salad of peanuts and crunchy vegetables.

1 Tip the pork into a bowl and, with your hands, mix in the water chestnuts, spring onions, ginger, hoisin sauce and soy sauce. Divide the mixture into 20 equal portions.

2 Brush a wonton wrapper with beaten egg and place a portion of the pork mixture in the centre. Gather up the wrapper around the pork and squeeze it together at the top to seal in the filling and form an old-fashioned moneybag shape. Repeat with the remaining pork and wonton wrappers.

3 Heat the oil in a large frying pan. Stand the dumplings in the pan, in one layer, cover and cook them very gently for 5 minutes or until they are lightly browned on the base.

4 Pour in enough hot stock to come halfway up the sides of the dumplings, then cover the pan again and simmer gently for 10 minutes or until the wonton wrappers are cooked.

5 Meanwhile, to make the salad, stir the cucumber, carrot, shallots and coriander together. Gradually add the dipping sauce, tasting the mixture to ensure that it is not too spicy for you, then add the peanuts and pepper to season.

6 To serve, arrange the lettuce leaves on four large plates and pile five drained dumplings on top of each. Spoon some of the spicy peanut salad around and garnish with coriander sprigs. Serve any remaining salad separately.

250g lean minced pork

55g drained canned water chestnuts, finely chopped

3 spring onions, finely chopped

1 tablespoon finely grated fresh root ginger

2 tablespoons hoisin sauce

1 tablespoon reduced-sodium soy sauce

20 wonton wrappers

1 egg, beaten

2 tablespoons sunflower oil

300ml hot low-sodium chicken stock or stock made without salt

4–8 crisp lettuce leaves to serve

SPICY PEANUT SALAD

7.5cm piece of cucumber, deseeded and finely diced

1 large carrot, finely diced

2 shallots, finely chopped

2–3 tablespoons chopped fresh coriander

2 tablespoons Thai dipping sauce for dim sum

4 tablespoons finely chopped unsalted peanuts

pepper to taste

---

preparation time **25 mins**
cooking time **15 mins**
serves **4** (makes 20)

PER SERVING

300 kcal

20.5g protein

20g total fat
4g saturated fat

97mg cholesterol

9g total carbohydrate
3g sugars

2g fibre

774mg sodium

COOK'S TIP

Instead of frying and then simmering the dumplings, they can be steamed as for the dim sum with dipping sauce (see opposite page).

roast salmon strips with potato salad

This elegant starter is what the French would call a 'salade composée' – a salad where the elements are arranged separately. In this healthy example, salmon shares the spotlight with a light potato salad and a healthy helping of greens.

370g salmon fillet (in one piece)
750g new potatoes, unpeeled
3 shallots, finely chopped
80ml white wine vinegar
2 tablespoons Dijon mustard
½ teaspoon pepper or to taste
10g fresh dill, finely chopped
225g radishes, cut into thin matchstick strips
250g mixed salad leaves

1 Preheat the oven to 230°C (gas mark 8). Place the salmon skin-side down in a roasting tin. Roast for 10–15 minutes or until it is just cooked through. Allow it to cool to room temperature, then remove the skin.

2 While the salmon is roasting, cook the potatoes in a pan of boiling water for about 20 minutes or until they are just tender. Drain the potatoes. When cool enough to handle, cut them into thin slices.

3 Combine the shallots, vinegar, mustard and pepper in a large bowl. Add the warm potatoes, tossing gently to combine. Just before serving, add the dill and radishes.

4 Slice the salmon into thin strips. Arrange the salmon, potato salad and mixed salad leaves on a serving platter and serve.

 Fb

preparation and cooking time **55 mins**

serves **4**

PER SERVING

329 kcal

22g protein

11g total fat
2g saturated fat

47mg cholesterol

36g total carbohydrate
4g sugars

4g fibre

62mg sodium

COOK'S TIP

You can prepare both the fish and the potato salad a day ahead of time and refrigerate, but be sure to allow time for them both to return to room temperature before serving.

salmon cakes with creamy tomato-garlic sauce

Give those fatty beefburgers a miss and try these heart-healthy, thick, juicy salmon 'burgers' instead. And while you're at it, leave the tomato ketchup in the fridge and slather the salmon cakes with a home-made tomato sauce.

1 To make the sauce, cook the sun-dried tomatoes and garlic in a small saucepan of boiling water for 3 minutes. Drain, reserving 80ml of the cooking liquid. Transfer the tomatoes and garlic to a food processor. Add the reserved cooking liquid, the yoghurt and hot chilli sauce and process until smooth.

2 Meanwhile, cook the potato and garlic in a medium saucepan of boiling water for 7 minutes or until tender. Drain and transfer to a large bowl. Use a potato masher to mash the potato and garlic.

3 Stir in the salmon, 2 tablespoons breadcrumbs, the dill and capers. Shape the salmon mixture into eight cakes.

4 Heat the oil in a large non-stick frying pan over moderate heat. Coat the salmon cakes in the remaining breadcrumbs. Add to the frying pan and sauté for about 3 minutes on each side or until golden brown. Serve with the tomato-garlic sauce.

1 large baking potato, thinly sliced
2 garlic cloves, peeled
1 can (about 415g) pink salmon, drained
2 tablespoons plus 50g dried breadcrumbs
10g fresh dill, finely chopped
1 tablespoon capers, thoroughly rinsed and drained
1 tablespoon olive oil

TOMATO-GARLIC SAUCE

30g sun-dried tomatoes (not oil-packed)
2 garlic cloves, peeled
100g plain low-fat yoghurt
½ teaspoon hot chilli sauce

preparation time **30 mins**
cooking time **6 mins**
serves **4**

PER SERVING

362 kcal

30g protein

14g total fat
2g saturated fat

30mg cholesterol

31g total carbohydrate
3g sugars

1.5g fibre

816mg sodium

HEART SUPERFOOD

Why is canned salmon so healthy? First, salmon is rich with omega-3 fatty acids, highly nutritious oils that keep the blood 'flowing freely'. In addition, canned salmon contains a useful amount of calcium, which helps lower blood pressure. The calcium comes from the salmon bones, which are softened and made edible in the canning process.

pasta, rice & grains

fresh tomato sauce

Vine-ripened or full-flavoured summer tomatoes are best for this recipe, but you can also use canned tomatoes.

2 tablespoons extra virgin olive oil

1 large onion, finely chopped

1 garlic clove, chopped

1kg tomatoes, skinned, deseeded and chopped

150ml red wine or low-sodium vegetable stock (or stock made without salt)

2 tablespoons chopped fresh basil or 1 teaspoon dried basil

pinch of sugar

pepper to taste

8–10 sprigs of fresh basil, shredded, to garnish (optional)

4 tablespoons freshly grated Parmesan cheese to serve (optional)

1 Heat the oil in a large saucepan. Add the onion and garlic, and cook gently, stirring occasionally, for 5 minutes or until softened but not browned.

2 Add the tomatoes, wine or stock and basil. Cook over moderate heat for 20–30 minutes or until the sauce is thick.

3 Process the sauce in a blender or food processor until smooth, then pass it through a fine sieve if a particularly smooth result is required.

4 Add the sugar to balance the acidity of the tomatoes. Stir in pepper to season and reheat the sauce.

5 Use the sauce as required. Or pour it over freshly cooked pasta, toss well and top with shredded basil and freshly grated Parmesan cheese.

preparation time **10 mins**

cooking time **25–35 mins**

serves **4** (makes 600ml)

PER SERVING

131 kcal

2g protein

6g total fat
1g saturated fat

0mg cholesterol

11g total carbohydrate
10g sugars

3g fibre

26mg sodium

béchamel sauce

This classic white sauce is used in a range of dishes, such as lasagne. Many ingredients can be added to vary the flavour.

600ml semi-skimmed milk

1 onion or 2 shallots, halved

1 bay leaf

6 black peppercorns

pinch of grated nutmeg or 1 blade of mace

55g margarine

55g plain flour

pepper to taste

1 Pour the milk into a heavy-based saucepan and add the onion or shallots, bay leaf, peppercorns and nutmeg or mace. Bring just to the boil over moderate heat, then remove from the heat, cover and set aside to infuse for 10 minutes. Strain the flavoured milk into a jug.

2 Melt the margarine in the rinsed-out pan. Stir in the flour and cook gently, stirring occasionally, for 1 minute. Do not allow the flour to brown.

3 Remove the pan from the heat and gradually pour in the milk, stirring or whisking constantly. Return the pan to the heat and bring to the boil, still stirring or whisking.

4 Reduce the heat and simmer the sauce gently for about 2 minutes, stirring occasionally, until it is smooth and thick.

5 Taste and add pepper. Serve or use immediately.

preparation time **5 mins** plus 10 mins infusing

cooking time **5 mins**

serves **4** (makes 600ml)

PER SERVING

220 kcal

6g protein

14g total fat
4g saturated fat

9mg cholesterol

18g total carbohydrate
7g sugars

0.5g fibre

160mg sodium

preparation time **10 mins** plus 30 mins infusing

cooking time **2 mins**

serves **4**

PER SERVING

124 kcal
0g protein
14g total fat
2g saturated fat
0mg cholesterol
0g total carbohydrate
0g sugars
0g fibre
0mg sodium

garlic and herb dressing

Pasta is superb with this simple dressing. The secret is to warm the garlic with bay leaves in the oil, to mellow the garlic flavour slightly. Then the dressing is left to stand so that the flavour of the garlic can infuse the oil.

1 Crease the bay leaves in half and place them in a small saucepan with the garlic. Add about 1 tablespoon olive oil and heat gently for 2 minutes or until the oil just begins to sizzle around the garlic. Remove from the heat.

2 Stir in the lemon zest, then pour in the remaining oil. Set aside to infuse for at least 30 minutes.

3 Remove the bay leaves and add the chopped herbs. Toss the dressing into hot pasta and serve.

2 fresh bay leaves
4 garlic cloves, thinly sliced
5 tablespoons extra virgin olive oil
grated zest of 1 lemon
4 tablespoons snipped fresh chives
4 tablespoons chopped fresh parsley
4 tablespoons chopped fresh tarragon, sage, marjoram or dill, or a mixture of fresh herbs

pesto sauce

A little home-made pesto sauce goes a long way. Toss this sauce into piping hot pasta just before eating. Store any leftover pesto in a screwtop jar in the refrigerator (cover the surface of the pesto with a little extra olive oil).

preparation time **10 mins**

serves **4** (makes 150ml)

PER SERVING

206 kcal
4g protein
21g total fat
4g saturated fat
7mg cholesterol
0.4g total carbohydrate
0.3g sugars
0g fibre
57mg sodium

1 Place the garlic in a food processor or blender. Add the pine nuts and Parmesan cheese, and process until the ingredients are finely chopped and thoroughly combined.

2 Add the basil, including all the soft stalks. Process until the basil is chopped and the mixture begins to clump together.

3 Add the olive oil and process until combined. The sauce should have a fine, slightly grainy texture. Serve with pasta.

2 garlic cloves, peeled
30g pine nuts
30g Parmesan cheese, freshly grated
20g fresh basil sprigs
5 tablespoons extra virgin olive oil

tagliatelle with meatballs

These little meatballs have aubergine added for a modern twist, and the sauce contains all the essential flavours of a classic Italian dish. Both meatballs and sauce can be made ahead, then reheated when you are ready to cook the pasta.

1 aubergine, about 200g
2 teaspoons extra virgin olive oil
340g lean minced beef
1 small onion, roughly chopped
1 garlic clove, crushed
100g fresh white breadcrumbs
grated zest of 1 lemon
1 tablespoon fresh basil leaves
pepper to taste
400g egg tagliatelle
fresh basil leaves to garnish

RICH TOMATO SAUCE
1 tablespoon extra virgin olive oil
4 lean back bacon rashers, about
    125g in total, derinded
    and chopped
1 onion, roughly chopped
1 medium-sized carrot, thinly sliced
1 celery stick, thinly sliced
1 garlic clove, crushed
2 cans (about 400g each) chopped
    tomatoes
150ml dry white wine
1 tablespoon chopped fresh basil

1 Preheat the grill to high. Halve the aubergine lengthways, then place skin side up on the rack in the grill pan and grill for 5 minutes. Turn the aubergine halves over, brush each cut side with 1 teaspoon oil and grill for a further 5 minutes or until the flesh is tender. Cool.

2 Peel away the aubergine skin, then place the flesh in a blender or food processor. Add the beef, onion, garlic, breadcrumbs, lemon zest, basil leaves and pepper to taste, and blend briefly. With wet hands, shape the mixture into 36 balls. Chill until ready to cook.

3 To make the sauce, heat the oil in a non-stick saucepan, add the bacon and onion, and fry, stirring, for 3–4 minutes or until softened. Stir in the carrot, celery and garlic and fry, stirring frequently, for a further 5 minutes. Add the tomatoes with their juice, the wine and pepper to taste. Bring to the boil, then reduce the heat, cover and simmer for 20 minutes.

4 While the sauce is simmering, fry the meatballs in a large non-stick frying pan without any fat. Fry in three batches, for 10–12 minutes each batch, until evenly browned and cooked through. As they are done, remove the meatballs with a draining spoon and drain on kitchen paper. When they are all cooked, add them to the sauce together with the chopped basil and keep warm.

5 Drop the tagliatelle into a large saucepan of boiling water. When the water returns to the boil, cook for 10–12 minutes, or according to the packet instructions, until al dente. Drain the pasta, toss with the meatballs and sauce and garnish with fresh basil leaves. Serve immediately.

preparation and cooking
time 1¼ **hours**
serves **6**

PER SERVING
545 kcal
28g protein
18g total fat
6g saturated fat
35mg cholesterol
68g total carbohydrate
8g sugars
5g fibre
633mg sodium

HEALTH HINT

Frying the meatballs without any fat or oil draws out some of the fat in the beef, which can then be drained off.

herb-infused vegetable lasagne

preparation time **1 hour** plus 10 mins standing

cooking time **45 mins**

serves **4**

PER SERVING

485 kcal

34g protein

17g total fat
6g saturated fat

84mg cholesterol

50g total carbohydrate
14g sugars

5g fibre

537mg sodium

HEALTH HINT

Aubergines do not have a strong flavour, but absorb other flavours in a dish well. They add 'bulk' for very few calories.

COOK'S TIP

Puréed cottage cheese makes a creamy base for a delicious low-fat lasagne topping.

For this zesty lasagne, pasta sheets are layered with a tomato, aubergine and mushroom sauce flavoured with marjoram and sage, then topped with a smooth cheese sauce and freshly grated Parmesan.

1 Heat the oil in a large saucepan. Add the fennel seeds and bay leaf and cook for a few seconds, pressing the bay leaf with a spoon to bring out its aroma. Add the onion, garlic, celery, carrot, mushrooms, marjoram and sage. Cook, stirring frequently, for 10 minutes or until the vegetables soften slightly.

2 Stir in the aubergine and lemon zest, mixing well. Continue to cook for 5 minutes, stirring frequently. Pour in the tomatoes with their juice and add pepper to taste. Bring to the boil, then reduce the heat and simmer for about 15 minutes. Preheat the oven to 180°C (gas mark 4).

3 While the sauce is simmering, cook the lasagne sheets in boiling water for 3–5 minutes, or according to the packet instructions, until al dente. Drain well and lay out the sheets on a clean tea towel, in a single layer, to dry.

4 Process the cottage cheese with the flour and egg in a food processor or blender until smooth. Add the milk and process again briefly. Season to taste with nutmeg and pepper.

5 Pour half the aubergine sauce into a large rectangular or square ovenproof dish. Discard the bay leaf. Cover with half the lasagne sheets, then add the remaining sauce and top with the rest of the lasagne, overlapping the sheets neatly.

6 Pour the cottage cheese mixture over the lasagne to cover it completely. Sprinkle the Parmesan cheese evenly over the top. Bake the lasagne for about 45 minutes or until the topping is set and deep golden.

7 Leave the lasagne to stand for 10 minutes before serving. This allows time for the pasta and sauce to cool and set slightly.

2 tablespoons extra virgin olive oil

1 tablespoon fennel seeds

1 bay leaf

1 large onion, chopped

1 garlic clove, crushed

1 celery stick, diced

1 carrot, diced

100g mushrooms, roughly chopped

3 tablespoons chopped fresh marjoram or 1 tablespoon dried oregano

6 fresh sage leaves, shredded, or 1 tablespoon dried sage

2 large aubergines, cut into 1cm dice

grated zest of 1 lemon

2 cans (about 400g each) chopped tomatoes

pepper to taste

12 sheets fresh lasagne, about 250g in total

450g cottage cheese

2 tablespoons plain flour

1 egg

100ml semi-skimmed milk

good pinch of freshly grated nutmeg

pepper to taste

2 tablespoons freshly grated Parmesan cheese

mushroom ravioli in herb jus

Bought stuffed pasta just does not taste anything like silken-textured home-made pasta with a freshly prepared savoury filling. This is not a convenience meal – making pasta does take time – but the result is well worth the effort!

3 tablespoons extra virgin olive oil

4 shallots, chopped

1 garlic clove, chopped

450g mushrooms, finely chopped

3 tablespoons brandy

pepper to taste

30g dried porcini mushrooms, soaked, drained and finely chopped

100g fresh wholemeal breadcrumbs

55g Parmesan cheese, freshly grated

2 eggs

2 tablespoons chopped fresh parsley or basil

1 teaspoon chopped fresh marjoram or ¼ teaspoon dried marjoram

2 tablespoons plain flour

250g mange-tout or sugarsnap peas

2 tablespoons tiny tender sprigs of fresh thyme to garnish

1 tablespoon extra virgin olive oil to serve (optional)

PASTA

450g white bread flour

4 eggs, beaten

1 tablespoon extra virgin olive oil

HERB JUS

750ml low-sodium chicken or vegetable stock or stock made without salt

175ml dry white wine

1 garlic clove, chopped

1 tablespoon fresh thyme leaves or ¼ teaspoon dried thyme

4 courgettes, thinly sliced or coarsely diced

1 Heat the olive oil in a large saucepan. Add the shallots and cook for a few seconds, then add the garlic and mushrooms. Cook over high heat, stirring, to brown the mushrooms, then reduce the heat and cook for 10 minutes or until the mixture has reduced in volume.

2 Pour in the brandy and cook, stirring, until it has evaporated. Remove from the heat and add pepper to taste.

3 Stir in the porcini mushrooms, breadcrumbs, Parmesan cheese, eggs, parsley and marjoram. The ingredients should form a moist paste. Place in the refrigerator while you make the pasta.

4 To make the pasta, sift the flour onto a work surface, make a well in the centre and add the eggs and oil. Using your hands, gradually mix the flour into the eggs and oil until the mixture begins to form a firm dough. If necessary, add a few drops of water.

5 Knead the dough for 10 minutes or until smooth and elastic. The dough should still be firm. Add a little extra flour if the dough becomes too sticky. Wrap the dough tightly in plastic wrap and set aside to rest for 30 minutes.

6 Cut the pasta dough into quarters and roll out each separately. If using a pasta machine to roll the dough, use the second-thinnest setting. Otherwise, roll it out by hand on an unfloured surface. Cut each rolled-out quarter into two strips, each about 10 x 50cm.

7 Lay a pasta strip on the work surface. Dot the filling on the dough in small mounds (about 1 teaspoon each) about 5cm apart. Ensure that there is enough room between the mounds of filling for the covering of dough to stick to the base.

8 Brush the dough around each mound with a little water. Top with a second strip of pasta and press it down firmly around the filling to seal. Cut between the mounds of filling with a fluted pastry wheel or sharp knife.

9 Carefully pull the ravioli apart and toss with the flour. Place in a single layer on a tray in the fridge. Repeat with the remaining dough and filling.

10 To make the herb jus, combine the stock, wine and garlic in a saucepan. Bring to the boil and cook over high heat for

preparation amd cooking time **1¾ hours** plus 30 mins resting

serves **6**

PER SERVING

573 kcal

25g protein

18g total fat
5g saturated fat

240mg cholesterol

70g total carbohydrate
5g sugars

6g fibre

320mg sodium

HEALTH HINT

Mushrooms are low in fat and calories, and they also provide useful amounts of copper as well as some of the B vitamins.

5–10 minutes or until the liquid is well flavoured. Add the thyme and courgettes and continue cooking over moderately high heat for 5–10 minutes or until the courgettes are quite tender but not mushy, and the liquid has evaporated slightly.

11 Meanwhile, cook the ravioli in boiling water for 4–5 minutes or until they rise to the surface. Add the mange-tout for the final 30–60 seconds of cooking. Drain well.

12 Serve the ravioli and mange-tout in shallow soup bowls with the courgettes and herb jus ladled over. Sprinkle tiny thyme sprigs over the top and drizzle with the optional olive oil. Serve immediately.

Variations Bought wonton wrappers can be used instead of home-made pasta dough. • Alternatively, you can buy fresh lasagne and roll it out slightly thinner, if necessary, then use it to make the ravioli.

macaroni and mushroom cheese

 Introduce vegetables to old favourites for healthy family meals. This well-loved pasta dish is delicious with mushrooms, peas and red pepper added. Using a small amount of powerful blue cheese adds flavour but not too much fat.

225g macaroni or rigatoni

170g frozen peas

2 tablespoons sunflower oil

1 red pepper, deseeded and chopped

225g mushrooms, quartered if large

30g plain flour

600ml semi-skimmed milk

1 tablespoon Dijon mustard

55g Roquefort cheese, chopped

pepper to taste

30g reduced-fat Cheddar
    cheese, grated

55g fresh wholemeal breadcrumbs

1 Preheat the oven to 220°C (gas mark 7). Cook the pasta in boiling water for 10–12 minutes, or according to the packet instructions, until almost al dente. Add the peas for the final 2 minutes of cooking. Drain the pasta and peas well.

2 Heat the oil in a heavy-based saucepan and cook the red pepper for 1–2 minutes. Add the mushrooms and cook for a further 2–3 minutes or until softened, stirring occasionally.

3 Stir in the flour, then gradually stir in the milk and bring to the boil, stirring. Simmer until thickened.

4 Add the mustard and Roquefort cheese with pepper to taste, and stir until the cheese has melted. Add the pasta and peas and mix thoroughly. Pour the mixture into an ovenproof dish.

5 Mix the Cheddar cheese with the breadcrumbs and sprinkle this over the pasta mixture. Bake for 10–15 minutes or until lightly browned and bubbling hot. Serve immediately.

preparation time **30 mins**

cooking time **10–15 mins**

serves **4**

PER SERVING

520 kcal

24g protein

16g total fat

6g saturated fat

25mg cholesterol

75g total carbohydrate

12g sugars

5g fibre

460mg sodium

HEALTH HINT

Frozen vegetables often contain more vitamin C than fresh ones. For example, frozen peas retain 60–70 per cent of their vitamin content after freezing and maintain this level throughout storage.

pumpkin, ricotta and sage gnocchi

There are numerous versions of gnocchi. Here a flour-based dough of ricotta cheese and mashed pumpkin, flavoured with sage and Parmesan cheese, is used. A colourful roast red pepper and onion sauce completes the dish.

Fb

preparation and cooking
time **about 2 hours**
plus 1–2 hours drying

serves **4**

PER SERVING

404 kcal	
18g protein	
15g total fat	
7g saturated fat	
96mg cholesterol	
52g total carbohydrate	
11g sugars	
5g fibre	
146mg sodium	

HEALTH HINT

Like other cheeses, ricotta is a good source of calcium. In addition, it offers good quantities of phosphorus, another mineral involved in ensuring that bones and teeth are healthy. Phosphorus is also important in the release of energy from food.

1 Preheat the oven to 200°C (gas mark 6). Spread the red pepper and onion halves, cut-side down, on a baking tray. Place the pumpkin wedges, skin-side up, on another baking tray. Bake the peppers and onion for 30–35 minutes and the pumpkin for 45–55 minutes or until all the vegetables are tender.

2 Transfer the red peppers and onions to a blender or food processor and add the oil. Blend until almost smooth. Season with pepper. Pour into a saucepan and set aside.

3 Leave the pumpkin until cool enough to handle, then scrape the flesh from the skin into a bowl. Mash until smooth. Beat in the ricotta cheese, egg, chopped sage and Parmesan cheese, then gradually work in the flour to make a soft dough.

4 Flour a work surface. Divide the dough into quarters and, with floured hands, roll each piece into a long, 2cm thick rope. Cut into 2cm lengths. Press the back of a fork into each piece of dough to make a pattern. Leave the gnocchi to dry at room temperature for 1–2 hours.

5 Bring a large saucepan of water to the boil. Drop in the gnocchi, 10–12 at a time, and poach for 2–3 minutes or until they bob up to the surface. Remove with a slotted spoon and drain well on kitchen paper. Set aside and keep warm until all the gnocchi are cooked. Meanwhile, gently warm the roasted pepper sauce over low heat. Spoon the sauce over the gnocchi, garnish with sage leaves and serve at once.

2 red peppers, halved and deseeded

1 onion, halved

500g pumpkin, cut into wedges
and deseeded

1 tablespoon extra virgin olive oil

pepper to taste

250g ricotta cheese

1 egg, beaten

3 tablespoons chopped fresh sage

30g Parmesan cheese, freshly grated

200g plain flour, plus extra
for rolling

fresh sage leaves to garnish

linguine with no-cook sauce

This quick and easy sauce is bursting with tomatoes and olive oil – foods that will keep your heart pumping strongly.

750g ripe plum tomatoes, deseeded and chopped

30g fresh basil leaves, chopped

4 tablespoons extra virgin olive oil

4 tablespoons chopped fresh flat-leaf parsley

2 tablespoons chopped fresh mint

2 teaspoons grated orange zest

3 garlic cloves, finely chopped

pepper to taste

370g linguine

4 tablespoons freshly grated Parmesan cheese to serve

1 Mix together the tomatoes, basil, oil, parsley, mint, orange zest, garlic and pepper in a bowl. Leave the mixture to infuse for between 30 minutes and 2 hours at room temperature.

2 Cook the pasta according to the packet directions until al dente. Drain well and place in a large bowl. Top with the sauce, sprinkle with the Parmesan cheese and serve.

 Fb GI

preparation and cooking time **30 mins** plus infusing

serves **4**

PER SERVING

500 kcal

18g protein

17g total fat
5g saturated fat

14mg cholesterol

74g total carbohydrate
8g sugars

4g fibre

190mg sodium

angel hair pasta with basil and walnut pesto

This pesto recipe adds the extra health boost of spinach and the peppery surprise of rocket, in true heart-healthy style.

100g fresh basil leaves

200g trimmed fresh spinach leaves

100g trimmed rocket leaves

40g walnut pieces

3 tablespoons freshly grated Parmesan cheese

3 garlic cloves, peeled

1 tablespoon extra virgin olive oil

370g angel hair pasta or spaghettini

½ lemon

fresh basil sprigs to garnish

1 Place the basil, spinach and rocket in a colander. Wash the leaves well under cold running water. Shake to dry. Transfer the leaves to a food processor.

2 Add the walnuts, Parmesan cheese and garlic and process until finely chopped. With the machine still running, slowly drizzle the oil through the feed tube, processing until the pesto is thick.

3 Cook the pasta according to the packet directions until al dente; drain. Toss the pasta with the pesto in a large serving bowl until evenly coated. Squeeze over the lemon juice, garnish with basil sprigs and serve.

30 Fb GI

preparation and cooking time **25 mins**

serves **4**

PER SERVING

473 kcal

18g protein

15g total fat
3g saturated fat

11mg cholesterol

70g total carbohydrate
4.5g sugars

4g fibre

160mg sodium

HEALTH HINT

This provides over 50 per cent of the recommended daily intake of vitamin B_1, essential for converting glucose into energy.

spaghetti with puttanesca sauce

Puttanesca is an Italian sauce that's hearty, spicy and rich in flavour. This version keeps in the traditional capers, anchovies and olives, but just uses fewer of them to keep down the level of salt.

1 Cook the spaghetti in boiling water for 10–12 minutes, or according to the packet instructions, until al dente. Meanwhile, finely chop the olives.

2 Heat the oil in a large non-stick frying pan over moderate heat. Add the garlic and cook briefly until golden, then stir in the tomatoes, capers, anchovies and chilli powder. Cook, stirring, for 10 minutes or until the sauce thickens slightly. Stir in the olives.

3 Drain the spaghetti, add to the sauce in the frying pan and toss to coat well. Sprinkle with the parsley and serve.

370g spaghetti
4 black olives, pitted
1 tablespoon extra virgin olive oil
2 garlic cloves, finely chopped
2 cans (about 400g each) chopped tomatoes
1 tablespoon capers, drained and rinsed
2 anchovies, finely chopped, or 1 teaspoon anchovy paste
¼ teaspoon chilli powder
1 tablespoon finely chopped fresh parsley to garnish

30 Kc Fb GI

preparation and cooking time **25 mins**

serves **4**

PER SERVING

381 kcal

14g protein

5g total fat
1g saturated fat

1mg cholesterol

75g total carbohydrate
8g sugars

4g fibre

281mg sodium

COOK'S TIP

To maximise the flavour of olives and minimise the salt and fat, opt for a tasty variety – a small amount delivers big taste. Look for black-purple kalamatas from Greece, wrinkled black gaetas from Italy or small black niçoise olives from France.

pasta and chicken salad with basil

 Quick to prepare, this salad makes an ideal midweek dinner and won't spoil if someone is late home. Tossing the pasta with lemon juice and white wine not only adds flavour but also means that the quantity of oil can be reduced.

300g pasta quills or shells

100g mange-tout

3 tablespoons extra virgin olive oil

finely shredded zest and juice
of 1 lemon

4 tablespoons dry white wine

pepper to taste

400g chicken breast fillets, cut
into bite-sized chunks

2 garlic cloves, thinly sliced

200g baby plum tomatoes, halved, or
3 medium-sized plum tomatoes,
each cut into 6 wedges

50g stoned black olives

20g fresh basil

1 Drop the pasta into a large saucepan of boiling water. When the water returns to the boil, cook for 10–12 minutes, or according to the packet instructions, until al dente. Add the mange-tout for the final minute of cooking. Drain, rinse with cold water and drain again well.

2 Mix 2 tablespoons of the oil with the lemon zest and juice and the wine in a large salad bowl. Season with pepper. Add the pasta and mange-tout, and toss to coat with the dressing. Set aside to cool slightly.

3 Meanwhile, heat the remaining 1 tablespoon of oil in a large frying pan. Add the chicken and garlic, and stir-fry over high heat for 5–6 minutes or until the chicken is lightly browned and thoroughly cooked. Add to the pasta.

4 Scatter the tomatoes and olives over the top. Sprinkle with the basil leaves, tearing larger ones into pieces. Toss the salad together and serve while the chicken is still warm.

30 **Fb** **GI**

preparation and cooking
time **30 mins**

serves **4**

PER SERVING

470 kcal

34g protein

12g total fat
2g saturated fat

70mg cholesterol

60g total carbohydrate
4g sugars

4g fibre

230mg sodium

HEALTH HINT

Pasta has a low GI (glycaemic index) so it is digested and absorbed slowly – you stay full for longer. The lemon juice in the dressing increases the acidity, which also works to delay digestion.

Oriental chicken and pasta salad

Pasta bows taste deliciously different when combined with an exotic dressing of fish sauce, fresh red chilli and rice vinegar in a moist chicken salad. Fresh crunchy vegetables complete this well-balanced main-course dish.

1 Place the chicken breasts in a large shallow pan and pour over enough water to cover them. Add the lemon or lime slices and the rice wine or sherry, and heat until just simmering. Reduce the heat and poach the chicken for 20 minutes or until cooked through. Remove from the heat and cover the pan, then leave the chicken to cool completely in the cooking liquid.

2 Meanwhile, cook the pasta in boiling water for about 10–12 minutes, or according to the packet instructions, until al dente. Drain, rinse under cold running water and drain again. Set the pasta aside until cool.

3 Place the carrot, red pepper, celery and cucumber in a large salad bowl. To make the dressing, mix together the fish sauce and sugar, stirring until the sugar dissolves, then add the vinegar, soy sauce, chilli and garlic. Pour the dressing over the raw vegetables in the salad bowl.

4 Drain the cooled chicken and pat dry on kitchen paper, then cut into bite-sized pieces. Stir the chicken and pasta into the dressed vegetables. Cover and leave to marinate in the refrigerator for about 1 hour. Bring the salad to room temperature before serving.

450g chicken breast fillets

2 lemon or lime slices

1 tablespoon rice wine (sake or mirin) or dry sherry

300g farfalle (pasta bows)

1 large carrot, about 150g, cut into matchstick strips

1 red pepper, deseeded and cut into matchstick strips

2 celery sticks, cut into matchstick strips

½ cucumber, halved, deseeded and cut into matchstick strips

DRESSING

2 tablespoons fish sauce

1 teaspoon caster sugar

1 tablespoon rice vinegar, cider vinegar or white wine vinegar

1 tablespoon reduced-sodium soy sauce

1 small fresh red chilli, deseeded and finely chopped

1 large garlic clove, crushed

preparation and cooking time **50 mins** plus cooling, 1 hour marinating and about 30 mins standing

serves **4**

PER SERVING

435 kcal

33g protein

7g total fat
2g saturated fat

80mg cholesterol

64g total carbohydrate
9g sugars

4.5g fibre

848mg sodium

HEALTH HINT

The combination of raw carrots, red pepper and celery makes this salad an excellent source of vitamins, particularly vitamin C.

spaghetti bolognese

Here's a new lower-fat version of a pasta classic, a full-flavoured meat sauce tossed with strands of spaghetti and served with Parmesan cheese. There's less beef than in traditional recipes, but low-fat chicken livers enrich the sauce.

2 tablespoons extra virgin olive oil

1 large onion, finely chopped

1 large carrot, finely chopped

2 celery sticks, finely chopped

2 garlic cloves, crushed

8 sun-dried tomatoes (not oil-packed), finely chopped

250g extra-lean minced beef

125g chicken livers, finely chopped

125ml red wine

1 can (about 400g) chopped tomatoes

125ml low-sodium beef stock or stock made without salt

1 teaspoon fresh thyme or marjoram or ½ teaspoon dried thyme or marjoram

3 tablespoons chopped fresh parsley

pepper to taste

350g spaghetti

30g Parmesan cheese, freshly grated

1 Heat the oil in a large saucepan and add the onion, carrot, celery, garlic and sun-dried tomatoes. Fry for 5–10 minutes, stirring frequently, until the vegetables start to brown.

2 Add the minced beef and chicken livers and fry, stirring, until the meat is browned. Pour in the wine, the tomatoes with their juice and the beef stock. Stir in the herbs and pepper to season. Cover the pan and simmer for 30 minutes, stirring occasionally.

3 Meanwhile, cook the spaghetti in boiling water for 10–12 minutes, or according to the packet instructions, until al dente.

4 Drain the spaghetti and mix it with the meat sauce, tossing until the strands are well coated. Sprinkle with Parmesan cheese and serve at once.

 Fb GI

preparation and cooking time **1 hour**

serves **4**

PER SERVING

621 kcal

37g protein

17g total fat
6g saturated fat

161mg cholesterol

80g total carbohydrate
14g sugars

6g fibre

289mg sodium

HEALTH HINT

Chicken livers are a good source of B vitamins, vitamin A, zinc and copper. They are also one of the richest sources of iron: a 100g serving provides about half the recommended daily intake.

spaghetti carbonara with roasted tomato salad

This version of an all-time favourite makes use of lower-fat dairy products and dry-cured ham instead of bacon to make a healthier dish with no compromise on flavour. To complete the meal, serve with a roasted tomato salad.

preparation and cooking time 35 mins

serves **4**

PER SERVING

580 kcal

32g protein

20g total fat
9g saturated fat

210mg cholesterol

73g total carbohydrate
10g sugars

5g fibre

260mg sodium

HEALTH HINT

Pasta scores healthily low on the glycaemic index, which means that it breaks down slowly into glucose in the body, providing long-lasting energy.

COOK'S TIP

Serving an interesting salad as a major part of a meal is a good way to avoid over-indulging in fatty foods.

1 Preheat the oven to 220°C (gas mark 7). To make the salad, place the tomatoes in a shallow ovenproof dish, cut-sides up, sprinkle with the garlic and basil and season with pepper. Drizzle over the olive oil, then roast for 10 minutes.

2 Mix the salad leaves in a serving dish. Add the onion, cucumber and fennel. When the tomatoes are done, spoon them, with all their hot juices, over the greens.

3 While the tomatoes are still roasting, cook the spaghetti in boiling water for 10–12 minutes, or according to the packet instructions, until al dente.

4 Meanwhile, dry-fry the slices of ham in a very hot, heavy-based frying pan for 2–3 minutes or until just crisp. Remove and drain on kitchen paper, then crumble or snip into small pieces. Set aside. Beat the eggs with the cream, then mix in the ricotta, half of the Parmesan cheese and a little pepper.

5 Drain the pasta. Return the empty pan to the heat and pour in the egg mixture. Heat for 1 minute over low heat, stirring constantly, then tip the drained pasta back into the pan. Toss the spaghetti with the creamy egg to coat the strands with the mixture. The heat of the pan and the hot pasta will lightly set the eggs to make a creamy sauce. Serve immediately, sprinkled with the remaining Parmesan cheese and the crisp ham, and accompanied by the roasted tomato salad.

350g spaghetti

100g Parma or Serrano ham, trimmed of visible fat

3 eggs

5 tablespoons reduced-fat single cream

3 tablespoons ricotta cheese

4 tablespoons freshly grated Parmesan cheese

ROASTED TOMATO SALAD

450g cherry tomatoes or baby plum tomatoes, halved

2 garlic cloves, very thinly sliced

8 large sprigs of fresh basil, shredded

pepper to taste

2 teaspoons extra virgin olive oil

mixed green salad leaves, such as frisée, rocket, watercress, Little Gem lettuce hearts and/or shredded Chinese leaves

1 red onion, thinly sliced

½ cucumber, thinly sliced

1 small bulb of fennel, halved and thinly sliced

stir-fried beef with fine noodles

Tangy tamarind and lemongrass infuse a Thai-inspired sauce for tender strips of beef and fine rice noodles. With mange-tout and baby corn adding all-important vegetable balance, this is an easy dish that is a meal in itself.

1 In a small bowl, combine the tamarind paste and boiling water and leave to soak for 10 minutes, stirring frequently to break down the paste. Mix the resulting tamarind liquid with the soy sauce, sesame oil and rice wine or sherry.

2 While the tamarind is soaking, soak the rice noodles in boiling water for 4 minutes, or according to the packet instructions. Then drain, rinse under cold running water and set aside to drain thoroughly.

3 Heat the sunflower oil in a wok or very large frying pan and stir-fry the beef over a high heat for about 3 minutes or until cooked. Use a slotted spoon to remove the beef from the wok and set it aside.

4 Add the onion, lemongrass, chilli and garlic to the wok and stir-fry over a high heat for 1 minute. Add the mange-tout, baby corn and mushrooms, and continue stir-frying for 2 minutes.

5 Return the beef to the wok. Add the tamarind liquid and the noodles and stir for about 1 minute to heat through. Serve immediately, while still hot.

Variations You can use strips of chicken breast instead of beef. • Other vegetables that work well in the stir-fry include strips of red or green pepper, sliced canned water chestnuts, chopped or shredded spring onions and bean sprouts.

1 teaspoon tamarind paste
3 tablespoons boiling water
2 tablespoons reduced-sodium soy sauce
2 teaspoons toasted sesame oil
1 tablespoon rice wine (sake or mirin) or sherry
100g fine rice noodles
1 tablespoon sunflower oil
225g lean rump steak, cut into strips
1 small onion, cut into wedges
2 teaspoons chopped lemongrass
1 fresh red chilli, deseeded and chopped
2 large garlic cloves, crushed
85g mange-tout, halved diagonally
6 baby corn, sliced
100g shiitake, chestnut or button mushrooms, sliced

30 **Fb**

preparation time **20 mins**
cooking time **10 mins**
serves **2**

PER SERVING

460 kcal

30g protein

15g total fat
3g saturated fat

68mg cholesterol

49g total carbohydrate
6.5g sugars

3g fibre

705mg sodium

HEALTH HINT

Weight for weight, chillies are richer in vitamin C than citrus fruits such as oranges. However, you would have to eat substantially more chillies than you are likely, or would want, to eat!

chicken and ricotta cannelloni

Cannelloni are often filled with rich beef or veal mixtures, but this lighter version uses chicken with fresh vegetables. The cannelloni can be assembled early in the day and left in the refrigerator until you are ready to bake them.

300g minced chicken

55g red pepper, deseeded and finely diced

½ small leek, finely chopped

55g frozen peas

250g ricotta cheese

55g mascarpone cheese

1 egg

4 tablespoons finely chopped fresh herbs, such as parsley, chives or basil, or a mixture

pepper to taste

24 no-precook cannelloni tubes, 7.5cm long, about 185g in total

SAUCE

900ml semi-skimmed milk

½ onion, studded with 4 cloves

1 bay leaf

pinch of freshly grated nutmeg

pepper to taste

55g plain flour

TOPPING

45g fine fresh wholemeal breadcrumbs

45g Parmesan cheese, freshly grated

1 To make the sauce, pour the milk into a heavy-based pan. Add the onion, bay leaf, nutmeg and pepper. Bring to the boil, then remove from the heat, cover and set aside to infuse.

2 Meanwhile, in a frying pan over moderately high heat, cook the chicken until white and crumbly. Set aside to cool slightly.

3 Place the diced red pepper, leek and frozen peas in a heatproof bowl, pour in enough boiling water to cover them and leave for 30 seconds. Drain the vegetables well.

4 Beat the ricotta, mascarpone and egg together, then mix in the chicken, drained vegetables, herbs and pepper to taste.

5 Using a slotted spoon, remove and discard the flavourings from the milk. Whisking constantly, sprinkle the flour into the milk. When incorporated, return the pan to moderate heat and bring the sauce to the boil, whisking. Reduce the heat and simmer gently, whisking frequently, for about 3 minutes.

6 Preheat the oven to 200°C (gas mark 6). Spread a layer of sauce on the bottom of a 30cm square ovenproof dish. Fill the cannelloni with the chicken mixture and arrange in a single layer on the sauce in the dish. Spoon over the remaining sauce. For the topping, mix together the breadcrumbs and Parmesan and sprinkle over the cannelloni. Bake for 35–40 minutes or until the topping is golden and the sauce bubbling. Leave to stand for 10 minutes before serving.

 GI

preparation time **45 mins**

cooking time **35–40 mins**

serves **6**

PER SERVING

445 kcal

29g protein

18g total fat
10g saturated fat

111mg cholesterol

43g total carbohydrate
10g sugars

2g fibre

290mg sodium

COOK'S TIP

Adding vegetables to cannelloni fillings will 'stretch' a small quantity of protein food, such as chicken. Frozen vegetables are better than canned vegetables as they retain more vitamins. However, when fresh or frozen vegetables are not available, use canned vegetables to contribute fibre, flavour and bulk.

cheesy rice with asparagus

This is an easy and attractive vegetarian dish. The rice is cooked in stock, then mixed with peas, asparagus and cheese, and baked in individual dishes. Choose a tangy Cheddar cheese for maximum flavour – a little will go a long way.

preparation time **25 mins**
cooking time **20 mins**
serves **4**

PER SERVING

508 kcal

22g protein

16g total fat
8g saturated fat

211mg cholesterol

70g total carbohydrate
2g sugars

3g fibre

409mg sodium

HEALTH HINT

Asparagus is a rich source of many of the B vitamins, especially folate. Folate not only helps to prevent birth defects such as spina bifida, if sufficient is consumed in the early stages of pregnancy, it may also help to protect against heart disease.

1 First prepare four individual baking dishes of 360ml capacity. Lightly grease with the melted margarine, then dust with the breadcrumbs to coat the bottom and sides. Preheat the oven to 190°C (gas mark 5).

2 Place the rice in a medium-sized saucepan, pour over the stock and bring to the boil. Reduce the heat, cover tightly and simmer gently for 5 minutes, without stirring.

3 Uncover the pan and stir in the peas and asparagus. Bring back to the boil, then reduce the heat and simmer gently, covered, for a further 5 minutes.

4 Remove the pan from the heat. Stir, then cover the pan again and leave the rice and vegetables to stand undisturbed for 5–7 minutes.

5 Combine the eggs and cheese in a mixing bowl. Add the chilli flakes and pepper to taste. Mix with a fork until well blended. Add the rice mixture and stir gently until thoroughly combined.

6 Divide the rice mixture evenly among the prepared dishes. Set them on a baking sheet and bake for 20 minutes or until set and the tops are golden and crisp. Serve hot.

1 tablespoon melted margarine
2 tablespoons dried breadcrumbs
300g long-grain or basmati rice
600ml low-sodium vegetable stock or stock made without salt
150g frozen peas
150g asparagus, cut into 5cm pieces
3 eggs
100g mature Cheddar cheese, grated
¼ teaspoon crushed dried chillies
pepper to taste

turkey biryani with cucumber raita

A biryani consists of curried meat, poultry, fish or vegetables combined with basmati rice to make a complete meal. Here a turkey curry is layered with the rice and baked, then served with a fresh cucumber raita.

1 tablespoon sunflower oil

1 large onion, chopped

450g skinless boneless turkey thigh meat, diced

15g fresh root ginger, finely chopped

1 small red or green chilli, deseeded and finely chopped

seeds from 10 cardamom pods, lightly crushed

1 tablespoon ground cumin

1 tablespoon ground coriander

6 cloves

1 cinnamon stick

2 bay leaves

½ teaspoon crushed black peppercorns

1 can (about 400g) chopped tomatoes

300ml low-sodium chicken stock or stock made without salt

55g sultanas

250g basmati rice, rinsed

½ teaspoon turmeric

30g toasted flaked almonds

CUCUMBER RAITA

100g plain Greek-style yoghurt

100g plain low-fat yoghurt

½ large cucumber, coarsely grated and squeezed dry

2 tablespoons chopped fresh mint

1 Heat the oil in a large frying pan, add the onion and cook gently for 5 minutes or until softened. Add the turkey and cook over moderate heat for 5 minutes or until browned.

2 Stir in the ginger, chilli, cardamom, cumin, coriander, cloves, cinnamon stick, bay leaves and peppercorns. Cook for 1 minute, stirring all the time to ensure the spices do not burn.

3 Add the tomatoes, the stock and sultanas. Bring to the boil, then reduce the heat, cover and cook for 45 minutes.

4 Meanwhile, preheat the oven to 160°C (gas mark 3). Place the rice in a saucepan, add 600ml water and the turmeric, and bring to the boil. Cover and simmer gently for 7 minutes or until the rice is almost tender. Drain off any excess water.

5 Layer the turkey curry and rice in a casserole dish. Cover and cook in the oven for 25 minutes, checking after 20 minutes and adding a little more stock if needed (there should be enough liquid for the rice to complete cooking).

6 Meanwhile, make the raita. Stir together the yoghurt, cucumber and mint. Season with pepper.

7 When the biryani is ready, stir it well, then scatter the toasted almonds on top. Serve with the raita.

preparation time **1¼ hours**

cooking time **25 mins**

serves **4**

PER SERVING	
518 kcal	
34g protein	
13g total fat	3g saturated fat
99mg cholesterol	
68g total carbohydrate	21g sugars
3g fibre	
334mg sodium	

HEALTH HINT

Mixing Greek-style and low-fat yoghurts keeps total fat low, but still makes a creamy raita.

preparation time **20 mins**
plus 1 hour marinating

cooking time **20 mins**

serves **4**

PER SERVING

440 kcal

20g protein

10g total fat
2g saturated fat

58mg cholesterol

63g total carbohydrate
11g sugars

3g fibre

852mg sodium

HEART SUPERFOOD

Tofu plays a very
important part in a
heart-healthy diet.
Soya protein lowers the
level of artery-clogging
LDL ('bad') cholesterol
without reducing the
beneficial HDL ('good')
cholesterol in the body.

fried rice with tofu and vegetables

 Soya foods can lower cholesterol levels and reduce the risk of heart disease. If you've been looking for a tasty tofu recipe, your search is over. Here, tofu is marinated in a sweet and savoury sauce and stir-fried with plenty of vegetables.

1 Place the wine or stock, 1 tablespoon soy sauce, the honey and 1 teaspoon ginger in a resealable plastic bag. Add the tofu, push out the excess air, close and shake gently to coat. Marinate in the refrigerator for 1 hour, turning occasionally.

2 Cook the rice according to the packet directions; keep warm. Lightly coat a wok or large deep frying pan with cooking spray and set over high heat. When hot add the garlic and remaining ginger and stir-fry for about 1 minute or until fragrant.

3 Add the mixed vegetables, half the spring onions, the rice, the remaining soy sauce and pepper to taste. Stir-fry for about 4 minutes or until the vegetables are heated through. Push the ingredients to one side of the wok and pour in the egg. Cook until almost set, cutting the egg into strips with a spatula.

4 Pour the tofu marinade into a small saucepan. Boil over high heat for 2 minutes. Add the tofu and marinade to the wok. Stir-fry for 4 minutes or until the tofu is heated through. Sprinkle with the remaining spring onions and serve.

250ml dry white wine or low-sodium chicken stock (or stock made without salt)

4 tablespoons reduced-sodium soy sauce

2 tablespoons clear honey

1 tablespoon grated fresh root ginger

370g extra-firm tofu, cut into 1cm dice

225g long-grain white rice

2 garlic cloves, finely chopped

500g frozen mixed Asian vegetables, slightly thawed

5 spring onions, cut into 5cm pieces

pepper to taste

1 large egg, lightly beaten

green coriander rice

Toasting the rice, then cooking with a herb and vegetable paste before adding stock and simmering, develops and enriches the flavour of this dish. The rice makes a great accompaniment to grilled or roast chicken.

1 large green pepper, quartered and deseeded

1 onion, quartered

1 garlic clove, crushed

15g fresh coriander

10g fresh flat-leaf parsley

10g margarine

2 teaspoons extra virgin olive oil

225g long-grain white rice

600ml boiling low-sodium chicken stock or stock made without salt

pepper to taste

sprigs of fresh coriander to garnish

1 Place the green pepper, onion, garlic, coriander and parsley in a food processor and blend to a very finely chopped paste. Alternatively, very finely chop them all together with a knife.

2 Heat the margarine and oil in a saucepan, add the rice and fry gently for 2–3 minutes or until the grains are translucent.

3 Remove from the heat and stir in the herb paste. Return to the heat and cook for 2 minutes, stirring constantly. Pour in the boiling stock, and season with pepper. Bring to the boil, then reduce the heat, cover the pan and cook gently for 10–15 minutes or until the rice is tender and all the stock has been absorbed.

4 Remove from the heat and leave to stand, with the pan still covered, for 3–4 minutes. Then fork through to separate the grains. Serve hot, garnished with the coriander sprigs.

 Kc

preparation time **20 mins** plus standing

cooking time **20 mins**

serves **4**

PER SERVING

258 kcal

5g protein

4g total fat
1g saturated fat

1mg cholesterol

53g total carbohydrate
3g sugars

2g fibre

322mg sodium

HEALTH HINT

Green peppers are a good source of vitamin C, which is important for maintaining the body's immune system. Even though some of the vitamin C is destroyed during cooking, useful amounts still remain.

risotto primavera

This risotto makes a great main dish, or it can be served as a starter for six. Springtime vegetables – asparagus, courgettes and peas – add vitamins A and C, and a small amount of Parmesan adds calcium, protein and lots of flavour.

1 Bring the stock to the boil in a medium saucepan. Reduce the heat to maintain a simmer.

2 Meanwhile, melt the margarine in a large heavy saucepan over moderate heat. Add the onion and cook for 3 minutes or until barely soft. Add the rice and 6 strips of red pepper and fry for about 2 minutes or until the rice is translucent. Add the wine and simmer, stirring, until it has been absorbed. Gradually add half of the stock, a ladleful at a time, and simmer, stirring; allow each addition to be absorbed before adding the next ladleful of stock.

3 Stir in the asparagus, the remaining red pepper and another ladleful of stock. Simmer, stirring, until the stock is absorbed, then add the courgette, peas and another ladleful of stock.

4 Continue simmering, stirring constantly and gradually adding the remaining stock, until the rice is creamy and tender but still firm. Remove from the heat and stir in the Parmesan and pepper.

1.2 litres low-sodium chicken stock or stock made without salt

15g margarine

1 medium onion, chopped

230g risotto rice

1 large red pepper, deseeded and cut into thin strips

125ml dry white wine

250g asparagus, trimmed and sliced

1 small yellow or green courgette, chopped

75g shelled fresh or frozen peas

50g Parmesan cheese, freshly grated

pepper to taste

preparation time **20 mins**
cooking time **40 mins**
serves **4**

PER SERVING

442 kcal

25g protein

12g total fat
6g saturated fat

20mg cholesterol

61g total carbohydrate
7g sugars

4g fibre

730mg sodium

COOK'S TIP

Risotto isn't difficult, but it does need constant attention. Stirring the rice continuously, while adding the stock gradually, helps the rice absorb the hot stock. This causes the rice grains to release starch, yielding a creamy dish.

rice with prawns and dill dressing

In this good-looking salad, quickly seared tiger prawns are served on a mixture of aromatic basmati and wild rice, crunchy broccoli, mange-tout and yellow pepper tossed in a fresh dill and lime juice dressing.

250g mixed basmati and wild rice, well rinsed

thinly pared zest and juice of 1 lime

3 tablespoons sunflower oil

2 teaspoons toasted sesame oil

1 tablespoon reduced-sodium soy sauce

pepper to taste

125g broccoli, broken into small florets

125g mange-tout, halved lengthways

400g raw tiger prawns, peeled but tails left on

1 small yellow pepper, deseeded and thinly sliced

75g spring onions, sliced

4 tablespoons coarsely chopped fresh dill

1 Cook the rice with the lime zest in a saucepan of boiling water for 20 minutes, or according to the packet instructions, until tender. Drain the rice and tip it into a wide salad bowl. Discard the lime zest.

2 Whisk together 1 tablespoon of the lime juice, 2 tablespoons of the sunflower oil, the sesame oil, soy sauce and pepper in a small bowl. Drizzle this dressing over the rice and stir to mix. Spread out the rice in the bowl and leave to cool.

3 Meanwhile, place the broccoli in a steamer basket set over a pan of boiling water and steam for 4 minutes. Add the mange-tout and steam for a further 2 minutes or until the vegetables are tender but still crisp. Tip the vegetables into a colander and refresh under cold running water.

4 Heat the remaining sunflower oil in a large frying pan. Add the prawns and cook over high heat for 1–2 minutes on each side or until pink and cooked through. Remove from the heat and sprinkle with the remaining lime juice.

5 Add the broccoli, mange-tout, yellow pepper, spring onions and 3 tablespoons of the dill to the rice and stir gently to mix. Pile the prawns on top and scatter over the rest of the dill.

 GI

preparation and cooking time **40 mins** plus cooling

serves **4**

PER SERVING

393 kcal

20g protein

11g total fat
1g saturated fat

81mg cholesterol

53g total carbohydrate
2g sugars

2g fibre

769mg sodium

HEALTH HINT

Although prawns are relatively high in cholesterol, they are low in saturated fat, which means they don't have an adverse effect on blood cholesterol levels.

seafood paella

No trip to Spain would be complete without sampling their famous rice dish, paella. The ingredients vary from region to region, but this recipe uses white fish fillets, squid and mussels. Serve with crusty wholemeal bread.

Fb

preparation and cooking time **about 1 hour**

serves **4**

PER SERVING

487 kcal	
34g protein	
9g total fat	
1.5g saturated fat	
240mg cholesterol	
71g total carbohydrate	
11g sugars	
5g fibre	
306mg sodium	

COOK'S TIP

Using the stock obtained by boiling the head, skin and bones from any white fish not only adds flavour to a dish but also some nutrients. Any vitamins and minerals that leach out into the water will make a nutritious contribution to the dish.

1 Place the saffron threads in a heavy-based saucepan over moderate heat and stir until they begin to give off their aroma. Add the stock and bring to the boil. Remove the pan from the heat, cover and set aside to infuse.

2 Slice the squid into thin strips. Set aside.

3 Heat 1 tablespoon of the oil in a frying pan. Add the pieces of monkfish and quickly fry on all sides until lightly browned. Remove and set aside. Add the remaining oil to the pan, then add the garlic, onion and paprika and cook over moderate heat for 2 minutes, stirring occasionally. Stir in the red pepper and cook for about 3 minutes or until softened but not brown.

4 Stir in the rice so all the grains are well coated with oil. Bring the saffron-infused stock to simmering point and add half of it to the rice. Stir, then bring to the boil. Reduce the heat to low and simmer for 5 minutes or until the liquid is almost all absorbed.

5 Add the rice mixture to the stock remaining in the large pan. Gently stir in the tomatoes with their juice, the peas and monkfish pieces. Arrange the mussels on the top. Simmer for about 5 minutes. Very gently stir in the squid, then simmer for a further 15 minutes or until the rice is tender and all the liquid has been absorbed. Season with pepper.

6 Remove the pan from the heat, cover and leave to stand for 5 minutes. Discard any mussels that have not opened. Sprinkle the top of the paella with the parsley and serve.

good pinch of saffron threads

900ml low-sodium fish stock or stock made without salt

400g squid, cleaned and prepared

2 tablespoons extra virgin olive oil

200g monkfish fillet, cut into bite-sized pieces

2 large garlic cloves, crushed

1 large onion, finely chopped

½ teaspoon paprika

2 large red peppers, deseeded and chopped

250g long-grain white rice

1 can (about 225g) chopped tomatoes

150g frozen peas

12 mussels, scrubbed and beards removed

pepper to taste

3 tablespoons finely chopped parsley to garnish

herbed polenta with Gorgonzola

Grilled slices of polenta topped with a creamy, melting mixture of Gorgonzola and ricotta cheeses is a delicious dish, ideal for a tempting starter. It is served hot with a garnish of mixed salad leaves.

750ml low-sodium vegetable stock or stock made without salt

170g instant polenta

2 tablespoons chopped fresh flat-leaf parsley

1 tablespoon chopped fresh oregano or marjoram

pepper to taste

115g Gorgonzola cheese

115g ricotta cheese

1 tablespoon extra virgin olive oil

mixed salad leaves to garnish

1 Bring the stock to the boil in a medium-sized saucepan. Add the polenta in a steady stream, stirring constantly, and cook for about 5 minutes, or according to the packet instructions, until the mixture has thickened and is pulling away from the sides of the saucepan.

2 Stir in the parsley and oregano or marjoram, and season with pepper. Pour the polenta onto a greased baking tray and spread out to make a rectangle about 20 x 18cm and 1cm thick. Leave in a cool place to set for about 1 hour.

3 Preheat the grill to high. In a bowl, mash the Gorgonzola with the ricotta cheese and set aside. Brush the top of the polenta lightly with the oil, then cut into 12 rectangles, each about 5 x 6cm. Place on the rack of the grill pan, oiled-side up, and grill for 8–10 minutes or until lightly browned.

4 Turn the polenta slices over and top with the Gorgonzola mixture. Grill for a further 2–3 minutes or until the cheese has melted and is beginning to brown. Serve at once, garnished with mixed salad leaves.

Variations You can substitute other herbs such as rosemary, basil or sage for the oregano or marjoram. • For grilled polenta with sautéed leeks and herbs, make the polenta mixture without the herbs. Melt 45g margarine in a pan, add 2 finely chopped leeks and 2 crushed garlic cloves, and cook over moderate heat for about 10 minutes or until soft, stirring occasionally. Stir in 3 tablespoons dry sherry and simmer briefly, then stir in 2–3 tablespoons chopped fresh mixed herbs and season to taste with pepper. Grill the polenta slices for 5–10 minutes on each side, then top with the hot leek mixture and serve.

 Kc

preparation time **20 mins** plus 1 hour cooling

cooking time **15 mins**

serves **4**

PER SERVING

352 kcal

14g protein

17g total fat
9g saturated fat

42mg cholesterol

33g total carbohydrate
2g sugars

2g fibre

350mg sodium

HEALTH HINTS

Like other grains, corn or maize – from which polenta is made – is rich in starchy carbohydrate and low in fat.

Gorgonzola is a semi-hard, blue-veined cheese with a rich, full flavour, while ricotta is much milder and lower in fat. Mixing the two cheeses together helps to keep the total fat content of this dish healthy.

Cajun-spiced barley

Barley is one of the crops that farmers love, due to its short growing season and hardy nature. We should love this nutty, wholesome grain too, since it is so good for us. Serve it with extra-lean, grilled beef sausages or lamb kebabs.

200g pearl barley

2 tablespoons extra virgin olive oil

4 spring onions, the white and green parts chopped separately

2 celery sticks, chopped

1 onion, chopped

1 green pepper, deseeded and chopped

1 large mild green chilli, deseeded and finely chopped

2 garlic cloves, finely chopped

1/2 teaspoon ground cumin

1/4 teaspoon dried thyme

1/4 teaspoon cracked black peppercorns

pinch of cayenne pepper

500ml low-sodium vegetable stock or stock made without salt

2 tablespoons lemon juice

lemon wedges to serve

1 Heat a heavy-based frying pan over moderate heat. Add the pearl barley and toast, stirring constantly, for about 4 minutes or until the grains just start to brown and smell fragrant. Remove from the heat immediately, transfer to a shallow bowl and set aside.

2 Heat the oil in a heavy-based saucepan over moderate heat. Add the white parts of the spring onions, the celery, onion and green pepper, and sauté for about 5 minutes or until slightly softened, stirring occasionally.

3 Stir in the chilli, garlic, cumin, thyme, peppercorns and cayenne pepper. Sauté for a further 5 minutes, stirring well.

4 Add the barley and stock. Bring to the boil, then cover, reduce the heat and simmer for 30–40 minutes or until the barley is tender and the liquid has been absorbed.

5 Stir in the lemon juice. Scatter over the green spring onion tops and serve with the lemon wedges.

preparation time **15 mins**

cooking time **50 mins**

serves **4**

PER SERVING

255 kcal

5g protein

7g total fat

1g saturated fat

0mg cholesterol

47g total carbohydrate

4g sugars

2g fibre

77mg sodium

HEART SUPERFOOD

Like oats, barley is rich in soluble fibre, the type of fibre that can bind the end-products of cholesterol metabolism and sweep them out of the body. When the outer bran and germ are removed to make pearl barley, there is some loss of vitamins, particularly vitamin B_1.

apricot lamb with minted couscous

 Based on the Moroccan way of stewing meat with fruit, here lamb is marinated with mushrooms and herbs, then cooked slowly with dried apricots. Shredded cabbage and fresh mint enliven the couscous accompaniment.

Fb

preparation time **15 mins** plus 12 hours marinating

cooking time **2½ hours**

serves **4**

PER SERVING

580 kcal

37g protein

12g total fat
5g saturated fat

85mg cholesterol

76g total carbohydrate
31g sugars

8g fibre

540mg sodium

HEALTH HINT

Combining cabbage and mint with couscous adds flavour and beneficial nutrients to the satisfying carbohydrate.

1 Place the lamb in a bowl with the mushrooms and onion. Tie the bay leaves and thyme together into a bouquet garni and add to the bowl with the garlic, carrots, celery and nutmeg. Pour over the ale and stir to mix, then cover and leave to marinate in the refrigerator for 12 hours.

2 Preheat the oven to 160°C (gas mark 3). Transfer the lamb, mushrooms and flavouring ingredients to a large casserole and pour over the marinade. Add the tomatoes and the stock. Cover and cook in the oven for 2 hours.

3 Discard the bouquet garni from the casserole. Stir in the apricots and pepper, then return the casserole to the oven to cook for a further 30 minutes.

4 Just before the casserole is ready, prepare the couscous. Bring the stock to the boil in a large saucepan. Add the cabbage and bring back to the boil, then remove from the heat and immediately add the couscous and mint. Stir once, then cover the pan and leave, off the heat, for about 5 minutes or until the couscous has absorbed all the stock. Use a fork to fluff up the couscous.

5 Divide the couscous among four bowls and ladle the lamb casserole over the top. Scatter over the chopped parsley and serve immediately while hot.

450g lean boneless lamb, cut into chunks

350g mushrooms, sliced

1 onion, thinly sliced

2 bay leaves

2 sprigs of fresh thyme

2 garlic cloves, crushed

2 carrots, sliced

2 celery sticks, sliced

¼ teaspoon freshly grated nutmeg

500ml strong brown ale

1 can (about 400g) chopped tomatoes

150ml low-sodium lamb or chicken stock or stock made without salt

150g dried apricots, halved

pepper to taste

2 tablespoons chopped parsley to garnish

MINTED COUSCOUS

750ml boiling low-sodium vegetable stock or stock made without salt

450g green cabbage, such as Savoy, finely shredded

350g couscous

4 tablespoons chopped fresh mint

fish & seafood

Japanese sushi rolls

Japanese food tends to be low in fat, and these stylish sushi rolls are no exception. Now that the ingredients are available in supermarkets, it is easy to make them yourself. You must use sushi rice, which is sticky when cooked.

300g sushi rice

2 tablespoons caster sugar

3 tablespoons rice wine vinegar

2 spring onions, very finely chopped

30g piece of cucumber, deseeded and finely chopped

115g smoked salmon

4 sheets of sushi nori, about 10g in total

2 teaspoons wasabi paste

gari (pickled ginger) to garnish

reduced-sodium soy sauce to serve

1 Cook the sushi rice in a saucepan of boiling water according to the packet instructions.

2 Meanwhile, place the sugar and vinegar in a small pan and heat gently until the sugar dissolves. When the rice is cooked, drizzle the mixture over it, then add the spring onions and cucumber, and mix. Cover with a tea-towel and leave to cool.

3 Divide the rice into four equal portions. Cut the salmon into strips about 1cm wide. Place a sheet of nori, shiny-side down, on a bamboo mat, or on a sheet of baking parchment on a board. Spread a portion of rice over the nori, pressing it down evenly and leaving a 1cm space at the top and bottom. Place one-quarter of the salmon along the middle of the layer of rice. Spread the salmon with ½ teaspoon of the wasabi paste.

4 With the help of the bamboo mat or paper, roll up the nori, rice and salmon into a neat tube. Roll tightly to ensure that the rice sticks together and holds the filling in place. Make three more rolls in the same way.

5 Using a wet knife, cut each roll across into eight slices and stand them upright on a serving plate. Rinse the knife between cuts. Garnish with pieces of gari and offer a small dish of soy sauce for dipping.

 Kc

preparation and cooking time **35 mins** plus cooling

makes **32 sushi rolls**

PER SUSHI ROLL

45 kcal

2g protein

0.4g total fat

0.1g saturated fat

1mg cholesterol

8g total carbohydrate

1g sugars

0.2g fibre

70mg sodium

HEALTH HINT

Like other foods from the sea, nori – a dark brownish seaweed – is a good source of iodine, essential for the healthy functioning of the thyroid gland. It also provides some calcium, potassium and beta carotene, which is converted to vitamin A in the body.

tuna provençale baguette

Flavoursome, savoury and full of heart-smart nutrients, this sandwich is sure to become a favourite. It's a variation of the classic 'pan bagnat', a baguette bursting with tuna, olives and garden-fresh vegetables.

1 Mix the tomatoes and olives in a medium-sized bowl, then leave for about 15 minutes or until juicy.

2 Meanwhile, cut the baguette lengthways almost in half (do not slice completely through). Open the baguette like a book, being careful not to separate the bread halves. Pull out some of the soft bready centre. Using ½ tablespoon oil, brush the cut sides of the bread, then spread over the tomato mixture and any juices that have collected in the bowl.

3 Cut the onion lengthways in half, then cut it across into thin slices. Cut the green pepper lengthways in half, then cut it across into thin slices. Layer the onion, green pepper and tuna over the tomato mixture. Whisk together the vinegar, garlic and remaining oil in a small bowl. Drizzle over the tuna.

4 Close the stuffed baguette and wrap tightly in cling film. Weight down with a heavy frying pan and leave at room temperature for 30 minutes or until the juices have soaked into the bread. Cut diagonally into four equal pieces to serve.

2 large tomatoes, skinned and chopped

5 black olives (not oil-packed), stoned and finely chopped

1 baguette (wholemeal if possible), about 60cm long

1½ tablespoons extra virgin olive oil

1 large onion

1 large green pepper

1½ cans (about 200g each) tuna in water, drained

2 tablespoons white wine vinegar

2 garlic cloves, finely chopped

Fb

preparation time **20 mins** plus 30 mins standing

serves **4**

PER SERVING

350 kcal

28g protein

6.5g total fat
1g saturated fat

4mg cholesterol

48g total carbohydrate
7g sugars

3g fibre

581mg sodium

HEALTH HINT

Canned tuna is a great storecupboard standby as it is so easy to use. Canned tuna that is packed in water contains half the calories of tuna canned in oil.

fennel, apple and herring salad

Oily fish such as herring are traditionally served with tart ingredients that offer a refreshing piquancy to balance the rich fish flavour. In this Scandinavian-style salad, apple, fennel and lemon juice offer the complementary contrast.

1 Rinse the herrings. Pour the cider and stock into a saucepan large enough to hold the fish. Add the shallots and bay leaf, cover and simmer over a moderately low heat for 10 minutes. Add the fish and continue simmering for 8 minutes or until the flesh looks opaque. Remove the herrings and set aside to cool. Strain the cooking liquid and reserve 270ml.

2 Put the couscous in a bowl and pour over the reserved fish cooking liquid. Cover and leave to soak for about 10 minutes or until the couscous has absorbed all the liquid. Add the mint, parsley and lemon juice, and fluff up the grains with a fork.

3 To make the dressing, in a small bowl stir together the lemon juice, mustard, mayonnaise and yoghurt until smooth, then stir in the dill.

4 Quarter, core and dice the apple. Put the apple, cucumber, fennel, spring onions and hazelnuts into a bowl and stir in half of the dressing. Season with pepper to taste.

5 Remove the skin from the herrings and carefully take the fillets off the backbone. Use tweezers, if necessary, to remove any remaining bones. Cut the flesh into large pieces and mix gently with the remaining dressing.

6 Pile the couscous on individual plates and arrange the apple salad and fish on top. Garnish with dill sprigs or fennel fronds and serve.

Variation For a delicious Italian-style mackerel and bean salad, wrap a 450g mackerel in foil and bake in a preheated 180°C (gas mark 4) oven for about 20 minutes. Cool, then remove the skin and bones and flake the flesh. Mix together 2 oranges, peeled and segmented, 1 small bulb of fennel, thinly sliced, 3 spring onions, thinly sliced and 1 can (about 400g) cannellini beans, rinsed and drained. Add the mackerel to the salad with 3 tablespoons chopped parsley. Make a dressing with 1 tablespoon freshly squeezed lemon juice, 1 teaspoon Dijon mustard, 2 tablespoons extra virgin olive oil and pepper to taste. Toss the salad with the dressing and serve on a bed of rocket, with crusty bread to accompany.

4 herrings, cleaned and heads removed (cleaned weight about 500g in total)

120ml dry cider

360ml low-sodium vegetable stock or stock made without salt

2 shallots, sliced

1 bay leaf

200g couscous

2 tablespoons chopped fresh mint

3 tablespoons chopped fresh parsley

1 tablespoon freshly squeezed lemon juice

1 red-skinned dessert apple

½ cucumber, diced

1 small bulb of fennel, diced

3 spring onions, finely chopped

45g hazelnuts, toasted and chopped

pepper to taste

sprigs of fresh dill or fennel fronds to garnish

DILL AND MUSTARD DRESSING

1 tablespoon freshly squeezed lemon juice

1 tablespoon Dijon mustard

2 tablespoons reduced-fat mayonnaise

4 tablespoons plain low-fat yoghurt

2 tablespoons chopped fresh dill

Fb GI

preparation time **45 mins**

serves **4**

PER SERVING

496 kcal

29g protein

26g total fat
5g saturated fat

64mg cholesterol

35g total carbohydrate
7g sugars

3g fibre

274mg sodium

HEALTH HINT

The fat content of herring (and of the fat-soluble vitamins A and D) varies according to the season, with highest values occurring in late summer and lowest values in spring. Vitamin A is essential for healthy skin, vision and eyes and, as with all vitamins, for growth; vitamin D is vital for the efficient absorption of calcium.

trio of warm seafood salad

Many different fish work well in this salad, so you can see what is the freshest at the fishmonger and make up your own mixture. Choose firm-fleshed white or oily fish and some shellfish. Serve with crusty bread.

SALAD

100g baby spinach leaves

1 Little Gem lettuce

1 small carrot

1 small courgette

FISH MIXTURE

600g mussels, scrubbed and
    beards removed

300ml low-sodium fish stock or stock
    made without salt

1 shallot, finely chopped

1 carrot, finely diced

1 celery stick, thinly sliced

2 thick parsley stalks

300g skinless halibut fillet

8 queen scallops, about 100g in total

2 tablespoons extra virgin olive oil

grated zest and juice of ½ lemon

pepper to taste

TO GARNISH

2 tablespoons chopped fresh
    flat-leaf parsley

sprigs of fresh dill

1 Divide the spinach leaves among four plates. Tear or shred the Little Gem lettuce and sprinkle over the spinach. With a vegetable peeler, make short curly ribbon shavings of carrot and courgette, and arrange them in the centre of the spinach and lettuce.

2 Put the mussels in a large saucepan and add 2 tablespoons of the stock. Cover tightly and cook over a high heat for 2-3 minutes, shaking the pan occasionally, until the shells open.

3 Tip the mussels into a colander over a large bowl, shaking them to make sure you catch all the cooking juices. Remove the mussels from the shells, discarding any mussels that have not opened. Set the mussels aside.

4 Pour the remaining stock and the reserved cooking juices into the saucepan. Add the shallot, carrot, celery and parsley stalks. Cover and bring to the boil, then simmer for 5 minutes. Remove the parsley stalks.

5 Cut the halibut into 2.5cm chunks. Add the halibut and scallops to the cooking liquid, cover again and poach gently for 2 minutes. Add the mussels and poach for a further minute or until all the fish is just cooked. Remove the fish from the liquid with a large draining spoon and put it onto a warm plate. Boil the liquid until it has reduced by half, to about 200ml. Divide the seafood and vegetables among the prepared plates, piling them in the middle of the salad.

6 Whisk the oil and lemon zest and juice into the reduced cooking liquid, and season with pepper to taste. Spoon over the fish, vegetables and salad, and sprinkle with the chopped parsley and dill. Serve immediately.

preparation and cooking
time **40 mins**

serves **4**

PER SERVING

227 kcal

30g protein

9g total fat
1g saturated fat

62mg cholesterol

6.5g total carbohydrate
4g sugars

2g fibre

324mg sodium

HEALTH HINT

Although classified as a white fish, halibut does contain some fat – about the same amount as in skinless chicken breast. The fat is present predominantly as polyunsaturated and monounsaturated fatty acids, which can help to improve health.

salade niçoise

Waxy new potatoes, such as Pink Fir Apple, La Ratte or Charlotte, are ideal for salads such as this classic, as they are firm enough to keep their shape when stirred with other ingredients. Serve with crusty French bread.

1 Cook the potatoes in a saucepan of boiling water for 10–15 minutes or until tender, adding the beans for the last 5 minutes of cooking. Drain and refresh under cold running water. Cut the potatoes in half, then transfer the potatoes and beans to a mixing bowl. Add the red pepper and fennel.

2 To make the anchovy dressing, put three of the anchovy fillets and the peeled garlic in a food processor and process to a purée. Add the mustard, lemon juice and oil, and process until smooth. Alternatively, use a pestle and mortar, pounding the anchovies and garlic to a paste before whisking in the remaining ingredients. Pour the dressing over the vegetables and toss to coat.

3 Brush the tuna steaks with the oil and season with pepper. Heat a non-stick frying pan or ridged cast-iron grill pan. Add the tuna steaks and cook over a moderately high heat for about 4 minutes on each side or until lightly browned. Do not overcook or the tuna will be dry.

4 Make a layer of lettuce leaves on each of four plates and divide the potato mixture among them. Top with the tuna steaks. Arrange the tomatoes and egg quarters around the edge and scatter over the olives and basil leaves. Finish with the rest of the anchovies, arranging two on top of each serving.

500g waxy new potatoes, scrubbed

340g thin green beans, halved

1 red or yellow pepper, deseeded and thinly sliced

1 small bulb of fennel, thinly sliced

4 tuna steaks, 5cm thick, about 400g in total

1 teaspoon extra virgin olive oil

pepper to taste

lettuce leaves

16 baby plum tomatoes, halved

3 hard-boiled eggs, quartered

12 black olives, stoned

handful of fresh basil leaves

ANCHOVY DRESSING

1 can (about 50g) anchovy fillets, drained, soaked in milk for 10 minutes and drained again

1 small garlic clove

2 teaspoons Dijon mustard

1 tablespoon freshly squeezed lemon juice

4 tablespoons extra virgin olive oil

Fb

preparation and cooking time **45 mins**

serves **4**

PER SERVING

483 kcal

37g protein

25g total fat

5g saturated fat

214mg cholesterol

28g total carbohydrate

9g sugars

5g fibre

500mg sodium

HEALTH HINT

Fresh tuna contains beneficial omega-3 fatty acids, which reduce the tendency of blood to clot and thus are helpful in preventing and treating heart disease. Tuna is also an excellent source of vitamins D and B$_{12}$ and a useful source of potassium.

smoked trout and pasta salad

Tempt your family with this delicious heart-healthy pasta salad. It makes an ideal midweek meal served with crusty wholemeal bread. If you wait until the last minute to add the rocket leaves, it won't spoil if anyone's late home.

1 red pepper, deseeded and quartered

1 yellow pepper, deseeded and quartered

280g penne rigati (ridged penne) or other pasta shapes

280g smoked trout fillets

1 orange

1 large avocado

2 spring onions, sliced

2 tablespoons capers, well drained

50g rocket leaves

DRESSING

4 tablespoons fromage frais

2 teaspoons freshly squeezed lemon juice

1 teaspoon Dijon mustard

2 tablespoons chopped fresh dill

½ teaspoon caster sugar

pepper to taste

1 Preheat the grill to high. Place the peppers on the grill rack, skin-side up, and grill for about 10 minutes or until the skins are blistered and blackened. Remove from the grill and place in a plastic bag. Seal and set aside to cool.

2 Meanwhile, bring a large pan of water to the boil and add the pasta. Cook for 10–12 minutes, or according to the packet instructions, until al dente. Drain, rinse with cold water and drain well again. Tip the pasta into a large salad bowl.

3 Flake the trout fillets into bite-sized pieces, discarding the skin and any bones. Cut all the skin and pith from the orange and cut out the segments from between the membranes. Halve the segments. Halve, stone and peel the avocado, and cut into small chunks. Mix together the dressing ingredients and season with pepper.

4 Peel the peppers and cut into strips. Add the peppers to the pasta together with the trout, orange, avocado, spring onions and capers. Add the dressing and toss gently but thoroughly. Just before serving, toss in the rocket leaves.

preparation and cooking time **40 mins**

serves **4**

PER SERVING
525 kcal
28g protein
18g total fat
5g saturated fat
1mg cholesterol
66.5g total carbohydrate
14g sugars
6g fibre
8mg sodium

HEALTH HINT

Smoked trout is usually prepared from rainbow trout and, like its fresh counterpart, is an excellent source of many vitamins, minerals and healthy omega-3 fatty acids.

Thai fish cakes with dipping sauce

These delicious fish cakes are flavoured with lemongrass and coriander, and spiced with Thai red curry paste. They're served with a tangy lime and honey dipping sauce, and a lettuce, cucumber and mint salad.

Fb

preparation time **40 mins** plus 1 hour chilling

cooking time **15 mins**

serves **8**

PER SERVING

295 kcal	
19g protein	
7g total fat	
1g saturated fat	
80mg cholesterol	
41g total carbohydrate	
8g sugars	
3g fibre	
400mg sodium	

HEART SUPERFOOD

Research suggests that garlic may help to reduce high blood cholesterol levels and inhibit blood clotting, thereby reducing the risk of heart disease and strokes.

1 Cook the potatoes in a saucepan of boiling water for 15–20 minutes or until tender. Drain well, then mash.

2 Meanwhile, place the fish in a shallow pan with enough cold water to cover and add half the lime juice. Bring to the boil, reduce the heat to low and simmer for 1 minute. Remove from the heat, cover and leave to cool for 4 minutes. Drain the fish and flake the flesh with a fork, discarding skin and bones.

3 Mix together the potatoes and fish with a fork, adding the lemongrass, curry paste, spring onions, garlic, coriander, ginger and the remaining lime juice.

4 Tip the flour onto one plate, the eggs onto a second plate and the breadcrumbs onto a third plate. Take about 1 tablespoon of the fish mixture and shape into a cake. Turn first in the flour, then dip into the egg and, finally, coat with crumbs. Shape and coat the remaining fish cakes in the same way, making 24 in all. Chill the fish cakes for 1 hour.

5 Heat half the oil in a non-stick frying pan. Add half the fish cakes and cook over moderate heat for about 3 minutes on each side or until golden. Remove and keep warm while you cook the rest of the fish cakes, using the remaining oil.

6 For the dipping sauce, place all of the ingredients in a small pan and heat gently for 1 minute. Do not boil. Mix together the lettuce, cucumber and mint for the salad. Arrange the fish cakes on individual plates with the salad and serve each with a tiny dish of the dipping sauce.

350g floury potatoes, peeled

350g white fish fillets

juice of 1 lime

1 thin lemongrass stalk, thinly sliced and lightly crushed

2 teaspoons Thai red curry paste

3 spring onions, thinly sliced

3 garlic cloves, chopped

3 tablespoons chopped fresh coriander

1 teaspoon chopped fresh root ginger

4 tablespoons plain flour

2 eggs, lightly beaten

1 cup fresh wholemeal breadcrumbs

2 tablespoons extra virgin olive oil

LIME AND HONEY DIPPING SAUCE

juice of 3 limes

2 tablespoons clear honey

1 teaspoon chopped fresh root ginger

2 teaspoons reduced-sodium soy sauce

¾ teaspoon Thai red curry paste

1 large mild red chilli, deseeded and thinly sliced

CUCUMBER AND MINT SALAD

1 round lettuce, finely shredded

½ cucumber, diced

15g fresh mint leaves, shredded

fish steaks en papillote

Laying a piece of fish on a bed of greens, seasoning with a few aromatics and then sealing up tightly into a parcel is a simple and trouble-free way to cook fish. It's healthy too, as no water-soluble nutrients are lost.

280g mixed Asian greens, such as pak choy and Chinese cabbage, chopped

4 white fish steaks, such as hake or cod, about 140g each

grated zest and juice of ½ small orange

3 tablespoons shredded fresh basil

2 garlic cloves, finely chopped

120ml dry white wine

1 tablespoon extra virgin olive oil

½ medium-sized bulb of fennel, thinly sliced

1 carrot, cut into thin strips

pepper to taste

BULGHUR AND HERB PILAF

200g bulghur wheat

1 tablespoon extra virgin olive oil

juice of ½ lemon

1 garlic clove, finely chopped

2 tablespoons shredded fresh basil

2 tablespoons chopped fresh coriander

3 spring onions, sliced

1 Preheat the oven to 240°C (gas mark 9). Cut out four 30cm squares of foil or baking parchment. Arrange one-quarter of the chopped Asian greens in the middle of each square. Top with a fish steak, and sprinkle over the orange zest and juice, basil, garlic, white wine, olive oil, fennel, carrot, and pepper to taste. Fold over the foil or paper to form a parcel, leaving a little air inside so the ingredients can steam, and twist the edges to seal. Set the parcels on a baking sheet. Set aside.

2 Combine the bulghur wheat with 900ml water in a large saucepan and bring to the boil. Reduce the heat to moderately low, cover and cook for 12–15 minutes or until the bulghur is just tender. Drain the bulghur if necessary.

3 While the bulghur is cooking, put the fish parcels into the oven and bake for 10 minutes. Open one of the parcels to check that the fish is cooked and will flake easily.

4 Fork through the cooked bulghur and mix in the olive oil, lemon juice, garlic, basil, coriander and spring onions. Season with pepper to taste. Serve each person a fish parcel, letting them open them at the table, with the bulghur pilaf in a bowl.

Variations Replace the dry white wine with orange juice. • For salmon en papillote, divide 4 large tomatoes, sliced, among four foil or paper squares and lay 4 pieces of skinless salmon fillet, about 140g each, on top. Sprinkle with 2 garlic cloves, finely chopped, 1 fresh red chilli, deseeded and sliced, 4 spring onions, sliced, 3 tablespoons chopped fresh coriander, ½ teaspoon ground cumin and 2 tablespoons lemon juice. Wrap and bake for 10 minutes, and serve with the bulghur pilaf.

preparation time **20 mins**
cooking time **10 mins**
serves **4**

PER SERVING

417 kcal

34g protein

10g total fat
1g saturated fat

64mg cholesterol

44g total carbohydrate
5g sugars

3g fibre

193mg sodium

HEALTH HINT

Pak choy is a variety of Chinese cabbage, the Oriental species of the cabbage family. Its nutrient content is similar to cabbages such as Savoy, which means it is a particularly good source of beta carotene and folate.

Indian-style fish parcels

Fish fillets are flavoured with chilli, ginger, mint and coconut milk, then wrapped in parcels and baked in the oven. Courgettes tossed with mustard and sesame seeds and minted new potatoes are served alongside.

1kg small new potatoes, scrubbed

4 white fish fillets, such as plaice or sole, about 150g each

pepper to taste

2cm piece fresh root ginger, finely chopped

½ red onion, finely chopped

1 large mild red chilli, deseeded and finely chopped

4 tablespoons chopped fresh mint

4 tablespoons reduced-fat coconut milk

2 courgettes, cut into large dice

1 tablespoon sesame seeds

2 teaspoons yellow mustard seeds

2 teaspoons reduced-sodium soy sauce

1 Preheat the oven to 180°C (gas mark 4). Place the potatoes in a medium-sized saucepan, cover with boiling water and simmer for about 15 minutes or until tender.

2 Meanwhile, cut out four large pieces of baking parchment or foil, each large enough to enclose a fish fillet. Place a fillet on each piece of paper or foil and season with pepper.

3 Mix together the ginger, onion, chilli, half of the mint and the coconut milk, and spread over the fish. Fold over the paper or foil and pleat or twist the ends to seal. Place the parcels on a large baking sheet and bake for 10–12 minutes or until the fish flakes easily (open a parcel to check).

4 When the potatoes and fish are almost ready, steam the courgettes in a basket set above the potatoes for 4 minutes.

5 Heat a frying pan, add the sesame and mustard seeds, cover and fry over moderate heat for 2–3 minutes or until lightly toasted, shaking the pan frequently. Remove the pan from the heat. Add the soy sauce to the seeds and quickly stir, then re-cover the pan and set aside until the seeds stop 'popping'. Stir the courgettes into the seed mixture.

6 Drain the potatoes and toss with the remaining chopped mint. Arrange the fish parcels on serving plates and serve with the courgettes and the new potatoes.

 Kc Fb

preparation and cooking time **40 mins**

serves **4**

PER SERVING

355 kcal

35g protein

6g total fat
1.5g saturated fat

69mg cholesterol

45g total carbohydrate
3g sugars

4g fibre

217mg sodium

COOK'S TIP

Baking the fish in a parcel captures all the flavour and nutrients, and the fish stays deliciously moist.

baked trout with cucumber sauce

Orange and lemon slices add great flavour to this simple recipe for baked fish, and a cucumber and yoghurt sauce provides a refreshing contrast. New potatoes are roasted in the oven with the fish.

Fb

preparation and cooking time **40 mins**

serves **4**

PER SERVING

440 kcal

43g protein

13g total fat
3g saturated fat

0mg cholesterol

40g total carbohydrate
12g sugars

3.5g fibre

229mg sodium

HEALTH TIP

Like other oily fish, trout is rich in beneficial omega-3 fatty acids. It is also valuable for its high protein content and B vitamins, especially niacin and vitamin B_{12}.

1 Preheat the oven to 200°C (gas mark 6). Put two baking trays in the oven to heat. Place the potatoes in a large saucepan of boiling water, bring back to the boil and simmer for 5 minutes. Drain and return to the pan.

2 Drizzle the oil over the potatoes and toss them quickly to coat. Spread them out on one of the hot baking trays and roast for 10 minutes. Turn the potatoes over and roast for another 10 minutes, then turn them again and roast for a further 5 minutes or until crisp and tender.

3 Meanwhile, tuck the sprigs of tarragon inside the trout and season with pepper. Cut out four squares of foil, each large enough to wrap up a fish. Cut the orange and lemon slices in half. Divide half the orange and lemon slices among the foil squares, lay the fish on top and cover with the remaining fruit slices. Sprinkle 1 tablespoon orange juice over each fish. Wrap up the foil to enclose the fish completely, twisting the ends to seal. Place the parcels on the second hot baking tray and bake for 20 minutes.

4 While the fish and potatoes are cooking, make the cucumber sauce. Grate the cucumber, place it in a sieve and press to squeeze out excess liquid. Mix together the cucumber, yoghurt and mint, and season with pepper.

5 Arrange the fish, orange and lemon slices and roast potatoes on individual warm plates. Add a garnish of watercress leaves and serve with the cucumber sauce.

750g new potatoes, scrubbed and quartered lengthways

1 tablespoon extra virgin olive oil

4 sprigs of fresh tarragon

4 small whole trout, about 300g each, cleaned

pepper to taste

1 orange, cut into 8 slices

1 lemon, cut into 8 slices

4 tablespoons freshly squeezed orange juice

100g watercress to garnish

CUCUMBER SAUCE

200g cucumber

150g plain low-fat yoghurt

2 tablespoons chopped fresh mint

skate with citrus-honey sauce

Poaching skate in the oven with fresh fish stock couldn't be simpler, and accompanied by a simple orange and lemon sauce, it makes a no-hassle dinner. Serve with roast potato slices and courgettes or beans.

675g even-sized new potatoes, scrubbed and halved

1 tablespoon extra virgin olive oil

pepper to taste

4 pieces of skate wing, about 600g in total

250ml low-sodium fish stock or stock made without salt

3 oranges

juice of 1 lemon

30g margarine

4 tablespoons clear honey

1 tablespoon finely chopped parsley to garnish

1 Preheat the oven to 200°C (gas mark 6). Put the potatoes in a roasting tin, drizzle over the oil and add pepper to taste. Toss well. Roast on the top shelf of the oven for 25–30 minutes or until tender.

2 Meanwhile, arrange the skate in a single layer in a large shallow ovenproof dish and pour over the fish stock. Cover tightly with foil and poach in the oven for about 25 minutes or until the fish will flake easily.

3 While the fish and potatoes are cooking, make the sauce. Squeeze the juice from 2 of the oranges and pour into a small pan. Add the lemon juice, margarine and honey. Cut the peel and pith from the remaining orange. Working over the saucepan to catch the juice, cut in between the membranes to release the segments. Set the segments aside.

4 When the skate is cooked, carefully lift it from the stock and arrange on plates. Gently warm the sauce to melt the margarine, but don't allow it to boil. Add the orange segments and season with pepper. Pour over the fish, sprinkle with the parsley and serve, with the roast potatoes.

Variations For scallops with citrus and chive sauce, use 12 large scallops (without their corals). Heat 1 tablespoon extra virgin olive oil in a large non-stick frying pan, add the scallops and sear over a high heat for about 1 minute on each side or until caramelised on the outside, but still moist inside. Keep warm while you make the sauce as in the main recipe, replacing the parsley with 2 tablespoons snipped fresh chives. • Instead of roast potatoes, make a wild rice and lemongrass pilaf to serve with the skate. Fry 4 chopped shallots in 1 tablespoon extra virgin olive oil, then add 250g mixed long-grain and wild rice. Pour in 600ml low-sodium vegetable stock (or stock made without salt) and stir in 1 teaspoon finely chopped lemongrass. Cover and simmer for 20 minutes, or according to the packet instructions, until the rice is tender and the stock has been absorbed. Add 3 tablespoons chopped fresh coriander and serve.

preparation and cooking time **45 mins**

serves **4**

PER SERVING

420 kcal

28g protein

10g total fat
2g saturated fat

0mg cholesterol

58g total carbohydrate
30g sugars

4g fibre

281mg sodium

HEALTH HINTS

An orange can provide more than twice the recommended daily intake of vitamin C. This water-soluble vitamin cannot be stored by the body, so it is essential to eat fruit and vegetables containing vitamin C on a daily basis.

The vitamin C content of potatoes varies with their age, dropping from 21mg per 100g for freshly dug potatoes to 9mg after 3 months of storage.

mackerel with gooseberry sauce

Mackerel is a well-flavoured, highly nutritious fish and is good simply grilled and served with a fruity sauce – here gooseberry and fennel. A side dish of rosti potatoes and a green vegetable complete the meal.

3 medium-sized potatoes, about 600g in total, peeled and coarsely grated

3 medium-sized sweet potatoes, about 600g in total, peeled and coarsely grated

pepper to taste

40g margarine

4 mackerel, about 170g each, cleaned and trimmed

juice of ½ lemon

1 teaspoon extra virgin olive oil

300g fresh or frozen gooseberries

50g bulb of fennel, finely chopped

2 tablespoons concentrated elderflower cordial

1 Preheat the oven to 220°C (gas mark 7). Mix the potatoes and sweet potatoes in a large bowl. Season with pepper.

2 Put half the margarine in a round 25cm ovenproof dish or tin. Heat in the oven for 1–2 minutes or until the margarine starts to bubble, then remove. Turn the grated potatoes into the hot dish and press down firmly to make an even, compact cake. Dot with the remaining margarine, then return to the oven and bake for 25 minutes or until dark golden brown and the centre feels soft when pierced with a skewer.

3 Meanwhile, preheat the grill to high. Season the fish with pepper and make four slashes on each side. Cut a piece of foil to fit the grill pan and lay the fish on top. Mix the lemon juice with the oil and brush half over the fish. Grill for 4–5 minutes or until the flesh next to the bone will flake easily. Carefully turn the fish over, brush with the remaining lemon juice and oil mixture, and grill for a further 4–5 minutes.

4 While the fish is cooking, put the gooseberries, fennel, elderflower cordial and 75ml water into a non-aluminium saucepan and bring to the boil. Reduce the heat and simmer gently, stirring frequently, for 5 minutes or until all the gooseberries have popped and feel tender. Taste the sauce – it should have a pleasant sour tang. If it tastes too sweet, add a squeeze of lemon juice. Keep the sauce hot.

5 When the fish and potatoes are cooked, transfer the fish to a large serving platter or warmed dinner plates. Pour the sauce into a sauce boat and serve with the fish and rosti.

 Fb

preparation and cooking time **50 mins**

serves **4**

PER SERVING

687 kcal

34g protein

34g total fat
7g saturated fat

81mg cholesterol

65g total carbohydrate
16g sugars

7g fibre

240mg sodium

HEALTH HINTS

All oily fish must be eaten fresh as they spoil rapidly. The expression 'holy mackerel' comes from the days when a special licence was given to markets in Cornwall to sell fresh fish on a Sunday.

Gooseberries are a good source of vitamin C. Because of the high acidity of the fruit, the vitamin C is preserved when they are cooked.

seafood and mushroom pie

preparation time **40 mins**

cooking time **20 mins**

serves **4**

PER SERVING

440 kcal

38g protein

8g total fat
3g saturated fat

133mg cholesterol

58g total carbohydrate
9g sugars

3g fibre

380mg sodium

HEALTH HINT

Greek-style yoghurt is often used as an alternative to cream. This has the advantage of helping to lower the fat content of a recipe. In addition, yoghurt provides more calcium than cream.

A simple fish pie can be transformed into a feast by the addition of prawns and mushrooms. Serve with a colourful medley of steamed vegetables, such as mange-tout or sugarsnap peas, carrots and baby corn.

1 Preheat the oven to 180°C (gas mark 4). Place the potatoes in a saucepan of boiling water and cook for 15–20 minutes or until tender. When the potatoes are done, drain them well and mash with the yoghurt. Set aside and keep hot.

2 Meanwhile, melt the margarine in a flameproof casserole, add the onion and cook gently for 5 minutes or until soft. Place the fish on top, pour over 400ml of the milk and add the bay leaves and parsley. Cover and poach in the oven for 15 minutes or until the fish flakes easily.

3 Cook the pasta in a saucepan of boiling water for 10 minutes, or according to the packet instructions, until just al dente. Drain and set aside.

4 Place the cornflour and mustard in a saucepan, add the remaining milk and mix to a smooth paste. Strain the poaching milk from the fish into the saucepan, reserving the onion, and add nutmeg to taste. Bring to the boil, stirring well. Reduce the heat and simmer for 5 minutes or until thick.

5 Flake the fish, discarding the skin and any bones. Stir the fish, reserved onion, prawns, mushrooms, drained pasta shells and chopped parsley into the sauce, and season with pepper. Return the mixture to the casserole. Spoon the mashed potatoes over the fish mixture, spreading the potato evenly, right to the edge of the dish. Fork up the surface. Bake for about 20 minutes or until bubbling and browned. Serve hot.

550g potatoes, peeled and cut into chunks

4 tablespoons plain Greek-style yoghurt

15g margarine

1 small onion, sliced

400g haddock fillets

500ml semi-skimmed milk

2 bay leaves

4 sprigs of parsley

85g small pasta shells

3 tablespoons cornflour

½ teaspoon mustard powder

freshly grated nutmeg to taste

125g cooked peeled prawns

85g mushrooms, thinly sliced

3 tablespoons chopped parsley

pepper to taste

Chinese sea bass with noodles

A whole fish cooked with ginger, garlic and spring onions is a traditional centrepiece in a Chinese meal. Here, it is served with a mixture of noodles and bean sprouts to make a very special dish.

1 Preheat the oven to 200°C (gas mark 6). Brush a large sheet of thick foil with the oil and place the fish on top. Place the lime slices inside the fish and scatter over the spring onions, carrot, ginger and garlic. Drizzle over the soy sauce and sesame oil, and sprinkle over the coriander leaves. Bring the ends of the foil together and fold and twist to seal in the fish. Place on a baking tray. Bake for 30–35 minutes or until the fish flakes easily (open the parcel to check).

2 Meanwhile, place the noodles in a saucepan of boiling water, return to the boil and simmer for 3 minutes. Or cook them according to the packet instructions. Drain well. Heat the oil in a wok, add the onions and garlic, and cook over a high heat for 30 seconds. Add the bean sprouts and cook for 1 minute or until they begin to soften. Add the noodles together with the soy sauce. Cook over high heat for 2–3 minutes, stirring and tossing well.

3 Remove the fish from the oven, unwrap and transfer to a hot serving platter. Garnish with coriander leaves and lime halves. Serve the fish cut into slices, with the noodles.

Variation For Mediterranean-style baked sea bass, use 4 fillets, about 150g each, and place on four oiled pieces of foil. Mix together 4 tomatoes, deseeded and diced, 40g stoned black olives, quartered, 2 tablespoons drained capers, roughly chopped, 1 tablespoon chopped fresh parsley, 2 tablespoons extra virgin olive oil and some pepper. Divide the mixture among the fish and wrap in the foil. Bake for 15 minutes. Meanwhile, make a salad by mixing together 1 bulb of fennel, finely grated, 1 large courgette, sliced, and 2 red onions, cut into thin wedges. Toss with 2 tablespoons lemon juice, 1 tablespoon extra virgin olive oil and pepper to taste. Serve the fish with the salad and boiled new potatoes.

1 teaspoon sunflower oil

1 sea bass, about 800g, cleaned and scaled

1 lime, cut into 4 slices

6 spring onions, cut into fine shreds

1 carrot, cut into fine matchsticks

2.5cm piece fresh root ginger, cut into fine matchsticks

2 garlic cloves, thinly sliced

2 tablespoons reduced-sodium soy sauce

1 teaspoon toasted sesame oil

1 tablespoon fresh coriander leaves, plus extra leaves to garnish

lime halves to serve

NOODLES

250g fine Chinese egg noodles

1 tablespoon sunflower oil

2 small red onions, cut into very thin wedges

1 garlic clove, thinly sliced

300g bean sprouts

1 tablespoon reduced-sodium soy sauce

Fb GI

preparation time **15 mins**

cooking time **35 mins**

serves **4**

PER SERVING

485 kcal

39g protein

14g total fat
3g saturated fat

178mg cholesterol

55g total carbohydrate
7g sugars

4g fibre

610mg sodium

HEALTH HINTS

Sunflower is one of the most popular oils, having a mild flavour. It is a good source of vitamin E, which is a powerful antioxidant that protects cell membranes from damage by free radicals.

Eggs add flavour and colour to noodles and only a tiny amount of fat. Egg noodles are also an excellent source of starchy carbohydrate.

Parma-wrapped lemon sole

For this elegant dish, fillets of lemon sole are spread with a nutty herb filling, then rolled up in thin slices of Parma ham and baked with white wine. A potato and rocket mash and steamed asparagus are ideal accompaniments.

900g floury potatoes, peeled and cut into large chunks

8 very thin slices of Parma ham, about 125g in total, trimmed of fat

4 large lemon sole fillets, about 150g each, skinned

90g fresh wholemeal breadcrumbs

75g chopped toasted hazelnuts

2 tablespoons chopped fresh coriander

2 eggs, beaten

pepper to taste

4 tablespoons white wine

30g margarine

100ml semi-skimmed milk

2 tablespoons chopped rocket

500g asparagus spears

1 Preheat the oven to 190°C (gas mark 5). Put the potatoes into a large pan of boiling water and cook over a moderate heat for about 15 minutes or until tender.

2 Meanwhile, lay two overlapping slices of Parma ham on a board and place a fish fillet on top, skinned side up. Combine the breadcrumbs with the hazelnuts, coriander, eggs and a little pepper. Spread one-quarter of this mixture on top of the fish, pressing it over evenly. Carefully roll up the fish and ham like a swiss roll. Repeat with the remaining Parma ham, sole fillets and hazelnut filling.

3 Arrange the fish rolls in a lightly greased ovenproof dish. Pour over the wine. Using 15g of the margarine, put a dab on top of each roll. Cover the dish tightly with foil and bake for 20–25 minutes or until the fish will flake easily.

4 Meanwhile, drain the potatoes well and return to the pan. Mash them, then beat in the milk, remaining magarine and the rocket. Season with pepper to taste. Transfer to a serving dish and keep hot. Steam the asparagus for about 4 minutes or until just tender.

5 Serve the fish, cut into slices, on individual warmed dinner plates, with the asparagus and potatoes.

preparation and cooking time **45 mins**

serves **4**

PER SERVING

668 kcal

51g protein

28g total fat
5g saturated fat

203mg cholesterol

53g total carbohydrate
7g sugars

7g fibre

423mg sodium

HEALTH HINT

The low fat content of lemon sole allows for some higher fat ingredients to be used with it, particularly in a special recipe such as this. Even so, the saturated fat content of the dish is healthily low.

teriyaki swordfish kebabs

 Teriyaki is a popular cooking style in Japan. The teriyaki marinade for fish or meat is made with soy sauce, rice wine and sugar and can be bought ready made from most supermarkets. It is intense in flavour, so you only need a little.

preparation time **25 mins** plus 30 mins soaking of the skewers

cooking time **10 mins**

serves **4**

PER SERVING

538 kcal

36g protein

15g total fat
3g saturated fat

75mg cholesterol

69g total carbohydrate
21g sugars

5g fibre

1040mg sodium

HEALTH HINT

Swordfish is an excellent source of vitamin B$_{12}$, which apart from its role in the formation of red blood cells is involved in maintaining a healthy nervous system, as it helps to form the protective sheath around nerves.

1 If using wooden skewers, soak them in cold water for at least 30 minutes. Preheat the grill to high.

2 Cut the swordfish into 24 bite-sized pieces. Mix together the marinade ingredients in a bowl, add the fish and toss to coat. Thread the fish onto eight skewers, alternating the cubes with the onions, yellow pepper and limes.

3 Grill the kebabs for 8–10 minutes or until the fish is just cooked but still very slightly translucent in the centre and all the ingredients are golden brown. Turn the kebabs halfway through the cooking and baste with the remaining marinade.

4 While the kebabs are cooking, prepare the noodles. Place the noodles in a saucepan of boiling water, bring back to the boil and simmer for 3 minutes. Or cook the noodles according to the packet instructions. Drain well. Heat the oil in a wok over a high heat and cook the garlic and ginger for 30 seconds. Add the mange-tout and spring onions and stir-fry for 1 minute. Add the noodles with the sweet chilli and soy sauces, and stir and toss together for 1–2 minutes.

5 Spoon the noodle mixture onto warm plates and top with the fish kebabs. Garnish with the chopped coriander and serve.

550g thick swordfish steaks

4 small red onions, quartered

1 large yellow pepper, deseeded and cut into 16 cubes

2 limes, each cut into 8 slices

2 tablespoons chopped fresh coriander to garnish

MARINADE

2 tablespoons teriyaki marinade

1 tablespoon clear honey

1 teaspoon toasted sesame oil

1 garlic clove, crushed

SWEET CHILLI NOODLES

250g fine Chinese egg noodles

1 tablespoon sunflower oil

2 garlic cloves, sliced

1 tablespoon finely chopped fresh root ginger

125g mange-tout, sliced

6 spring onions, shredded

3 tablespoons sweet chilli sauce

1 tablespoon reduced-sodium soy sauce

Thai green curry with monkfish

This Thai green curry is wonderfully fragrant and is prepared with a homemade curry paste. Serve it with rice and a side dish of Chinese cabbage or broccoli florets stir-fried with garlic and a little reduced-sodium soy sauce.

preparation time **25 mins**
cooking time **20 mins**
serves **4**

PER SERVING

284 kcal

24g protein

9g total fat
5g saturated fat

17mg cholesterol

28g total carbohydrate
14g sugars

3g fibre

666mg sodium

HEALTH HINT

Shallots tend to be milder and more subtle in flavour than onions. Like onions, they contain some vitamin C and B vitamins.

COOK'S TIP

Galangal is a rhizome, similar to ginger, with a hot peppery flavour. It is usually available in Chinese markets.

2 tablespoons sunflower oil
600ml low-sodium fish stock or stock made without salt
2 tablespoons fish sauce
2 tablespoons sugar
300g new potatoes, halved
1 red pepper, deseeded and cut into strips
500g monkfish fillets, sliced across into medallions
115g small sugarsnap peas
100ml reduced-fat coconut milk
juice of 1 lime
1 tablespoon chopped fresh coriander

GREEN CURRY PASTE
2 tablespoons finely grated fresh galangal
2 teaspoons finely chopped lemongrass
4 lime leaves, shredded
6 tablespoons finely chopped fresh coriander
6 shallots, very finely chopped
4 garlic cloves, crushed
1 teaspoon ground coriander
1 teaspoon ground cumin
1 small red chilli, deseeded and finely chopped
finely grated zest of 1 lime

1 Mix together all the ingredients for the green curry paste and stir in 6 tablespoons water. (If you have a food processor, you can save chopping time by using the machine to blend all of the paste ingredients with the water until smooth.)

2 Heat the oil in a non-stick pan. Add the curry paste and fry for 5 minutes, stirring frequently, until the water has evaporated and the shallots have softened and are starting to colour.

3 Pour the fish stock and fish sauce into the pan and stir in the sugar, potatoes and red pepper. Bring to the boil, then cover and cook for about 10 minutes or until the potatoes are almost tender.

4 Add the monkfish, sugarsnap peas and coconut milk, then cover again and cook gently for 5 minutes or until the fish flakes easily. Remove from the heat, stir in the lime juice and scatter over the coriander to garnish. Serve hot.

Variation To make a speedy Thai prawn curry, fry the shallots and garlic in the sunflower oil until softened, then pour in the fish stock, fish sauce and sugar. Add 2–3 tablespoons ready-made green curry paste from a jar (compare brands to find the one with the lowest fat) and stir well. Simmer for 10 minutes. Add the sugarsnap peas and cook for 3 minutes, then add 200g peeled raw prawns. Cook for 1–2 minutes or until the prawns turn pink. Add the lime juice and 4 tablespoons chopped fresh basil and serve.

seafood lasagne

Packed with seafood and vegetables, this lasagne is a superb vitamin-rich, nutritious meal. Choose vegetables that are fresh and in season – when fresh peas, asparagus and beans are past, try broccoli and sautéed mushrooms.

Fb – GI

preparation time **1½ hours**
cooking time **30 mins**
serves **6**

PER SERVING

595 kcal

38g protein

22g total fat
8g saturated fat

174mg cholesterol

60g total carbohydrate
11g sugars

6g fibre

400mg sodium

HEART SUPERFOOD

Oily fish, such as salmon, is rich in omega-3 fatty acids, which are a type of polyunsaturated fat believed to help protect against coronary heart disease and strokes.

1 Preheat the oven to 180°C (gas mark 4). Heat 2 tablespoons of the oil in a saucepan. Add the fennel, onion and half the garlic. Cook for 5 minutes or until the onion softens. Add the parsley, fennel seeds, Italian herbs and chilli and cook for 1–2 minutes. Add the squid and salmon and cook for 1 minute. Stir in the prawns and mixed shellfish and cook for 30 seconds. Use a slotted spoon to transfer the seafood to a bowl and set aside.

2 Add the wine, stock, lemon zest, bay leaves and carrot to the juices remaining in the pan. Boil for 5 minutes or until the liquid is reduced to about 100ml. Stir in the tomatoes and cook over high heat for 3–4 minutes or until the sauce has reduced. Add the beans and remaining garlic. Cover and cook for 10 minutes. Add the courgettes, cover and cook for 5 minutes. Add the asparagus and peas and cook, covered, for another 5 minutes.

3 Lightly grease a deep 30cm ovenproof dish with a little oil. Place two-thirds of the vegetables in the dish, lifting them out of the sauce with a slotted spoon and discarding the bay leaves. Top with a layer of lasagne, overlapping the sheets slightly. Add the seafood and a second layer of lasagne. Pour on the remaining vegetables and sauce. Top with the remaining lasagne.

4 Mix the ricotta with the eggs and Parmesan cheese. Season with a little nutmeg, pepper and cayenne. Pour this evenly over the top of the lasagne and drizzle with the remaining olive oil.

5 Bake for 30 minutes or until the lasagne is bubbling hot and the top is speckled golden brown. Serve immediately.

3 tablespoons extra virgin olive oil
1 small bulb of fennel, diced
1 onion, chopped
4 garlic cloves, coarsely chopped
2 tablespoons chopped fresh parsley
¼–½ teaspoon fennel seeds
½ teaspoon dried mixed Italian herbs
pinch of crushed dried chillies
125g prepared squid
125g salmon fillet, cut into chunks
125g raw tiger prawns, peeled
125g mixed shellfish
150ml dry white wine
150ml low-sodium fish stock
grated zest of ½ lemon
2 bay leaves
1 carrot, roughly chopped
1kg tomatoes, diced
5 runner beans, sliced
1 courgette, sliced or diced
250g asparagus tips
170g shelled fresh or frozen peas
400g no-precook lasagne
250g ricotta cheese
2 eggs, lightly beaten
85g Parmesan cheese, freshly grated
freshly grated nutmeg, pepper and cayenne pepper to taste

salmon koulibiac

This updated version of a traditional Russian dish is made with poached salmon, rice and mushrooms wrapped in crisp filo rather than the usual puff pastry. As all the preparation can be done ahead, it is ideal for a dinner party.

400g piece of salmon fillet

3 tablespoons dry white wine

1 bay leaf

6 black peppercorns

30g margarine

2 onions, finely chopped

200g button mushrooms, thinly sliced

pepper to taste

200g basmati rice, rinsed

2 tablespoons finely chopped
    fresh dill

2 tablespoons extra virgin olive oil

7 sheets of filo pastry, about
    200g in total

1 egg, beaten

lemon wedges to serve

1 Put the salmon in a non-aluminium pan with the wine, bay leaf and peppercorns. Pour in enough cold water just to cover the fish. Set the pan over a moderate heat and bring to a gentle boil. Reduce the heat so the liquid just simmers, then cover the pan and cook for 10 minutes. Remove the pan from the heat and let the fish cool in the poaching liquid.

2 Meanwhile, melt 15g of the margarine in a large frying pan. Add the onions and stir well, then cover and cook over a low heat for 8–10 minutes or until very soft and translucent. Add the mushrooms and season with pepper. Turn up the heat and cook uncovered, stirring, for 5 minutes or until the mushrooms have softened. Remove from the heat and leave to cool.

3 Cook the rice in a pan of boiling water for 10–12 minutes, or according to the packet instructions, until just tender. Drain the rice and turn it out onto a large plate or tray to cool.

4 Drain the cooled salmon and flake the flesh, discarding the skin and any bones; set aside. Gently combine the rice with the mushroom mixture. Add the dill and season with pepper.

5 Melt the remaining 15g margarine with the oil in a small saucepan. Arrange three overlapping sheets of pastry on a lightly oiled baking sheet to make a 40cm square, brushing each sheet sparingly with the oil mixture. Arrange three more sheets on top, brushing with the oil.

6 Spoon half the rice mixture down the centre of the pastry to make a neat shape about 30 x 17cm. Top with the flaked salmon. Spoon the rest of the rice on top of the fish and mound into a neat shape. Lightly brush the edges of the pastry with beaten egg, then wrap the pastry over the filling to enclose it completely. Brush the last sheet of pastry with the remaining oil mixture, then cut into quarters. Lightly crumple each piece and secure on top of the koulibiac with a little beaten egg, to make a neat decoration. Cover and chill for up to 4 hours until ready to cook.

7 When ready to cook, preheat the oven to 200°C (gas mark 6). Lightly brush the koulibiac with beaten egg to glaze, then bake for 35–40 minutes or until golden brown and the centre is piping hot (check with a skewer). Transfer the koulibiac to a serving platter and add lemon wedges. Cut into slices to serve.

preparation time **50 mins**
plus 1½ hours cooling
cooking time **40 mins**
serves **6**

PER SERVING

447 kcal

21g protein

17g total fat
3g saturated fat

72mg cholesterol

50g total carbohydrate
2g sugars

1g fibre

82mg sodium

HEALTH HINT

Black peppercorns are the dried fruit of a tropical vine native to India. They are picked when green and allowed to ferment in the sun before drying. Herbal practitioners believe that black pepper can have a stimulatory effect on the digestive system.

smoked fish paella

 One of the reasons the so-called Mediterranean diet is considered healthy is that it features many dishes like this one from Spain, based on rice cooked in olive oil with lots of vegetables and a modest amount of protein foods.

900ml low-sodium vegetable or fish stock, or stock made without salt

large pinch of saffron threads

50g thin chorizo sausage

400g undyed smoked haddock fillet, skinned

2 tablespoons extra virgin olive oil

1 large onion, finely chopped

2 large garlic cloves, crushed

250g green beans, cut into bite-sized pieces

250g paella or other short-grain rice

pepper to taste

150g frozen peas

finely chopped parsley to garnish

1 Bring the stock to the boil in a pan over a high heat. Add the saffron threads, reduce the heat and leave to simmer gently while preparing the other ingredients.

2 Remove the thick skin from the chorizo sausage and thinly slice the sausage. Cut the haddock into large chunks. Heat the olive oil in a 30cm round, shallow flameproof casserole, paella pan or frying pan. Add the chorizo, onion, garlic and green beans and fry for 2 minutes, stirring occasionally.

3 Add the rice and stir until all the grains are coated with oil. Add the saffron-flavoured stock and stir. Season with pepper to taste. Bring to the boil, then reduce the heat to low and simmer for 3 minutes.

4 Gently stir in the haddock pieces and peas. Simmer for a further 20 minutes or until all the liquid has been absorbed and the rice is tender. Stir halfway through the cooking time, taking care not to break up the haddock too much. Sprinkle with parsley and serve.

preparation time **10 mins**

cooking time **20 mins**

serves **4**

PER SERVING

465 kcal	
28g protein	
13g total fat	
1g saturated fat	
36mg cholesterol	
58g total carbohydrate	
4g sugars	
4g fibre	
945mg sodium	

HEALTH HINT

Smoked haddock, like other fish, is an excellent low-fat source of protein. It is also an excellent source of iodine, and a useful source of potassium and vitamin B_6.

teriyaki-glazed prawn salad

East meets West in this intriguing salad of skewered tiger prawns, Parma ham, courgettes and tomatoes with Chinese leaves and spinach in a Japanese-style dressing. Serve it as a stylish lunch dish, with French bread or ciabatta.

1 Place all the ingredients for the glaze in a small bowl and stir to dissolve the sugar. Set aside.

2 Preheat the grill to high, and line the grill pan with foil. Peel the prawns, leaving on the tails. Cut each slice of Parma ham lengthways into three strips. Wrap a strip around each prawn, pressing the ham so it stays in position.

3 Thread the prawns, courgette slices and cherry tomatoes onto four metal skewers, alternating the ingredients so you start and finish with courgette slices. Pour half the glaze into a large mixing bowl and reserve for making the dressing. Generously brush some of the remaining glaze over the ingredients on the skewers, then place on the grill rack.

4 Brush with glaze again and grill for 3 minutes. Turn the skewers over and brush with the remaining glaze. Grill for another 3 minutes or until the prawns are pink.

5 Meanwhile, add the sesame oil and sunflower oil to the reserved glaze and whisk to mix. Add the Chinese leaves, spinach, spring onions, chives, parsley and coriander. Toss everything together to coat with the dressing.

6 Divide the salad among four plates. Place a kebab on each plate (remove the skewers, if liked). Sprinkle with the sesame seeds and serve at once, garnished with orange wedges.

12 large raw tiger prawns, about 400g in total
4 paper-thin slices of Parma ham, about 45g in total, trimmed of visible fat
1 courgette, cut into 16 slices
12 cherry tomatoes
1 tablespoon toasted sesame oil
1 tablespoon sunflower oil
225g Chinese leaves, shredded
100g baby spinach leaves
4 spring onions, green part only, chopped
4 tablespoons snipped fresh chives
4 tablespoons chopped fresh flat-leaf parsley
4 tablespoons chopped fresh coriander
2 tablespoons sesame seeds
1 orange, cut into wedges, to garnish

TERIYAKI-STYLE GLAZE
juice of 1 large orange
2 tablespoons sake or dry sherry
1 tablespoons soft light brown sugar
1½ teaspoons reduced-sodium soy sauce
1 garlic clove, crushed

preparation and cooking time **45 mins**
serves **4**

PER SERVING

245 kcal

23g protein

11g total fat
2g saturated fat

105mg cholesterol

12g total carbohydrate
11g sugars

3g fibre

745mg sodium

HEALTH HINTS

Spring onions contain vitamin C, which helps your body absorb the iron from the tiger prawns in this salad.

Sesame seeds come from a herbaceous plant native to Indonesia and East Africa – the first known evidence of its cultivation is from the Middle East in 3000BC. As well as contributing a distinctive flavour, they provide useful amounts of calcium.

heringsalat

Horseradish, caraway and dill flavour this tasty Danish-style salad of pickled herrings, apples and new potatoes.

800g new potatoes, thickly sliced
2 red-skinned dessert apples
4 teaspoons lemon juice
115g radishes, sliced
115g radicchio, separated into leaves
2 heads of chicory, divided into leaves
50g walnut pieces
400g sweet-cured herrings in dill marinade, drained
1/4 teaspoon caraway seeds
1 tablespoon chopped fresh dill

HORSERADISH AND CARAWAY DRESSING
150g plain low-fat yoghurt
2 tablespoons reduced-fat mayonnaise
2 teaspoons creamed horseradish
1 teaspoon clear honey
1/2 teaspoon caraway seeds
pepper to taste

1 Cook the potatoes in boiling water for 5 minutes or until just tender. Drain, rinse with cold water and drain again.

2 To make the dressing, combine the yoghurt, mayonnaise, creamed horseradish, honey and caraway seeds in a large mixing bowl. Season with pepper to taste. Add the potatoes and stir to coat them with the dressing.

3 Quarter, core and dice the apples. Toss them in the lemon juice, then add to the potatoes together with the radishes. Fold in gently.

4 Divide the radicchio and chicory leaves among four serving plates and sprinkle with the walnut pieces. Spoon the potato salad over the leaves. Arrange the herring on top, cutting it into bite-sized pieces if necessary. Sprinkle with the caraway seeds and chopped dill, and serve.

 30 Kc Fb

preparation time **30 mins**
serves **4**

PER SERVING

521 kcal

25g protein

23g total fat
1.5g saturated fat

44mg cholesterol

56g total carbohydrate
21g sugars

4g fibre

945mg sodium

barbecued prawns with mustard sauce

Next time you have a barbecue, treat yourself to a little luxury – skewers of juicy prawns in an exotically spiced marinade.

2 1/2 tablespoons Dijon mustard
1 1/2 tablespoons freshly squeezed lemon juice
2 teaspoons ground coriander
2 teaspoons ground cumin
1/2 teaspoon pepper
24 raw tiger prawns, peeled and deveined

1 To make the mustard dipping sauce, stir together the mustard, lemon juice, 1/2 teaspoon coriander, 1/2 teaspoon cumin and 1/4 teaspoon pepper in a small bowl. Set aside.

2 Combine the remaining 1 1/2 teaspoons coriander, 1 1/2 teaspoons cumin and 1/4 teaspoon pepper in a large bowl. Add the prawns, tossing to coat.

3 Preheat the barbecue (or the grill). Thread the prawns onto four long metal skewers. Place the prawns on the barbecue and cook for about 1 minute on each side or until opaque throughout. Serve hot or at room temperature, with the mustard dipping sauce.

 30 Kc

preparation time **10 mins**
cooking time **2 mins**
serves **4**

PER SERVING

71 kcal

16g protein

0.5g total fat
0g saturated fat

182mg cholesterol

0.5g total carbohydrate
0g sugars

0g fibre

180mg sodium

preparation and cooking
time **40 mins**

serves **4**

PER SERVING

414 kcal

25g protein

14g total fat

2g saturated fat

32mg cholesterol

51g total carbohydrate

5g sugars

7g fibre

622mg sodium

HEALTH HINT

Buckwheat contains useful amounts of beta carotene and vitamins from the B group. It is low in fat and rich in starchy carbohydrate. It is not related to wheat so can be eaten by those with wheat intolerance.

scallops with noodles and ginger

This salad is based on soba – Japanese buckwheat noodles. They are tossed with bean sprouts, Chinese leaves, fresh coriander and an intensely flavoured dressing, then topped with juicy soy-grilled scallops and mushrooms.

1 Line the grill pan and a baking tray with foil. To make the baste, mix together the garlic, oil, soy sauce and sugar. Set aside one-third of the baste in a large mixing bowl. Brush some of the remaining baste over both sides of the mushrooms and place on the grill pan. Brush the scallops with the rest of the baste and place on the baking tray.

2 Bring a large saucepan of water to the boil and cook the soba for about 6 minutes, or according to the packet instructions, until just tender. Drain well.

3 Meanwhile, to make the dressing, add all the dressing ingredients to the baste in the salad bowl and stir until smooth.

4 Add the drained noodles to the dressing and toss to coat. Add the Chinese leaves, bean sprouts, spring onions and coriander. Toss well again. Divide among four shallow bowls.

5 Preheat the grill to high. Grill the mushrooms for 10 minutes or until tender, turning once. Remove from the heat, then grill the scallops for 2 minutes or until cooked. Slice the mushrooms and scatter over the salad with any cooking juices. Add the scallops and nori and serve.

350g large flat mushrooms

250g queen scallops

200g soba (buckwheat noodles)

125g Chinese leaves, shredded

170g bean sprouts

4 spring onions, shredded

4 tablespoons chopped coriander

1 sheet toasted sushi nori, about
    20 x 18cm, cut into fine strips

SOY AND GARLIC BASTE

2 garlic cloves, crushed

4 tablespoons sunflower oil

2 tablespoons reduced-sodium
    soy sauce

2 teaspoons caster sugar

SOY DRESSING

juice of 1 large lemon

2 teaspoons finely grated fresh ginger

1 tablespoon reduced-sodium
    soy sauce

$^1/_2$ small red chilli, deseeded and
    finely chopped

pesto fish cakes

Fish cakes are popular with all the family and are a great way to encourage children to eat fish or to tempt fussy eaters. These cakes are easy to make and can be prepared ahead, then chilled until ready to cook.

400g potatoes, peeled and cubed

375g white fish fillets, such as cod or haddock

100ml semi-skimmed milk

pepper to taste

3 spring onions, finely chopped

finely grated zest of 1 lemon

2½ tablespoons pesto

30g plain flour

1 large egg, beaten

85g fresh wholemeal breadcrumbs

30g Parmesan cheese, freshly grated

8 tomatoes, halved

sprigs of fresh flat-leaf parsley to garnish

1 Place the potatoes in a saucepan of boiling water and cook gently for 15 minutes or until tender.

2 Meanwhile, put the fish in a deep-sided non-stick frying pan, pour over the milk and add pepper to taste. Bring almost to boiling point, then reduce the heat, cover and poach the fish gently for 5–6 minutes or until it will flake easily. Remove the fish and flake the flesh, discarding the skin and any bones. Reserve the milk.

3 Drain the potatoes and mash or crush with a fork. Add the fish to the potatoes with the spring onions, lemon zest, pesto and 2 tablespoons of the poaching milk to make a soft mixture. Season with pepper to taste. Allow to cool.

4 Shape the fish mixture into eight thick, flat cakes and dust on both sides with the flour. Place the egg on a plate and combine the breadcrumbs and Parmesan on another plate. Coat the fish cakes in the egg and then the crumbs. Chill until ready to cook.

5 Preheat the oven to 190°C (gas mark 5). Place the fish cakes on a non-stick baking sheet (or line it with baking parchment). Arrange the halved tomatoes on the baking sheet and sprinkle with pepper. Bake for 20 minutes. Serve the fish cakes and baked tomatoes garnished with parsley.

Fb

preparation time **40 mins** plus cooling

cooking time **20 mins**

serves **4**

PER SERVING

405 kcal

32g protein

14g total fat
5g saturated fat

120mg cholesterol

39g total carbohydrate
8g sugars

5g fibre

291mg sodium

HEALTH HINT

Both cod and haddock are excellent sources of iodine, needed for the synthesis of thyroid hormones, which regulate many body functions. Sea fish and seaweed are the only reliable natural sources of iodine.

prawn and vegetable stir-fry

Stir-frying is quick, so it limits nutrient loss – fast food that's healthy too. Fresh prawns, crisp yet tender vegetables, a hint of soy and the zing of ginger make this stir-fry special. Serve on white or brown rice.

1 Stir the soy sauce, wine, cornflour and ginger with 150ml water in a small bowl until smooth. Set aside.

2 Heat the oil in a large wok or large, deep frying pan over moderately high heat. When hot, add the garlic and stir-fry for 30 seconds or until just softened. Add the prawns and stir-fry for about 3 minutes or until pink. Remove the prawns with a slotted spoon and set aside.

3 Add the broccoli florets to the wok and stir-fry for 2 minutes. Add the red and yellow pepper strips and the mange-tout and stir-fry for a further 1 minute or until all the vegetables are just tender but still crisp.

4 Return the prawns to the wok. Add the baby corn, water chestnuts and spring onions. Stir the soy sauce mixture again, then pour into the wok. Stir-fry for 1 minute or until the sauce thickens and boils. Serve immediately.

60ml reduced-sodium soy sauce

3 tablespoons white wine

2 tablespoons cornflour

1½ teaspoons grated fresh root ginger

1 tablespoon vegetable oil

2 garlic cloves, finely chopped

500g raw tiger prawns, peeled and deveined

250g broccoli florets

1 large red pepper, cut into strips

1 large yellow pepper, cut into strips

125g mange-tout

100g baby corn

125g canned water chestnuts, sliced

4 spring onions, cut diagonally into 5cm pieces

preparation time **20 mins**

cooking time **10 mins**

serves **4**

PER SERVING

275 kcal

34g protein

5g total fat
1g saturated fat

350mg cholesterol

23g total carbohydrate
10g sugars

3.5g fibre

900mg sodium

COOK'S TIP

Stir-frying is an ideal method for cooking prawns. If cooked too long or at too high a temperature, prawns become unpleasantly dry and tough.

poultry

Southeast Asian chicken salad

This salad has an exotic twist. Grilled chicken is tossed with oranges, spring onions, mange-tout and lychees and is then crowned with a drizzle of creamy peanut dressing. What a treat for your heart and your taste buds!

500g cos lettuce

150g mange-tout

1 can (about 565g) lychees, drained and cut in half

1 large navel orange, peeled and cut into segments

1 red plum, stoned and sliced

4 spring onions, thinly sliced

370g chicken breast fillets

CREAMY PEANUT DRESSING

80ml reduced-fat mayonnaise

3 tablespoons creamy peanut butter

1 garlic clove, finely chopped

1 Finely shred the lettuce and place in a salad bowl. Cut the mange-tout in half on the diagonal and add them to the bowl. Add the lychees, orange segments, plum and spring onions and toss to combine.

2 Coat a heavy-based frying pan with cooking spray and set over moderately high heat. When the pan is hot, add the chicken breast fillets and sauté for about 4 minutes on each side or until cooked through. Allow to cool.

3 To make the dressing, whisk the mayonnaise with the peanut butter and garlic. Cut the chicken diagonally into thin slices and add the strips to the salad bowl. Just before serving, drizzle the dressing over the salad and toss to coat.

preparation and cooking time **30 mins** plus cooling

serves **4**

PER SERVING

356 kcal

29g protein

14g total fat
3g saturated fat

69mg cholesterol

32g total carbohydrate
29g sugars

4,5g fibre

292mg sodium

COOK'S TIP

This salad works with many types of cooked lean meat and seafood. In place of the chicken, cook the same amount of boneless lamb, turkey breast, pork fillet, beef fillet or large prawns.

chicken liver and raspberry salad

The fruity flavour of raspberries and a splash of raspberry vinegar balance the richness of chicken livers in this warm salad. Cooking the livers in a non-stick pan means the minimum of oil is needed. Serve with French country bread.

30 Kc

preparation and cooking time **20 mins**

serves **4**

PER SERVING

196 kcal

20g protein

11g total fat
2g saturated fat

380mg cholesterol

4g total carbohydrate
3g sugars

2g fibre

114mg sodium

HEALTH HINT

Chicken livers are an excellent source of iron, with 100g cooked chicken livers providing over half of the recommended daily intake. They are also an excellent source of several of the B vitamins, vitamin A, zinc and copper.

1 Trim the chicken livers, removing any cores and green bits. Cut any large pieces in half. Pat the livers dry with kitchen paper and set aside.

2 Arrange the lettuce and spinach leaves on a platter. Sprinkle with the parsley and chives. Set aside.

3 Heat 2 tablespoons of the olive oil in a large non-stick frying pan. Add the shallots and garlic and fry over a low heat for about 3 minutes or until softened, stirring occasionally.

4 Increase the heat to moderate and add the remaining oil to the pan. Add the chicken livers and fry, stirring occasionally, for 5 minutes or until they are cooked through – remove one piece and cut it open; it should be light pink in the centre.

5 Turn the heat to high, add the raspberry vinegar and stir. Season with pepper to taste. Pour the hot liver mixture over the salad, scatter on the raspberries and serve at once.

Variation For a chicken liver and sultana salad, poach the livers rather than frying them. Put them in a pan with 1 chopped carrot, 1 chopped celery stick and a bay leaf. Cover with water and bring to the boil, skimming the surface as necessary. Reduce the heat and simmer for about 5 minutes or until the livers are cooked through but still pink in the centre. Meanwhile, whisk 4 tablespoons extra virgin olive oil, 2 tablespoons balsamic vinegar and pepper to taste in a salad bowl. Add the lettuce and spinach leaves and toss to coat with the dressing. Drain the chicken livers well (discard the vegetables and bay leaf) and add to the salad bowl together with 4 tablespoons sultanas or raisins. Toss again, then sprinkle with chopped parsley and serve.

400g chicken livers
150g mixed lettuce leaves, such as Oak Leaf, romaine and Lollo Rosso
100g baby spinach leaves
4 tablespoons chopped fresh flat-leaf parsley
4 tablespoons snipped fresh chives
3 tablespoons extra virgin olive oil
100g shallots, finely chopped
1 large garlic clove, crushed
3 tablespoons raspberry vinegar
pepper to taste
125g raspberries

chicken satay salad

 Here's a flavourful salad based on the popular Thai dish of satay skewers. Marinated strips of chicken are threaded onto skewers and grilled, then served atop a rice and crunchy vegetable mixture drizzled with a spicy dressing.

550g chicken breast fillets

2 tablespoons sunflower oil

3 tablespoons reduced-sodium soy sauce

1 tablespoon fish sauce

2 garlic cloves, crushed

2.5cm fresh root ginger, finely chopped

250g basmati rice, well rinsed

100g mange-tout, halved

grated zest and juice of 2 limes

2 tablespoons chopped fresh coriander

½ small head of Chinese leaves, about 225g, shredded

¼ cucumber, diced

4 spring onions, cut into thin strips

SPICY PEANUT DRESSING

1 small onion, finely chopped

3 tablespoons crunchy peanut butter

1 fresh mild red chilli, deseeded and finely chopped

100ml reduced-fat coconut milk

1 teaspoon caster sugar

1 Cut the chicken breasts into long strips about 1cm wide. Mix together half of the oil, 2 tablespoons of the soy sauce, the fish sauce, garlic and ginger in a bowl. Add the chicken and toss to coat. Cover and marinate for at least 3 hours.

2 Cook the rice in a saucepan of boiling water for 8 minutes or until almost tender. Add the mange-tout and cook for a further 2 minutes. Drain in a sieve and rinse with cold water.

3 Combine the lime zest and juice with the remaining oil and soy sauce in a large salad bowl. Add the rice and mange-tout, the chopped coriander, Chinese leaves, cucumber and spring onions, and toss together.

4 Preheat the grill. Lift the strips of chicken out of the marinade, reserving the marinade, and thread onto metal skewers (or onto soaked wooden satay sticks if you want to leave the chicken on them for serving). Grill for 8–10 minutes or until cooked through, turning to brown the chicken evenly.

5 Meanwhile, make the dressing. Put the onion, peanut butter, chilli, coconut milk, sugar and reserved marinade into a small saucepan. Bring to the boil, then simmer gently for about 5 minutes, stirring. If the dressing is too thick, stir in 2–3 tablespoons water.

6 Take the chicken off the skewers and add it to the salad (or lay the skewers on top of the salad). Drizzle the dressing over the salad. Serve warm or at cool room temperature.

 GI

preparation and cooking time **50 mins** plus 3 hours marinating

serves **4**

PER SERVING

574 kcal

47g protein

17g total fat
2g saturated fat

96mg cholesterol

65g total carbohydrate
6g sugars

2g fibre

893mg sodium

HEALTH HINT

Although peanuts contain large amounts of fat, the majority of it is in the healthy monounsaturated form, which is thought to assist in lowering blood cholesterol levels.

coronation chicken

Specially created for Queen Elizabeth's coronation, this curry-flavoured salad with a fruity pilaf makes a lovely summer dish. Often made with cream and mayonnaise, this version cuts the fat content down significantly.

GI

preparation and cooking time **1½ hours** plus cooling
serves **6**

PER SERVING

618 kcal

42g protein

21g total fat
3g saturated fat

146mg cholesterol

65g total carbohydrate
14g sugars

2g fibre

245mg sodium

COOK'S TIP

Using the chicken stock to cook the rice ensures that none of the water-soluble vitamins that seeped into the water while the chicken was being poached are lost.

1 Place the chicken in a large pan and cover with water. Add the onion, carrot and celery and bring almost to the boil, skimming any fat off the surface. When bubbles begin to break through the surface, reduce the heat to a simmer. Add the peppercorns and bay leaf, then simmer for 45 minutes or until the juices run clear from the chicken when you pierce the thigh.

2 Remove the chicken from the liquid and set aside to cool. Pour the cooking liquid through a fine sieve into a measuring jug. Discard the vegetables.

3 To make the pilaf, place the rice in a saucepan and add 600ml of the strained cooking liquid. Stir in the raisins and mango. Bring to the boil, then reduce the heat, cover and simmer for 8–10 minutes, or according to the packet instructions, until all the liquid has been absorbed and the rice is tender.

4 Remove the rice from the heat and set aside, covered, for 5 minutes. Transfer the rice to a bowl to cool completely.

5 To make the curry dressing, place the yoghurt, mayonnaise, curry paste and lemon zest and juice in a bowl and mix until well blended. Stir in the chives, mint, parsley and pepper.

6 When the chicken is cool, cut into bite-sized pieces and fold into the curry dressing. Slice the banana and add to the chicken mixture. Stir the pecans into the rice pilaf and spoon onto six plates. Arrange the courgette ribbons on the pilaf and top with the chicken mixture. Garnish with fresh mint sprigs and serve.

1 chicken, about 1.7kg
1 onion, sliced
1 large carrot, coarsely chopped
1 celery stick, chopped
6 black peppercorns, lightly crushed
1 bay leaf
1 large banana
2 courgettes, cut into thin ribbons with a vegetable peeler
sprigs of fresh mint to garnish

MANGO AND RAISIN PILAF

375g basmati rice, well rinsed
45g raisins
45g dried mango, chopped
75g pecan nuts

CURRY DRESSING

150g plain low-fat yoghurt
4 tablespoons mayonnaise
2 tablespoons korma-flavoured curry paste
grated zest of 1 large lemon
1 tablespoon freshly squeezed lemon juice, or to taste
2 tablespoons snipped fresh chives
2 tablespoons chopped fresh mint
2 tablespoons chopped parsley
pepper to taste

summer chicken and pasta salad

Full of flavour and contrasting textures, the ingredients for this refreshing salad are mixed together in a smooth, creamy anchovy dressing. It's a good way to make the most of fresh broad beans during their short summer season.

1 red pepper, quartered and deseeded

1 yellow pepper, quartered and deseeded

3 tablespoons extra virgin olive oil

1 tablespoon freshly squeezed lemon juice

2 chicken breast fillets, about 340g in total

1 can (about 50g) anchovy fillets, drained and soaked in a little milk to remove excess salt

2 teaspoons Dijon mustard

1 small garlic clove, crushed

2 tablespoons plain Greek-style yoghurt

2 tablespoons warm water

pepper to taste

1 red onion, thinly sliced

125g plump asparagus spears

250g fusilli (pasta spirals)

200g podded fresh young broad beans

115g mixed salad leaves

1 Preheat the grill. Arrange the pepper quarters, skin side up, on the grill rack and grill for 5 minutes or until the skins are lightly charred. Turn the peppers over and grill for a further 2–3 minutes or until tender. Transfer to a polythene bag and leave until cool enough to handle, then peel off the skins and slice the peppers.

2 While the peppers are cooling, heat a ridged cast-iron grill pan or frying pan until very hot. Mix together half of the oil and 1 teaspoon of the lemon juice and brush this all over the chicken fillets. Add them to the pan, reduce the heat and cook for about 15 minutes, turning once, until the chicken is tender and cooked through; the juices should run clear when the thickest part is pierced with a knife.

3 Meanwhile, make the dressing. Put the anchovies in a blender with the remaining olive oil and lemon juice, the mustard, garlic, yoghurt, water and pepper to taste. Blend until smooth and thick. Put the onion in a large bowl and pour over the dressing. Set aside.

4 When the chicken is cooked, remove it from the pan and set aside to cool. Add the asparagus to the pan and cook for 3–4 minutes, turning once, until tender. Remove from the pan and cut the spears in half. Set aside.

5 Cook the pasta in a large pan of boiling water for 10–12 minutes, or according to the packet instructions, until al dente. Add the broad beans for the last 3–4 minutes of cooking. Drain and rinse with cold water. Set aside.

6 Cut or tear the cooked chicken into strips. Add to the onions together with the pepper slices, asparagus, broad beans and pasta. Toss to coat everything with the dressing. Cover and chill for up to 12 hours. Remove from the fridge at least 15 minutes before serving, piled on a bed of salad leaves.

preparation and cooking time **1 hour** plus 12 hours chilling serves **4**

PER SERVING

533 kcal

35g protein

18g total fat
2g saturated fat

68mg cholesterol

61g total carbohydrate
10g sugars

8g fibre

566mg sodium

HEALTH HINT

Serving a starchy carbohydrate like pasta with a small portion of low-fat protein in the form of lean meat, plus lots of vegetables, means this dish achieves a good, healthy balance from the different food groups.

sweet and sour chicken pancakes

This is a novel way of serving the popular Chinese dish of stir-fried sweet and sour chicken. Here, courgettes and bean sprouts are added to the chicken, and the whole mixture is folded up in lacy pancakes.

115g plain flour
2 eggs, beaten
200ml semi-skimmed milk

CHICKEN FILLING
2 tablespoons tomato purée
3 tablespoons sunflower oil
grated zest and juice of 1 lemon
1 teaspoon malt vinegar
1 tablespoon demerara sugar
2 teaspoons clear honey
450g chicken breast fillets,
    cut into long thin strips
1 onion, halved and sliced
1 courgette, cut into 5cm matchsticks
225g bean sprouts
1 teaspoon sesame seeds
2 tablespoons reduced-sodium
    soy sauce
spring onions, sliced, to garnish

1 To make the pancakes, sift the flour into a bowl and make a well in the centre. Beat together the eggs, milk and 90ml water and pour into the well; whisk in the flour to form a smooth batter. Cover and set aside while you make the filling.

2 Mix together the tomato purée, 1 tablespoon of the oil, the lemon zest and juice, vinegar, sugar and honey in a bowl. Add the chicken and toss to coat the strips.

3 Heat a wok and add 1 tablespoon oil. When hot, add the onion and stir-fry for 5 minutes or until softened. Add the courgette and stir-fry for 3 minutes. Using a slotted spoon, remove the vegetables from the wok and set aside. Reheat the wok, then add the chicken mixture and stir-fry for 3–4 minutes or until cooked. Return the vegetables to the wok and toss together, then remove from the heat and set aside.

4 Heat a 20cm non-stick frying pan and grease with a little oil. Pour in a little batter and tilt the pan so the batter spreads evenly; tip any excess back into the bowl. Cook the pancake over moderately high heat for 2 minutes, then loosen the edges, flip it over and cook for 30 seconds. Slide the pancake onto a plate and cover with greaseproof paper. Repeat with the remaining batter to make eight pancakes (keep them warm, covered with foil, over a pan of simmering water).

5 Reheat the filling. Add the bean sprouts, sesame seeds and soy sauce, and stir-fry for 1–2 minutes or until hot. Fill the pancakes, fold into quarters and garnish with spring onions.

Fb

preparation time **15 mins**
cooking time **40 mins**
serves **4** (makes 8)

PER SERVING

445 kcal

36g protein

17g total fat
4g saturated fat

180mg cholesterol

38g total carbohydrate
14g sugars

3g fibre

463mg sodium

HEALTH HINT

Bean sprouts, along with other sprouted seeds, are rich in B vitamins and vitamin C. Although some of the vitamin C will be destroyed by cooking, the bean sprouts still contribute good amounts in this recipe.

chicken and rosemary cobbler

This deep-dish pie is filled with succulent chunks of chicken, sliced peppers, mushrooms and black olives in a tomato sauce, and is topped with fresh rosemary scone wedges. Serve it with a crunchy raw vegetable salad.

1 Put the chicken in a large saucepan with the rosemary sprigs and bay leaf. Cover with water and bring to the boil, then reduce the heat and simmer for 1 hour or until tender.

2 Remove the chicken from the liquid. When cool enough to handle, take the meat from the carcass, discarding all the skin. Cut the meat into bite-sized chunks and set aside.

3 Preheat the oven to 230°C (gas mark 8). Heat the oil in a large saucepan. Add the onion, garlic, peppers and mushrooms, and cook for 5 minutes, stirring occasionally, until the onion is beginning to brown. Stir in the tomatoes with their juice, the sherry and olives. Season with pepper. Remove from the heat.

4 To make the scone topping, put the white and wholemeal flours, baking powder, rosemary and some pepper in a bowl. Rub in the margarine until the mixture resembles fine crumbs. Add the milk and mix to make a fairly soft, but not sticky, dough, adding more milk if necessary. Transfer the dough to a floured surface and knead briefly, then roll out to a round about 1cm thick and 18cm in diameter. Cut into six wedges.

5 Add the chunks of chicken to the vegetable mixture. Put the saucepan back on the heat and bring to the boil, then simmer for 2–3 minutes to reheat, stirring occasionally. Transfer to a deep 2 litre pie dish.

6 Arrange the scone wedges on top of the filling and brush them with a little extra milk, if liked. Bake for 10–15 minutes or until the scone wedges are risen and golden brown. Serve hot.

1 chicken, about 1.1kg
2 sprigs of fresh rosemary
1 bay leaf
1 tablespoon sunflower oil
1 onion, sliced
1 garlic clove, chopped
2 green peppers, deseeded and thickly sliced
170g button mushrooms, quartered
2 cans (about 400g each) chopped tomatoes
2 tablespoons medium dry sherry (optional)
115g stoned black olives
pepper to taste

ROSEMARY SCONE TOPPING
100g self-raising white flour
100g self-raising wholemeal flour
1 teaspoon baking powder
2 teaspoons chopped fresh rosemary
30g margarine
100ml semi-skimmed milk

Fb

preparation time **25 mins**
cooking time **1¼ hours**
serves **6**

PER SERVING

340 kcal

35g protein

8g total fat
2g saturated fat

112mg cholesterol

33g total carbohydrate
9g sugars

5g fibre

432mg sodium

HEART SUPERFOOD

Peppers are packed with vitamin C – weight for weight they offer twice as much vitamin C as oranges. They are also rich in beta carotene, which the body converts into vitamin A.

turkey empanadas

 There are lots of variations on these savoury Mexican pastries, which are similar to Cornish pasties. The filling here is a blend of lean turkey and vegetables, subtly flavoured with spices, nuts and dried fruit.

175ml warm water

1 packet (about 250g) wholemeal bread dough mix

1 small egg, beaten

¼ teaspoon paprika

SPICY TURKEY FILLING

1 tablespoon sunflower oil

1 onion, thinly sliced

1 garlic clove, crushed

1 green or red chilli, deseeded and finely chopped

250g minced turkey

300g potatoes, peeled and cut into 1cm dice

½ teaspoon ground cinnamon

½ teaspoon ground coriander

½ teaspoon ground cumin

4 tablespoons dry sherry or white wine

1 large carrot, coarsely grated

45g raisins

30g blanched almonds, toasted and roughly chopped

2 tablespoons tomato purée

2 tablespoons chopped fresh coriander

pepper to taste

1 First make the filling. Heat the oil in a frying pan and cook the onion, garlic and chilli over moderately high heat for 2–3 minutes, stirring, until softened and lightly browned. Add the minced turkey and stir for a further 4–5 minutes.

2 Meanwhile, parboil the diced potatoes in a saucepan of boiling water for 5 minutes. Drain well.

3 Stir the cinnamon, coriander and cumin into the turkey mixture and cook for 30 seconds. Add the sherry or wine and simmer for 2–3 minutes or until most of the liquid has evaporated. Stir in the potatoes, carrot, raisins, almonds, tomato purée, coriander and pepper. Remove from the heat.

4 Stir the water into the bread mix and knead for 2 minutes or until smooth. Cover and leave to rest for 5 minutes, then divide into five equal pieces. Roll out each piece on a lightly floured surface to a 20cm round.

5 Preheat the oven to 220°C (gas mark 7). Divide the filling among the dough rounds, spooning it into the centre. Brush the edge of each round with egg, then fold over into a half-moon shape. Press the edges together and roll over to seal. Place on a non-stick baking tray, cover with oiled cling film and leave in a warm place for 10–15 minutes.

6 Uncover the pasties, glaze them with the rest of the beaten egg and sprinkle with the paprika. Bake for 10 minutes, then reduce the temperature to 180°C (gas mark 4) and bake for a further 15 minutes. Serve hot or at room temperature.

preparation time **30 mins** plus 15 mins rising

cooking time **25 mins**

serves **5** (makes 5)

PER SERVING

424 kcal

24g protein

10g total fat
2g saturated fat

91mg cholesterol

58g total carbohydrate
12g sugars

2g fibre

95mg sodium

HEALTH HINT

Raisins, like other dried fruit, are a very good source of dietary fibre. They are also virtually fat-free and provide useful amounts of iron.

turkey burgers with tropical fruit salsa

There's no need to give up burgers just because you're on a heart-smart diet. These juicy turkey burgers, topped with a Caribbean-inspired salsa, are absolutely delicious. Complete the meal with oven-baked chips.

1 To make the salsa, peel, core and finely chop the pineapple, then place in a bowl. Mix in the mango, onion, coriander, lemon juice and oil. Cover and set aside.

2 Mix together the turkey, apple and breadcrumbs in another bowl. Divide the mixture into four equal portions and shape into patties about 1cm thick. Place the patties on a plate, cover and chill in the freezer for 20 minutes or the fridge for 1 hour.

3 Preheat the grill to moderate. Grill the turkey burgers for about 8 minutes on each side or until they are browned and cooked through.

4 Place a slice of cheese on the bottom of each hamburger bun, cover with lettuce, add a burger and top with salsa. Put the tops of the buns in place and serve.

1 small pineapple

1 small mango, peeled and finely chopped

1 small red onion, finely chopped

2 tablespoons finely chopped fresh coriander

1 tablespoon fresh lemon juice

1 teaspoon sunflower oil

500g minced turkey or chicken

1 large Granny Smith apple, peeled and shredded

25g dried breadcrumbs

4 thin slices of reduced-fat Cheddar cheese

4 hamburger buns or soft rolls, preferably wholemeal, split

4 lettuce leaves

preparation time **20 mins** plus chilling

cooking time **15 mins**

serves **4**

PER SERVING

446 kcal

44g protein

6.5g total fat
3g saturated fat

79mg cholesterol

59g total carbohydrate
26g sugars

5g fibre

526mg sodium

COOK'S TIP

To keep the burgers in shape during cooking, so they will hold together when turned over, firm them up first by chilling in the freezer or fridge.

spicy chicken tostadas

'Tostadas' comes from the Spanish word for toasted. These flat, crisply toasted corn tortillas can be topped with all sorts of savoury things. Here, a delicious spicy chicken, red pepper, bean and tomato mixture is used.

Fb **GI**

preparation time **35 mins**
cooking time **20 mins**
serves **4**

PER SERVING

425 kcal

31g protein

11g total fat
3g saturated fat

96mg cholesterol

53g total carbohydrate
14g sugars

10g fibre

300mg sodium

HEALTH HINT

Radishes are low in fat and calories, and provide useful amounts of vitamin C. They also contain phytochemicals that may help to protect the body against cancer.

HEART SUPERFOOD

Pulses such as borlotti and pinto beans are a good source of protein for vegetarians. They are rich in soluble fibre, which helps sweep 'used' cholesterol out of the body. They have little fat, plenty of B vitamins and the minerals potassium and magnesium, all of which help keep your heart in good health.

1 Place the chicken in a saucepan with cold water to cover. Bring to the boil, then reduce the heat and simmer for 10–15 minutes. Remove from the heat and leave to cool in the liquid. When cool enough to handle, drain and shred the meat, discarding the bones. Set the meat aside.

2 Heat the olive oil in a frying pan and add the peppers, onion and garlic. Fry over moderate heat for 5 minutes or until softened. Add the chilli powder, paprika and cumin, stir well and cook for a few more minutes. Stir in the tomatoes with their juice and the sugar. Simmer for 5–8 minutes or until thick. Season with pepper. Remove from the heat and keep warm.

3 Heat a heavy-based frying pan. Fry the tortillas, one at a time, for about 15 seconds on each side or until slightly crisp and lightly browned. As they are done, keep them warm stacked in a tea towel. Meanwhile, in a small pan, warm the beans in their can liquid. Drain well.

4 Place two toasted tortillas on each plate. Spread with the tomato mixture, then spoon on the beans and chicken. Add the diced tomato, pickled jalapeños, if using, lettuce and radishes, piling up these toppings. Finish with a spoonful of soured cream and serve with Tabasco sauce.

Variation Instead of beans, you can use a mixture of sweetcorn and courgette. Cook 1 corn-on-the-cob and 1 whole courgette in separate pans of boiling water until tender – about 10 minutes for the corn and 5 minutes for the courgette. Drain. Dice the courgette, and cut the kernels of corn from the cob. Scatter the vegetables over each sauce-spread tortilla, then add the chicken and toppings.

2 chicken breasts, about 500g in total, skinned

2 tablespoons extra virgin olive oil

2 red peppers, deseeded and coarsely chopped

1 onion, coarsely chopped

2 garlic cloves, thinly sliced

1 tablespoon mild chilli powder

2 teaspoons paprika

1 teaspoon ground cumin

1 can (about 400g) chopped tomatoes

pinch of sugar

pepper to taste

8 corn tortillas

1 can (about 400g) borlotti or pinto beans

TO SERVE

1 tomato, diced

pickled jalapeño chilli peppers (optional)

125g iceberg lettuce, shredded

8 radishes, sliced

4 tablespoons soured cream

Tabasco or other hot chilli sauce

chicken fajitas with tomato salsa

Although in Mexico 'fajitas' refers to a specific cut of beef, the term has come to describe a combination of sizzling chicken with peppers and onions, wrapped in a tortilla. The dish has very little fat, but lots of fresh flavours.

400g chicken breast fillets, cut into strips

2 garlic cloves, chopped

1 teaspoon ground cumin

1 teaspoon mild chilli powder

1 teaspoon paprika

¼ teaspoon dried oregano

grated zest and juice of ½ orange

juice of ½ lemon

2 tablespoons sunflower oil

30g fresh coriander leaves, chopped

2 green peppers, deseeded and thinly sliced lengthways

2 onions, thinly sliced lengthways

8 flour tortillas

sprigs of fresh coriander to garnish

120ml soured cream

TOMATO SALSA

4 spring onions, thinly sliced

125g ripe tomatoes, diced

1 medium-hot green chilli, deseeded and chopped, or to taste

2 tablespoons tomato passata

2 garlic cloves, chopped

½ teaspoon ground cumin

freshly squeezed lemon juice to taste

pepper to taste

1 In a bowl combine the chicken with the garlic, cumin, chilli, paprika, oregano, orange zest and juice, lemon juice, 1 tablespoon oil and 3 tablespoons chopped coriander. Mix well so that all the chicken strips are coated, then leave to marinate for at least 15 minutes, or while you prepare the rest of the dish.

2 To make the salsa, combine all the ingredients in a bowl. Add the remaining chopped coriander and mix.

3 Preheat the oven to 180°C (gas mark 4). Heat a heavy-based frying pan until very hot. Brush with the remaining oil. Add the green peppers and onions and cook for 6–8 minutes or until tender and lightly charred (do this in batches, if necessary). Remove from the pan and set aside.

4 Wrap the tortillas, stacked up, in foil and place in the oven to warm for 10 minutes. Meanwhile, preheat the grill to high. Spread out the chicken in a shallow layer in the grill pan. Grill close to the heat, turning once or twice, for about 5 minutes or until thoroughly cooked.

5 To serve, divide the chicken, onions and peppers among the warm tortillas and roll up. Garnish with sprigs of coriander and serve with the salsa and soured cream. Or, present the ingredients separately, with the tortillas wrapped in a cloth to keep them warm, and let your guests make their own fajitas.

preparation time **30 mins**

cooking time **25 mins**

serves **4**

PER SERVING

495 kcal

29g protein

17g total fat
6g saturated fat

88mg cholesterol

60g total carbohydrate
10g sugars

5g fibre

500mg sodium

HEART SUPERFOOD

Onions and garlic are not just valuable assets in the kitchen, they have been used throughout history as a cure-all. Recent research suggests that they can help to lower blood cholesterol and so reduce the risk of heart disease. They also prevent blood clotting and are a natural decongestant. Therefore, include onions and garlic in your cooking regularly.

Fb GI

preparation time **20 mins**

cooking time **1 hour**

serves **2**

PER SERVING

570 kcal

52g protein

6g total fat

1.5g saturated fat

105mg cholesterol

72g total carbohydrate

16g sugars

8g fibre

290mg sodium

HEALTH HINT

Nutritionists recommend 30g fibre every day, but most of us consume only half that amount. Much of the fibre in this dish comes from the tomatoes, which also provide healthy amounts of vitamin C and beta carotene.

COOK'S TIP

Roasted garlic can also be stirred into soup, tossed in salad or spread on bread.

chicken breasts with roasted garlic and tomato sauce

Here's a recipe that turns the ordinary into the extraordinary. This chicken dish, simmered in a rich tomato sauce seasoned with roasted garlic, is high in vitamins B$_6$, C and niacin but low in fat, and fabulous in flavour.

1 Preheat the oven to 180°C (gas mark 4). Cut the top off each bulb of garlic, then wrap the bulbs in foil. Bake for about 1 hour or until soft.

2 Meanwhile, coat a medium-sized flameproof casserole with cooking spray and set over moderately high heat. Sprinkle the chicken with pepper, then add to the casserole and cook for 4–5 minutes on each side or until golden brown. Transfer the chicken to a plate.

3 Add the carrots and shallot to the casserole and fry for about 2 minutes or until the shallot is soft. Return the chicken, skinned-side down, to the casserole. Add the tomatoes, stock, wine and rosemary. Bring to a simmer, then cover and transfer to the oven. Bake the chicken for 30–45 minutes or until the juices run clear.

4 Remove the garlic cloves from their skins using the tip of a sharp knife and mash until smooth. Stir the garlic into the tomato sauce. Ladle over the freshly cooked fettuccine, sprinkle with the parsley and serve.

2 bulbs of garlic, papery skin removed

2 chicken breasts, about 150g each, skinned

½ teaspoon pepper

2 carrots, thinly sliced

1 large shallot, finely chopped

4 canned whole tomatoes, seeded and chopped

125ml low-sodium chicken stock or stock made without salt

125ml dry white wine or additional stock

1 teaspoon chopped fresh rosemary or ¼ teaspoon dried rosemary

350g freshly cooked fettuccine

1 tablespoon chopped fresh flat-leaf parsley

chicken with lemongrass

A cross between a soup and stew, this dish captures the exciting spicy and sour flavours of Southeast Asia. Lemongrass gives a citrus touch, and light coconut milk – using just the minimum for flavour – adds richness without excessive fat.

1 small red chilli, split open lengthways but left whole

1 garlic clove, cut in half

1cm piece fresh root ginger, peeled and cut into 4 slices

2 stalks lemongrass, bruised and cut in half

4 chicken joints, such as breasts or thighs, about 170g each, skinned

1 shallot, finely chopped

250g French beans, trimmed and cut into bite-sized pieces

1 courgette, sliced lengthways with a vegetable peeler into thin strips

75g creamed coconut

finely grated zest and juice of 1 lime

pepper to taste

2 tablespoons chopped fresh coriander to garnish

1 Place 1 litre water in a saucepan over high heat. Spear the chilli, garlic and ginger on a wooden cocktail stick or skewer (this makes them easy to remove later) and add to the pan together with the lemongrass. Bring to the boil and boil for 1 minute. Remove from the heat, cover and set aside to infuse for about 30 minutes.

2 Return the liquid to the boil, then reduce the heat to low. Add the chicken joints, shallot and French beans, and poach for 12–15 minutes or until the chicken is cooked (test with the tip of a knife – the juices should run clear). Add the courgette slices for the last 2 minutes of cooking.

3 Using a slotted spoon, transfer the chicken, beans and courgette to a warmed bowl. Add a little of the poaching liquid to keep them moist, then cover tightly and keep warm.

4 Return the liquid to the boil and add the coconut milk. Continue boiling for 5–6 minutes or until the liquid has reduced by about one-third.

5 Remove the chicken meat from the bones and shred it roughly. Return the chicken meat, beans and courgette to the soup and stir, then reheat briefly. Stir in the grated lime zest and juice. Season with pepper.

6 Divide the chicken and vegetables among four soup bowls. Spoon over the liquid, discarding the lemongrass and stick of chilli, garlic and ginger. Sprinkle with the coriander and serve.

Variation To turn this into a more filling dish, add some noodles. Soak 100g Chinese egg noodles in boiling water for 3 minutes, or according to the packet instructions, then drain. Stir into the reduced cooking liquid with the chicken and vegetables in step 5.

Kc

preparation time **25 mins** plus 30 mins infusing

cooking time **25 mins**

serves **4**

PER SERVING

299 kcal

35g protein

16g total fat
12g saturated fat

135mg cholesterol

3g total carbohydrate
3g sugars

1g fibre

122mg sodium

HEALTH HINT

Green beans are a good source of the B vitamin folate, essential for a healthy pregnancy. It is important to ensure a good intake of folate in the early stages of pregnancy, and 3 months before, to prevent spina bifida. Folate may also have a role in helping to protect the body against heart disease.

chicken cacciatore

This rich-tasting Italian classic is perfect for a chilly night. Skinless chicken thighs keep the fat figures in check and a combination of mushrooms, tomatoes and herbs provide just the right flavour. Serve with polenta and green beans.

750g chicken thighs

½ teaspoon pepper

1 large onion, chopped

2 celery sticks, thinly sliced

250g button mushrooms, quartered

125ml dry red wine or low-sodium chicken stock (or stock made without salt)

2 cans (about 400g each) chopped tomatoes

1 bay leaf

2 sprigs of fresh rosemary

6 sprigs of fresh flat-leaf parsley, plus 1 tablespoon chopped flat-leaf parsley to garnish

¼ teaspoon paprika

1 Remove the skin from the chicken thighs, then sprinkle them with pepper. Lightly coat with cooking spray (preferably olive oil flavoured). Coat a large non-stick frying pan with cooking spray and set over high heat until hot but not smoking. Add the chicken and sauté for 5 minutes on each side or until golden brown. Transfer the chicken to a plate.

2 Reduce the heat to moderate and add the onion, celery and mushrooms. Fry for about 5 minutes or until the mushrooms are soft. Pour in the wine or stock. Reduce the heat to moderately low and simmer for 1 minute. Stir in the tomatoes, bay leaf, rosemary, parsley sprigs and paprika.

3 Return the chicken to the frying pan. Simmer, partly covered, for about 30 minutes or until the juices run clear. Remove the bay leaf, rosemary and parsley. Sprinkle the chicken with the chopped parsley and serve.

preparation time **20 mins**

cooking time **45 mins**

serves **4**

PER SERVING

274 kcal

45g protein

5g total fat
1g saturated fat

169mg cholesterol

8g total carbohydrate
7g sugars

3g fibre

237mg sodium

HEALTH HINT

A chicken thigh provides about 50 per cent more iron per 100g serving than an equal weight of chicken breast meat.

COOK'S TIP

During cooking, the alcohol in the wine evaporates, leaving just its concentrated flavour. The better the wine, the more mellow the flavour!

turkey and spinach roulades

Fresh spinach, roasted red pepper, ricotta and a touch of Parmesan together make a fantastic filling for tender turkey roulades. Braised in stock and vermouth and served with asparagus, this makes an elegant, attractive dish.

Kc — Fb

preparation time **30 mins**
cooking time **35 mins**
serves **4**

PER SERVING

344 kcal	
44g protein	
10g total fat	
5g saturated fat	
158mg cholesterol	
10g total carbohydrate	
7g sugars	
3g fibre	
252mg sodium	

HEALTH HINT

Asparagus is a rich source of many of the B vitamins, especially folate. New research suggests that folate may have a role in helping to protect against heart disease.

1 Put the turkey steaks between sheets of cling film and bat out into rough squares about 5mm thick. Set aside.

2 Place the spinach in a large pan, with just the water clinging to the leaves after washing. Cover and cook for 2 minutes or until wilted. Drain well, squeezing out all the excess liquid, then chop the spinach finely and place in a large bowl.

3 Preheat the grill. Grill the red pepper quarters, skin side up, for 6 minutes or until the skin is charred. Transfer to a plastic bag and seal. When cool enough to handle, peel and dice.

4 Add the red pepper to the spinach together with the ricotta, egg, Parmesan cheese, breadcrumbs, basil and nutmeg. Season with pepper. Mix well. Divide the filling among the turkey steaks, spreading it over them evenly. Roll up each one, folding in the sides to enclose the filling, and secure with wooden cocktail sticks or skewers. Place the roulades in a frying pan and pour over the vermouth and stock. Cover and bring to the boil, then reduce the heat and simmer for 20 minutes.

5 Remove the roulades from the pan and keep hot. Bring the liquid back to the boil and boil until reduced. Stir in the crème fraîche and boil for a further 1–2 minutes or until thickened.

6 While the liquid is reducing, cook the asparagus spears in boiling water for 2–3 minutes or until just tender. Drain, refresh with cold water and keep warm.

7 Remove and discard the cocktail sticks from the turkey roulades, then cut into neat slices. Serve garnished with the asparagus spears and with the sauce drizzled round.

4 skinless turkey breast steaks, about 140g each

150g spinach leaves

1 small red pepper, deseeded and quartered

150g ricotta cheese

1 egg, beaten

2 tablespoons freshly grated Parmesan cheese

2 tablespoons fresh wholemeal breadcrumbs

2 tablespoons chopped fresh basil

pinch of freshly grated nutmeg

pepper to taste

150ml dry vermouth

150ml low-sodium chicken stock or stock made without salt

4 tablespoons half-fat crème fraîche

250g thin asparagus spears to serve

chicken with asparagus and pepper

Stir-frying is not just for Chinese dishes. This quick and healthy method of cooking works just as beautifully in this chicken and vegetable sauté, seasoned with garlic and rosemary. A bowl of basmati rice is the perfect complement.

2 teaspoons extra virgin olive oil

1 yellow pepper, deseeded and cut into 1cm wide strips

3 garlic cloves, finely chopped

3 spring onions, cut into 2cm lengths

370g chicken breast fillets, cut crossways into 1cm wide strips

750g asparagus, cut into 5cm lengths

1½ teaspoons grated lemon zest

½ teaspoon chopped fresh rosemary

175ml low-sodium chicken stock or stock made without salt

1½ teaspoons cornflour blended with 1 tablespoon water

2 tablespoons toasted, finely chopped walnuts

1 Heat the oil in a large non-stick frying pan over moderately high heat. Add the yellow pepper, garlic and spring onions and sauté, stirring, for 2 minutes.

2 Add the chicken, asparagus, lemon zest and rosemary. Continue to sauté, stirring, for about 5 minutes or until the chicken is cooked through and the asparagus is tender.

3 Add the stock and bring to the boil. Stir in the cornflour mixture and simmer for 1 minute or until the sauce has thickened. Add the walnuts and toss to combine, then serve.

30

preparation time **20 mins**
cooking time **10 mins**
serves **4**

PER SERVING

290 kcal

30g protein

14g total fat

2g saturated fat

83mg cholesterol

12g total carbohydrate

7g sugars

4g fibre

166mg sodium

COOK'S TIP

The grated lemon zest and rosemary in this dish have such powerful flavours that you will never miss the amount of fat that would ordinarily have been used for sautéing.

chicken and potato curry

Letting the chicken pieces sit for half an hour in a gingery marinade makes all the difference to this curry. Skinning the chicken not only does away with most of the bird's fat, it also lets the spicy flavours really permeate the flesh.

1 Remove the skin from the chicken joints. Cut three or four slashes in the flesh of each joint, right to the bone. Rub the turmeric, ginger and lemon juice all over the chicken joints, then leave to marinate for about 30 minutes.

2 Heat the oil in a large, heavy-based frying pan. Add the dried chilli, mustard seeds, fennel seeds and cumin seeds, and let them sputter and pop for a few minutes. Stir in the ground cumin, cinnamon and chickpea flour. Watch carefully to be sure you do not burn the spices, as this can happen very quickly.

3 Add the garlic, green pepper and onion to the spice mixture and cook for a few minutes, stirring. Add the chicken and tomatoes and stir to mix. Cover and cook for 15 minutes.

4 Meanwhile, cook the potatoes in boiling water for 5 minutes; drain and cut into bite-sized pieces. Blanch the cabbage in a separate pan of boiling water for 1 minute, then drain.

5 Add the potatoes and cabbage to the curried chicken and stir in. Cover the pan again and continue to simmer over a moderately low heat for 20–25 minutes or until the chicken is completely cooked and tender. Add the peas and warm through for a few minutes. Serve hot, with Indian breads and pickles.

Kc **Fb**

preparation time **30 mins** plus 30 mins marinating

cooking time **45 mins**

serves **4**

PER SERVING

350 kcal

39g protein

11g total fat
2g saturated fat

150mg cholesterol

26g total carbohydrate
10g sugars

6g fibre

218mg sodium

HEALTH HINT

The vitamin C provided by the peas, tomatoes and potatoes will increase the absorption of iron from the chicken.

---

1 chicken, about 1.35kg, jointed into 8 pieces

½ teaspoon turmeric

4cm piece fresh root ginger, peeled and finely chopped

juice of ½ lemon

2 tablespoons sunflower oil

1 dried red chilli, broken into 2–3 pieces

1 teaspoon mustard seeds

½ teaspoon fennel seeds

¼ teaspoon cumin seeds

¼ teaspoon ground cumin

¼ teaspoon ground cinnamon

1 tablespoon chickpea flour (gram flour)

3 garlic cloves, roughly crushed

½ green pepper, deseeded and thinly sliced

1 large onion, sliced

1 can (about 400g) chopped tomatoes

250g potatoes, peeled

¼ green cabbage, about 140g, thinly sliced

140g frozen peas, thawed with boiling water and drained

Tex-Mex chicken pie

Teenagers especially will love this pie, which layers flour tortillas with diced chicken and red kidney beans in a spicy tomato, sweetcorn and pepper sauce. Serve with a green salad and some diced avocado sprinkled with lime juice.

Fb

preparation time **35 mins**
cooking time **25 mins**
serves **6**

PER SERVING

517 kcal

29g protein

13g total fat
5.5g saturated fat

66mg cholesterol

75g total carbohydrate
17g sugars

7.5g fibre

581mg sodium

HEALTH HINTS

Tortillas, whether made from masa harina – a type of cornmeal – or wheat, are a good source of starchy carbohydrates.

There is little nutritional difference between canned red kidney beans and cooked dried ones, and canned beans are certainly a lot more convenient.

Eaten without the skin, chicken is low in fat and the fat that is present in the meat is mainly the more beneficial unsaturated type.

1 First make the filling. Heat the oil in a large pan, add the onion and cook for 10 minutes or until softened. Stir in the garlic, green pepper, baby corn and fresh chilli, and cook for 5 more minutes.

2 Add the tomatoes with their juice, the ground coriander, cumin, sugar and crumbled stock cube. Season with pepper and stir well. Bring to the boil, then reduce the heat and simmer for 10 minutes.

3 Stir in the chicken, kidney beans and half the fresh coriander. Heat through gently for 5 minutes. Preheat the oven to 200°C (gas mark 6).

4 Lightly oil a large china flan dish, measuring about 28cm in diameter and 5cm deep. Place a tortilla on the bottom and spoon over one-fifth of the filling. Cover with a second tortilla, then spread over another fifth of the filling. Continue layering, finishing with the last tortilla on top. The stack will be slightly higher than the side of the dish.

5 Mix the yoghurt with the soured cream, 50g of the cheese and 2 tablespoons of the remaining coriander. Spoon over the top of the pie and sprinkle with the remaining cheese. Bake for 25 minutes or until the top is golden. Sprinkle with the rest of the coriander and serve hot, cut into wedges.

Variations As an alternative topping, mix 200g fromage frais with 85g finely grated Manchego cheese and 2 tablespoons chopped fresh coriander.
• To make a tortilla pie without chicken, soften the onion, then add the crushed garlic, 1 deseeded and chopped yellow pepper, 250g chopped courgettes and 500g chopped bulb fennel. Cook for 5 minutes, then stir in the tomatoes, ground coriander, sugar, stock cube and pepper to taste. Simmer for 10 minutes. Add 2 cans (about 410g each) borlotti beans, drained and rinsed, and heat through. Layer the bean mixture with the flour tortillas, top with the yoghurt mixture or the fromage frais mixture and bake as in the main recipe.

6 large flour tortillas (wraps)
150g plain low-fat yoghurt
90ml soured cream
75g mature Cheddar cheese, finely grated

CHICKEN AND CORN FILLING

2 tablespoons extra virgin olive oil
1 large Spanish onion, chopped
2 garlic cloves, crushed
1 green pepper, deseeded and chopped
200g baby corn, chopped
1 fresh red chilli, deseeded and chopped
2 cans (about 400g each) chopped tomatoes
1 teaspoon ground coriander
1 teaspoon ground cumin
1 teaspoon caster sugar
1 low-sodium chicken stock cube
pepper to taste
300g cooked chicken breast fillets, diced
1 can (about 410g) red kidney beans, drained and rinsed
6 tablespoons chopped fresh coriander

Hungarian-style chicken meatballs

Minced chicken and mushrooms make succulent meatballs – delicious simmered in a smooth tomato sauce with red and green peppers. Paprika warms the flavour and new potatoes turn it into a complete one-dish meal.

30g margarine
1 small onion, finely chopped
350g mushrooms, finely chopped
350g minced chicken
50g fresh wholemeal breadcrumbs
1 egg, beaten
2 tablespoons chopped parsley
pepper to taste
550g small new potatoes
4 tablespoons plain low-fat
    yoghurt to serve
fresh flat-leaf parsley to garnish

PAPRIKA AND PEPPER SAUCE
2 tablespoons extra virgin
    olive oil
1 onion, finely chopped
2 garlic cloves, crushed
1 red pepper, deseeded and
    thinly sliced
1 green pepper, deseeded and
    thinly sliced
1 tablespoon mild paprika
1 litre tomato passata
pinch of caraway seeds

1 Melt the margarine in a frying pan. Add the onion and mushrooms, and cook over moderate heat, stirring frequently, for about 10 minutes or until the mixture is reduced, dark in colour and very thick. Transfer the mixture to a bowl and allow it to cool slightly.

2 Add the chicken to the mushroom mixture and use a fork to break up the mince. Add the breadcrumbs, egg, parsley and pepper. Mix the ingredients until thoroughly combined. Wet your hands, then shape it into 20 walnut-sized balls. Set aside.

3 To make the sauce, heat the oil in a flameproof casserole. Add the onion and cook for 4–5 minutes, stirring frequently, until softened. Add the garlic and peppers, then cook, stirring constantly, for 2–3 minutes. Stir in the paprika and cook for 1 minute, then pour in the tomato passata and bring to the boil over high heat.

4 Stir in the caraway seeds and pepper to taste. Add the meatballs and the potatoes to the simmering sauce, taking care not to break up the meatballs. Bring the sauce back to simmering point, then cover and simmer gently for 35 minutes or until the potatoes are tender.

5 Ladle the meatballs, potatoes and sauce into bowls and swirl on a little yoghurt. Garnish with parsley and serve.

 Fb

preparation time **35 mins**
cooking time **45 mins**
serves **4**

PER SERVING

477 kcal

31g protein

17g total fat
3.5g saturated fat

137mg cholesterol

51g total carbohydrate
21g sugars

7g fibre

491mg sodium

HEALTH HINT

When eaten regularly and in quantity, potatoes are a useful source of vitamin C – new potatoes contain the most, and eating them unpeeled retains the maximum goodness as the nutrients are concentrated under the skin.

preparation time **10 mins**

cooking time **20 mins**

serves **4**

PER SERVING

288 kcal

40g protein

3.5g total fat

1.5g saturated fat

105mg cholesterol

25g total carbohydrate

13g sugars

1.5g fibre

183mg sodium

HEART SUPERFOOD

An apple a day may not keep the doctor away, but several studies suggest a link between apple consumption and reduced risk of cardiovascular disease. Apples contain flavonoids, a group of antioxidants that protect against heart disease and cancer. They're also a good source of cholesterol-lowering soluble fibre.

chicken with apples and Calvados

 Looking for a meal that can be on the table in thirty minutes yet is elegant enough to serve at a dinner party? This dish tastes like it came from a French bistro. Serve with wild rice and steamed green beans.

1 Lightly coat a large frying pan with cooking spray and set over moderately high heat. Add the shallots and sauté for about 2 minutes to soften. Add the apples and sauté for 3 minutes or until lightly browned. Add the apple juice, stock and Calvados. Cook, stirring, for a further 5 minutes or until the apples are tender. Transfer to a bowl. Wipe the frying pan clean.

2 Combine the flour and pepper on a sheet of greaseproof paper. Coat the chicken breasts with the seasoned flour, pressing with your hands so the flour adheres and the chicken is flattened evenly.

3 Lightly coat the frying pan again with cooking spray and set over moderately high heat. Add the chicken and cook for about 3 minutes on each side or until browned and almost cooked through. Return the apple mixture and any juices to the frying pan and bring to the boil. Reduce the heat and simmer for 2 minutes. Stir in the crème fraîche and serve.

2 shallots, finely chopped

2 tart dessert apples, peeled and cut into 5mm slices

250ml apple juice

175ml low-sodium chicken stock or stock made without salt

1 tablespoon Calvados (apple brandy) or apple juice

4 tablespoons plain flour

$\frac{1}{2}$ teaspoon pepper

4 chicken breast fillets, about 150g each

2 tablespoons half-fat crème fraîche

citrus-grilled chicken with melon salsa

Capture the spirit of the tropics and serve it on your dinner table! This sunny mix of melon, salad greens, chicken and citrus, spiked with jalapeño chilli, is healthy carefree eating at its best.

500g chicken breast fillets
½ teaspoon pepper
80ml freshly squeezed lime juice
1 garlic clove, finely chopped
2 teaspoons reduced-sodium
    soy sauce
1 fresh jalapeño chilli, deseeded and
    finely chopped
100g mixed salad leaves

MELON SALSA
1 large cucumber
1 Charentais melon, cut into
    2cm dice
½ punnet cherry tomatoes, halved
2 tablespoons very thinly sliced
    fresh basil

1 Sprinkle the chicken on both sides with pepper. Stir together 2 tablespoons lime juice, the garlic, soy sauce and 1 teaspoon of the jalapeño chilli in a pie dish. Add the chicken and turn to coat. Leave to marinate at room temperature, turning once, while preparing the melon salsa.

2 Halve the cucumber lengthways. Remove the seeds by dragging the tip of a spoon down the centre. Place the cucumber cut-side down on a board and cut across into 2mm thick slices. Toss the cucumber, melon, tomatoes, basil and remaining jalapeño and lime juice in a mixing bowl. Set aside.

3 Preheat a barbecue or grill to moderate. Lift the chicken out of the marinade (discard the marinade) and lightly coat both sides of the chicken with cooking spray (preferably olive oil flavoured). Barbecue or grill the chicken for about 5 minutes on each side, turning only once, until the juices run clear.

4 Transfer the chicken to a carving board and cut the meat diagonally into strips about 1cm thick. Toss with the melon salsa. Divide the salad leaves among four plates and spoon the chicken and melon mixture on top.

 30 **Kc**

preparation and cooking
time **30 mins**
serves **4**

PER SERVING

170 kcal

31g protein

2g total fat
0.5g saturated fat

89mg cholesterol

7g total carbohydrate
7g sugars

1g fibre

211mg sodium

HEALTH HINTS

Orange-fleshed melons are an excellent source of beta carotene, a powerful antioxidant that the body converts into vitamin A.

Vitamin C in the fruit and lime juice aids in the absorption of iron, which is present in the mix of leafy salad greens.

chicken and yellow pepper loaf

This mustardy chicken and pepper loaf, wrapped in thin slices of courgette instead of high-fat bacon, is perfectly complemented by the fresh tomato and basil sauce – a very colourful dish, full of savoury flavours.

1 Heat a ridged cast-iron grill pan, then brush it with about 1 teaspoon of the oil. Char-grill the courgette slices, in batches, until tender, turning to mark both sides with charred lines. Add a little more oil if necessary.

2 Heat the remaining 1 tablespoon olive oil in a frying pan, add the peppers and cook for 5–6 minutes, stirring frequently, until softened and golden. Add the spring onions and garlic and cook for a further 2–3 minutes. Sprinkle over the mustard and stir well. Transfer the mixture to a bowl and cool slightly, then add the minced chicken and some pepper. Mix thoroughly.

3 Preheat the oven to 180°C (gas mark 4). Use the courgette slices to line a 900g loaf tin, laying them crossways and slightly overlapping. Arrange them so the ends hang over the sides of the loaf tin. Spoon the chicken mixture into the tin, pushing the mixture into the corners, and smooth the surface. Fold the ends of the courgette slices over the top of the chicken filling.

4 Set the loaf tin in a roasting tin of water. Bake for 1 hour or until the loaf is cooked through – the juices should run clear when a knife is inserted into the centre.

5 About 30 minutes before the end of the cooking time, put all the sauce ingredients in a medium-sized saucepan, reserving a few small basil sprigs for garnish. Bring to a gentle simmer, then cook, stirring occasionally, for 15–20 minutes or until the excess tomato liquid has evaporated. Press the sauce through a sieve into a clean pan and season with pepper. Reheat the sauce.

6 Drain off the juices from the loaf tin, then slice the loaf. Serve hot, with the tomato sauce and garnished with the reserved basil sprigs.

2 tablespoons extra virgin olive oil

3 large courgettes, thinly sliced lengthways

2 yellow peppers, deseeded and diced

2 bunches of spring onions, thinly sliced

1 garlic clove, crushed

1 teaspoon mustard powder

500g minced chicken

pepper to taste

TOMATO AND BASIL SAUCE

1 onion, finely chopped

450g plum tomatoes, coarsely chopped

1 bunch of fresh basil, about 20g, stalks discarded and large leaves torn into smaller pieces

pinch of caster sugar

few drops of Tabasco sauce

preparation time **30 mins**

cooking time **1¼ hours**

serves **4**

PER SERVING

300 kcal

29g protein

14g total fat

3g saturated fat

90mg cholesterol

15g total carbohydrate

14g sugars

5g fibre

96mg sodium

HEALTH HINT

Both the yellow peppers and courgettes provide vitamin C and beta-carotene, which the body converts into vitamin A. The courgettes also contribute folate.

marinated duck and kasha salad

Kasha, or buckwheat grain, is available either plain or roasted. When plain kasha is toasted and then simmered in stock, it develops a rich nutty flavour. It works perfectly with duck in this hearty main-dish salad.

450g boneless duck breasts, skinned and all visible fat removed

2 garlic cloves, chopped

juice of 1 lemon

12 sprigs of fresh thyme

1 teaspoon chopped fresh rosemary

3 tablespoons extra virgin olive oil

225g plain kasha

750ml chicken stock

125g thin green beans

200g mixed salad leaves, such as frisée, lamb's lettuce, mizuna and rocket

5 sprigs of fresh basil, finely shredded

½ red onion, thinly sliced

8 green olives, stoned

8 black olives, stoned

2 courgettes, thinly sliced lengthways

12 small spring onions

12 small tomatoes

1½ tablespoons red wine vinegar, or a combination of sherry and balsamic vinegars

pepper to taste

1 With a sharp knife, score the duck breasts on both sides in a criss-cross pattern. Put the breasts in a bowl and add about two-thirds of the garlic, the lemon juice, half of the thyme sprigs, the rosemary and 1 tablespoon of the oil. Coat the breasts with the flavourings, then set aside to marinate.

2 Put the kasha in a heavy frying pan and toast over a moderate heat, stirring and tossing, for 4–5 minutes or until it has become slightly darker in colour. Remove from the heat.

3 Bring the stock to the boil in a saucepan. Stir in the toasted kasha. Bring back to the boil, then cover and cook gently for 10–15 minutes or until the stock has been absorbed and the kasha is tender. Remove from the heat and set aside, covered.

4 Heat a ridged cast-iron grill pan. Meanwhile, blanch the green beans in boiling water for 1–2 minutes; drain and refresh. Cut the beans in half and put into a salad bowl. Add the salad leaves, basil, red onion and olives, and toss to mix.

5 Remove the duck breasts from the marinade and place on the hot grill pan. Cook for 3 minutes, then turn the breasts over and cook for another 3 minutes (the meat will be rare, so cook longer if you prefer it well done). Remove the duck to a board. Place the courgettes, spring onions and tomatoes on the grill pan and cook for 1–2 minutes or until lightly charred.

6 Combine the remaining garlic and oil with the vinegar in a small bowl, add the leaves from the remaining thyme sprigs and whisk together. Drizzle over the salad. Spoon on the kasha and arrange the courgettes, spring onions and tomatoes on top. Slice the duck breasts, place over the vegetables and serve.

 Fb

preparation and cooking time **50 mins**

serves **4**

PER SERVING

483 kcal

30g protein

18g total fat
4g saturated fat

124mg cholesterol

55g total carbohydrate
6g sugars

5g fibre

512mg sodium

HEALTH HINT

Despite its name, buckwheat is not a true grain, but a plant that produces cereal-like seeds. It is gluten-free, so it is suitable for anyone with gluten intolerance. It contains a phytochemical called rutin, which is believed to help reduce high blood pressure.

turkey, pasta and leek crisp

This warming dish appeals to children and adults alike, so it makes an ideal family meal. It is a good example of an everyday dish in which vegetables, pasta and breadcrumbs extend a modest portion of a protein food.

1 Place the carrots and leeks in a saucepan. Add the stock and the wine, if using, and bring to the boil. Reduce the heat, cover the pan and simmer for about 15 minutes or until the carrots are tender but not soft.

2 Drain the carrots and leeks, reserving the stock. Place the vegetables in a large ovenproof dish. Return the stock to the saucepan and boil it until it is reduced to about 300ml. Set aside to cool.

3 Cook the pasta in boiling water for 10–12 minutes, or according to the packet instructions, until al dente. Drain well and add to the vegetables; mix together. Preheat the oven to 190°C (gas mark 5).

4 Heat the oil in a saucepan. Add the turkey and cook, stirring, for 5–10 minutes or until lightly browned. Use a draining spoon to remove the turkey from the pan and mix it with the pasta and vegetables.

5 Remove the pan from the heat and pour in the milk and cooled stock. Whisking constantly, sprinkle the flour into the liquid. Return the pan to the heat and bring the sauce to the boil, still whisking. Reduce the heat and simmer gently for 3 minutes, whisking frequently, until the sauce is thick and smooth. Add pepper to taste. Pour the sauce over the pasta and vegetable mixture, coating it evenly.

6 Mix together the breadcrumbs, cheese and parsley, and sprinkle this evenly over the top. Bake for about 15 minutes or until the topping is crisp and golden.

2 carrots, sliced

400g leeks, sliced

450ml low-sodium vegetable or chicken stock or stock made without salt

300ml white wine or additional stock

300g cavatelli (fluted pasta shells) or other shapes

2 tablespoons extra virgin olive oil

400g turkey breast fillet, skinned and cut into thin strips

300ml semi-skimmed milk

45g plain flour

pepper to taste

CRISP TOPPING

50g fresh wholemeal breadcrumbs

2 tablespoons grated Cheddar cheese

2 tablespoons chopped fresh parsley

preparation time **1 hour**
cooking time **15 mins**
serves **4**

PER SERVING

635 kcal

40g protein

14g total fat
4g saturated fat

69mg cholesterol

80g total carbohydrate
10g sugars

6.5g fibre

473mg sodium

HEALTH HINT

Being a starchy carbohydrate, pasta is an excellent energy-giving and satisfying food for all the family. The energy is slowly released as the pasta is digested, so helping to prevent between-meal hunger pangs.

duck and wild mushroom risotto

Risotto rice absorbs delectable flavours from dried porcini mushrooms, herbs, garlic and vegetable stock, before being tossed with sautéed fresh mushrooms and slices of tender duck to make a spectacular supper dish.

1 Put the porcini mushrooms in a bowl and pour over the boiling water. Leave to soak for 20 minutes, then drain, reserving the soaking liquid. Finely chop the mushrooms and set aside. Strain the liquid into a saucepan. Add the stock and keep hot over a very low heat.

2 Heat a ridged cast-iron grill pan. Brush with 1 teaspoon oil and add the duck breasts. Reduce the heat to moderate and cook for 8–12 minutes, turning once, until done to your taste. Remove the duck breasts from the pan and leave to rest in a warm place for 10 minutes, then cut the breasts into thin slices. Keep them warm.

3 Meanwhile, heat 1 tablespoon of the remaining oil in a heavy-based saucepan, add the onion and garlic and fry gently for 4–5 minutes or until softened. Add the rice and stir for about 1 minute to coat it with the oil.

4 Add the wine and bubble until it has almost all been absorbed. Stir in the lemon zest, thyme and porcini mushrooms, then add a ladleful of the stock. Bubble, stirring frequently, until it has almost all been absorbed, then add another ladleful of stock. Continue adding the stock gradually in this way – total cooking time will be 15–20 minutes. The risotto is ready when the rice is tender but still firm and the texture is moist and creamy.

5 About 5 minutes before the end of cooking time, heat the remaining 2 teaspoons of oil and the margarine in a large frying pan. Add the fresh mushrooms and sauté over a high heat for 4 minutes or until tender.

6 Stir the mushrooms into the risotto together with the duck and any duck juices. Add the parsley and season with pepper. Remove from the heat, cover the pan and leave to stand for 5 minutes before serving.

10g dried porcini mushrooms

300ml boiling water

750ml hot low-sodium vegetable stock or stock made without salt

2 tablespoons sunflower oil

2 duck breasts, about 340g in total, skinned

1 red onion, finely chopped

1 garlic clove, crushed

340g risotto rice

150ml dry white wine

1 teaspoon finely grated lemon zest

2 teaspoons chopped fresh thyme

15g margarine

450g mixed fresh mushrooms, such as oyster mushrooms, ceps and shiitake, sliced if large

3 tablespoons chopped fresh parsley

pepper to taste

---

preparation and cooking time **1 hour**
plus 20 mins soaking
serves **4**

PER SERVING

558 kcal

27g protein

16g total fat
5g saturated fat

94mg cholesterol

68g total carbohydrate
3g sugars

2g fibre

500mg sodium

HEALTH HINT

Most recipes use mushrooms in such small quantities that the nutritional contribution they make is not as great as the flavour and texture they provide. Here a good quantity is used, which boosts the B vitamins and minerals in the dish.

turkey escalopes with chestnut mushrooms and Madeira

Lean and tender turkey escalopes – breast steaks pounded until thin – only need brief cooking. Simmered with chestnut mushrooms and a Madeira sauce finished with crème fraîche, they make a dish that is perfect for entertaining.

4 small skinless turkey breast steaks, about 115g each

2 tablespoons plain flour

pepper to taste

1 tablespoon sunflower oil

25g margarine

1 small onion, finely chopped

250g chestnut mushrooms, sliced

4 tablespoons Madeira

2 teaspoons wholegrain mustard

1 tablespoon chopped fresh oregano or 1 teaspoon dried oregano

150ml low-sodium chicken or turkey stock or stock made without salt

2 tablespoons crème fraîche

2 tablespoons chopped fresh parsley to garnish

1 Put the turkey steaks between sheets of cling film and pound them to flatten to about 5mm thickness. Season the flour with some pepper and use to coat the escalopes, shaking off the excess.

2 Heat the oil and margarine in a large frying pan. Add the turkey escalopes, in one layer, and fry for 2–3 minutes on each side. Transfer the turkey to a plate and keep warm.

3 Add the onion to the pan and cook gently for 2–3 minutes to soften. Add the mushrooms and cook for 1 minute or they are softened.

4 Stir in the Madeira and allow to bubble for 2 minutes, then stir in the mustard, oregano and stock. Return the escalopes to the pan and simmer gently for 3–4 minutes.

5 Using a draining spoon, spoon the turkey and mushrooms onto a warm serving platter. Stir the crème fraîche into the sauce and warm through, then check the seasoning. Pour the sauce over the turkey, sprinkle with parsley and serve.

30 **Kc**

preparation time **15 mins**

cooking time **15 mins**

serves **4**

PER SERVING

290 kcal

32g protein

13g total fat
4g saturated fat

74mg cholesterol

7g total carbohydrate
1g sugars

1g fibre

300mg sodium

HEALTH HINTS

Turkey has even less fat than chicken and it contains slightly more vitamin B_{12}, niacin and zinc.

Mushrooms are low in fat and calories, with 0.5g fat and 13 kcal in 100g.

hot turkey and Stilton bagels

Favourite Christmas flavours make this a most glamorous toasted open-face sandwich. If you keep a supply of bagels in the freezer, you can rustle up a great snack meal like this whenever you have some leftover turkey or chicken.

30 Fb

preparation time **10 mins**
cooking time **5 mins**
serves **4**

PER SERVING

490 kcal

31g protein

18g total fat
8g saturated fat

80mg cholesterol

52g total carbohydrate
16g sugars

3g fibre

688mg sodium

HEALTH HINT

Although Stilton is relatively high in fat, it has a strong flavour so a little goes a long way. Like all cheese, it is a good source of protein and a valuable source of calcium, phosphorus, vitamin B$_{12}$ and niacin.

1 Preheat the grill. Split the bagels in half horizontally, then toast both sides under the grill.

2 Spread the cut surfaces of the bagel halves lightly with margarine, then spread over the cranberry jelly. Arrange the sliced turkey on the bagel halves.

3 Slice or crumble the Stilton cheese and place on top of the turkey. Return to the grill to cook for 1–2 minutes, just to melt the cheese.

4 Serve hot, with the orange wedges and salad leaves.

Variations Instead of bagels, use English muffins or ciabatta rolls split in half. • Cooked chicken can be substituted for the roast turkey. • Blue Vinney is a lower-fat alternative to Stilton. If you're not fond of blue cheese, use thinly sliced Gruyère or Camembert, or even a well-flavoured Cheddar, coarsely grated; sliced Gouda will reduce the fat. • For another hot turkey sandwich, toast 8 thick slices of brioche loaf, or split brioche buns, on both sides and spread very lightly with margarine. Warm 120ml leftover turkey gravy (or make a sauce from 4 tablespoons each red wine and stock, thickened with 2 teaspoons cornflour mixed with a little water). Add the sliced turkey to the hot gravy or sauce and heat through, then spoon on top of the toasted brioche. Top each slice with 1 teaspoon cranberry or redcurrant jelly, garnish with watercress and serve.

4 bagels, plain or onion-flavoured
30g margarine
2 tablespoons cranberry jelly
225g cold roast turkey meat, skin removed, then thinly sliced
100g Stilton cheese

TO SERVE
2 oranges, cut into wedges
salad leaves

meat dishes

beef salade niçoise

In this hearty, French-style salad, slices of quickly char-grilled rump steak top a mixture of colourful vegetables in a tangy Dijon mustard dressing. Serve with a warm baguette to mop up all the delicious juices.

1 thick-cut lean rump steak, about 340g, trimmed of visible fat

coarsely ground black pepper

¼ teaspoon dried herbes de Provence, or to taste

500g small new potatoes, scrubbed

200g French beans, trimmed

200g shelled fresh or frozen broad beans

200g cherry tomatoes, halved

100g mixed black and green olives, stoned

2 tablespoons snipped fresh chives

3 tablespoons chopped fresh parsley

100g baby leaf spinach

3 Little Gem lettuces, separated into leaves

MUSTARD VINAIGRETTE

2 tablespoons extra virgin olive oil

1 tablespoon red wine vinegar

2 teaspoons Dijon mustard

pepper to taste

1 Pat the steak dry with kitchen paper. Season on both sides with coarse pepper and herbes de Provence. Set aside.

2 Place the potatoes in a saucepan of boiling water and cook for 10 minutes. Add the French and broad beans and cook for a further 5 minutes or until all the vegetables are just tender. Drain in a colander and rinse with cold water to cool a bit.

3 Put the potatoes and beans in a large bowl and add the tomatoes, olives, chives and parsley. Set aside.

4 Heat a ridged cast-iron grill pan or a non-stick frying pan until hot. Cook the steak for 2½ minutes on each side. It will be rare; cook longer if you prefer it medium or well-done. Remove to a plate and leave to rest for 5 minutes.

5 Meanwhile, place the dressing ingredients in a screw-top jar with 2 tablespoons water and season with pepper. Put on the lid and shake to mix.

6 Cut the steak into slices about 5mm thick and add to the vegetables. Pour any juices that have collected on the plate into the dressing. Pour the dressing over the meat and vegetables and toss until thoroughly combined. Arrange the spinach and lettuce leaves in a large salad bowl or on a large platter. Spoon on the steak salad and serve immediately.

preparation and cooking time **50 mins**

serves **4**

PER SERVING
339 kcal
26g protein
14g total fat 3g saturated fat
50mg cholesterol
28g total carbohydrate 6g sugars
7g fibre
324mg sodium

COOK'S TIP

Robust broad beans go well with beef and they bring valuable dietary fibre to the dish.

Kc

preparation time **35 mins**
plus 30 mins marinating

cooking time **8 mins**

serves **4**

PER SERVING

344 kcal

33g protein

7g total fat
2.5g saturated fat

74mg cholesterol

37g total carbohydrate
8g sugars

2g fibre

522mg sodium

HEALTH HINT

There are two good reasons to serve meat and potatoes on a bed of salad greens: the fresh greens provide a delicious contrast and, at the same time, they round out the meal with important nutrients, including carotenoids, vitamin C, folate and fibre.

grilled steak with mustard-glazed potatoes

Here lean beef is flavoured with a honey-mustard marinade and served with potatoes that are first boiled, then tossed in the marinade and grilled with the meat for a barbecued effect. Both are served on a bed of peppery watercress.

1 Combine the mustard, honey, vinegar, garlic and pepper in a large bowl and stir well to combine. Place the steak in a shallow bowl. Measure out 2 tablespoons of the mustard mixture and rub all over the steak. Leave to marinate for 30 minutes at room temperature or overnight in the refrigerator.

2 With a vegetable peeler, remove a strip of skin from around each potato. Drop the potatoes into a large pan of boiling water and cook for 20 minutes or until they are just tender. Drain well, then add to mustard mixture in the bowl and toss to coat. With a slotted spoon, transfer the potatoes to the rack in the grill pan. (Leave room for the onion wedges and beef.)

3 Preheat the grill. Add the onion to the mustard mixture in the bowl, turning the wedges to coat. Arrange on the grill pan.

4 Place the steak on the grill rack alongside the potatoes and onion. Grill 8cm from the heat for 8 minutes, turning everything over halfway through the cooking. Allow the beef to rest for 5 minutes before slicing. Serve with the watercress.

4 tablespoons Dijon mustard
1 tablespoon clear honey
1 tablespoon cider vinegar
2 garlic cloves, finely chopped
¼ teaspoon pepper
500g beef fillet or rump steak
750g new potatoes
1 large onion, cut into 8 wedges
1 bunch of watercress, tough
 ends trimmed

pepper steak with leek mash

Potatoes – as chips, jacket baked or mashed – are a popular partner for steak. Here a mash with leeks and mustard accompanies pepper-coated fillet steaks. Serve with a fresh seasonal green vegetable such as green beans or broccoli.

2 tablespoons mixed or black peppercorns, coarsely crushed

4 beef fillet steaks, 2.5cm thick, about 140g each, trimmed of visible fat

1 teaspoon extra virgin olive oil

chopped fresh parsley or snipped fresh chives to garnish

LEEK AND MUSTARD MASH

900g floury potatoes, peeled and cut into chunks

2 teaspoons extra virgin olive oil

200g young leeks, finely shredded

120ml semi-skimmed milk

1 tablespoon wholegrain mustard

25g margarine

pepper to taste

1 To make the leek and mustard mash, place the potatoes in a saucepan and pour over boiling water to cover by 5cm. Bring back to the boil, then reduce the heat and cook for 15–20 minutes or until the potatoes are very tender.

2 Meanwhile, spread out the crushed peppercorns on a plate and press the steaks into them until they are coated with peppercorns on all sides. Set aside.

3 Heat the oil for the mash in a non-stick frying pan. Add the leeks and cook, stirring constantly, for 3–5 minutes or until tender. Transfer to a plate lined with a double thickness of kitchen paper to drain. Heat the milk in a saucepan until hot.

4 When the potatoes are tender, drain them, shaking the colander or sieve to remove any excess water, and return them to the pan. Pour the hot milk over the potatoes, then mash them until they are completely smooth. Add the leeks, mustard and margarine, and season with pepper. Beat well to mix, then cover and keep warm.

5 Heat a ridged cast-iron grill pan over a high heat until hot. Brush the pan with the olive oil, then reduce the heat to moderately high. Place the steaks in the pan and cook for 3 minutes on each side for rare, 3½ minutes on each side for medium-rare, 4 minutes on each side for medium or 5 minutes on each side for well done.

6 Spoon a mound of mash on each warmed plate and place a steak next to it. Drizzle any pan juices over the steaks and sprinkle with parsley or chives. Serve immediately.

Variation Veal loin chops can be cooked in the same way. Use 4 chops, 2cm thick and about 250g each. (This weight includes the bone; it should give about 140g meat.) Brush the chops with oil and season with pepper to taste, omitting the peppercorns. Cook as for the fillet steaks, allowing 3 minutes on each side for medium-rare, 3½ minutes on each side for medium or 4½ minutes on each side for well done.

 Fb

preparation and cooking time **about 1 hour**

serves **4**

PER SERVING

466 kcal

36g protein

18g total fat
6g saturated fat

90mg cholesterol

42g total carbohydrate
4g sugars

4g fibre

195mg sodium

HEALTH HINT

Adding leeks to mashed potatoes not only boosts their flavour but also adds vitamins B_1, B_6 and folate. If you include the green part of the leeks this will also provide beta carotene. Eaten regularly, leeks are believed to help reduce the risk of heart disease and stroke.

Argentinian char-grilled steak with crisp potatoes

In this recipe, slices of beef are marinated in a tangy herb-based sauce, called chimichurri sauce, which hails from Argentina, making them tender and juicy. They are complemented nicely by crisp char-grilled potatoes.

1 beef rump steak, 2cm thick, about 500g

¼ teaspoon pepper

4 medium baking potatoes, scrubbed and sliced lengthways into 1cm slices

CHIMICHURRI SAUCE

80ml low-sodium chicken stock or stock made without salt

1 tablespoon extra virgin olive oil

2 teaspoons freshly squeezed lemon juice

2 large garlic cloves, finely chopped

1 tablespoon chopped fresh oregano or 1 teaspoon dried oregano

½ teaspoon crushed dried chillies, or to taste

1 small onion, finely chopped

15g fresh flat-leaf parsley, finely chopped

1 Put all the sauce ingredients in a resealable plastic bag and shake to mix well. Rub the steak on both sides with the pepper, then put the steak in the bag and close. Refrigerate for 30 minutes, or up to 2 hours, turning once.

2 Meanwhile, place a wire rack over kitchen paper. Cook the potatoes in a saucepan of boiling water for 10 minutes or until they are almost tender. Transfer the potatoes to the rack. Lightly coat the potatoes on both sides with cooking spray (preferably olive oil flavoured).

3 Remove the steak from the sauce. Pour the sauce into a small saucepan, bring to the boil and boil for 3 minutes, stirring constantly. Remove from the heat and cover to keep warm. Set aside.

4 Meanwhile, heat a ridged cast-iron grill pan over moderately high heat. Char-grill the steak and potatoes until the steak is cooked to your taste (3–4 minutes on each side for medium-rare, 4–5 minutes for medium) and the potatoes are crisp (about 4 minutes per side). Thinly slice the steak across the grain. Divide the potato and steak slices among four plates and spoon about 2 tablespoons warm sauce over each serving.

 Kc Fb

preparation time **30 mins** plus 30 mins marinating

cooking time **10 mins**

serves **4**

PER SERVING

381 kcal

34g protein

9g total fat
3g saturated fat

74mg cholesterol

45g total carbohydrate
3g sugars

3g fibre

133mg sodium

COOK'S TIP

Ideal potato varieties to use for this recipe would be King Edward or Desiree.

seared sirloin steak with soba

Strips of richly flavoured sirloin steak and shiitake mushrooms sit on a bed of slightly wilted mixed salad leaves, with a mound of warm soba (buckwheat noodles) and a soy, ginger and sesame dressing.

1 Mix together the garlic, 1 teaspoon of the soy sauce and the groundnut oil. Rub into both sides of the steaks and leave to marinate for a few minutes.

2 Meanwhile, put the remaining soy sauce, the ginger, sugar, vinegar and sesame oil in a small bowl and whisk together to make the dressing.

3 Cook the soba in a large pan of boiling water for 5 minutes, or according to the packet instructions, adding the sugarsnap peas for the last 2 minutes of the cooking time. Drain the noodles and peas.

4 Heat a ridged cast-iron grill pan. Add the steaks and cook over a high heat for 2½ minutes. Turn them over and cook for 1 minute. Add the shiitake mushrooms to the pan, cup side down. Cook for a further 1½–2 minutes. The steaks will be rare, so cook longer if you prefer them medium or well done. Remove the steaks to a board and cut into thin slices.

5 Place the mixed leaves in a large bowl and add the sugarsnap peas, mooli, spring onions and basil. Stir the dressing, then pour about two-thirds over the salad and toss. Add the rest of the dressing to the noodles and mix.

6 Arrange the leafy salad on a serving platter or on four plates and top with the soba, mushrooms and steak slices.

1 garlic clove, chopped

4½ teaspoons reduced-sodium soy sauce

1 teaspoon groundnut oil

2 thick-cut lean sirloin steaks, about 450g in total, trimmed of visible fat

2 teaspoons grated fresh root ginger

1 tablespoon caster sugar

3 tablespoons rice vinegar or cider vinegar

2 tablespoons toasted sesame oil

250g soba (Japanese buckwheat noodles)

200g sugarsnap peas

115g shiitake mushrooms, stalks removed

200g mixed salad leaves, including frisée, mizuna, baby sorrel, baby spinach and coriander leaves

7.5cm piece of mooli (white radish), cut into matchstick strips

5 spring onions, thinly sliced

10 sprigs of fresh basil, leaves torn

preparation and cooking time **40 mins**

serves **4**

PER SERVING

490 kcal

33g protein

15g total fat
3g saturated fat

76mg cholesterol

56g total carbohydrate
9g sugars

3g fibre

435mg sodium

HEALTH HINT

Red meat such as beef is a nutritious protein-rich food. Beef is an excellent source of zinc and a useful source of iron, and it provides B vitamins and vitamin D.

Sunday special roast beef

Succulent roast beef, crisp roast potatoes and root vegetables and feather-light, old-fashioned Yorkshire puddings make one of the best loved of Sunday lunches. This healthy version will please everyone, even the traditionalists.

1.5kg boned, rolled and tied lean sirloin of beef, trimmed of visible fat

pepper to taste

4 teaspoons prepared English mustard (optional)

1.35kg floury potatoes, peeled and cut into even-sized pieces

675g baby parsnips, halved lengthways

675g baby carrots, halved lengthways

3 tablespoons sunflower oil

675g broccoli florets

450ml low-sodium beef stock or stock made without salt

pepper to taste

YORKSHIRE PUDDINGS

50g plain flour

1 egg

100ml semi-skimmed milk

2 teaspoons sunflower oil

1 Preheat the oven to 180°C (gas mark 4). Put the meat, fat-side up, on a rack in a roasting tin. Season with pepper, then spread with 3 teaspoons of the English mustard, if using. Roast the meat in the oven for the calculated time (see the cook's tip). Baste occasionally with the juices in the tin.

2 Meanwhile, prepare the Yorkshire pudding batter. Place the flour in a bowl. Make a well in the centre and add the egg. Add a little of the milk and beat together, gradually working in the flour. Slowly beat in the remaining milk and 4 tablespoons water until all the flour is incorporated and the batter is smooth. Set aside.

3 Place the potatoes in a large saucepan of boiling water and boil for 5 minutes. Drain well and return to the pan, then cover and shake vigorously to roughen the surface of the potatoes (this helps to make them crisp during roasting).

4 Place the parsnips and carrots in another large saucepan of boiling water and boil for 3 minutes, then drain.

5 One hour before the end of the roasting time for the beef, put 2 tablespoons of the oil in a non-stick roasting tin and the remaining 1 tablespoon oil in another non-stick roasting tin. Heat on top of the cooker, then add the potatoes to the 2 tablespoons oil and the parsnips and carrots to the 1 tablespoon oil. Baste each piece of vegetable with oil, then quickly place the tins in the oven with the beef. (With a gas oven, put the potatoes above the meat, and the carrots and parsnips below.) After 30 minutes, turn all the vegetables so they crisp and brown evenly.

6 When the beef is cooked, remove it from the oven and increase the heat to 220°C (gas mark 7). Place the beef on a warmed plate, cover with foil and keep warm. Set the roasting tin aside for the gravy.

7 Divide the oil for the Yorkshire puddings among 12 non-stick patty tins and put into the top of the oven to heat for 2–3 minutes. (Move the potatoes down a shelf.) Stir the batter, then pour it into the tins. Bake for 15 minutes or until the puddings are risen and golden brown.

8 Meanwhile, steam the broccoli for 10 minutes or until tender. To make the gravy, pour the fat very slowly out of the roasting tin, leaving the sediment behind. Place the tin on

 Fb

preparation and cooking time **2¼–2¾ hours**

serves **8**

PER SERVING

514 kcal

53g protein

13g total fat
5g saturated fat

121mg cholesterol

51g total carbohydrate
11g sugars

8g fibre

275mg sodium

COOK'S TIP

For rare roast beef, cook for 20 minutes per 500g plus an extra 20 minutes. For medium, cook for 25 minutes per 500g plus 25 minutes. For well done, cook for 30 minutes per 500g plus 30 minutes.

top of the cooker and pour in the stock. Bring to the boil, stirring and scraping up the browned cooking residue on the bottom of the tin, then simmer until slightly reduced. Season with pepper and stir in the remaining mustard, if using.

9 To serve, transfer the meat to a warmed serving platter and surround with the roast potatoes, carrots and parsnips and the Yorkshire puddings. Place the broccoli in a warmed serving dish. Add any meat juices that have collected on the plate to the gravy and stir to combine, then skim off any fat. Pour the gravy into a gravy boat and serve immediately.

roast fillet of beef in red wine

Cancel those dinner reservations – you can make the kind of dinner you find in fine restaurants, and you don't have to be a chef to do it. The fillet almost cooks itself, and the vegetables complement the meat perfectly.

2kg fillet of beef, trimmed

1½ teaspoons coarsely ground black pepper

500ml dry red wine

1kg onions, chopped

3 garlic cloves, crushed

6 sprigs of fresh thyme

300g button mushrooms, trimmed and sliced

1 tablespoon sugar

370g baby carrots

1 punnet red or yellow cherry tomatoes

500g pappardelle or other wide egg noodles

1 Preheat the oven to 230°C (gas mark 8). Rub the fillet with the pepper. Tuck the ends under and tie with string. Mix the red wine with 350ml water. Coat a frying pan with cooking spray and set over moderately high heat. Add the fillet, one-third of the onions and the garlic and sear the fillet for 10 minutes or until browned on all sides. Transfer the fillet to a roasting tin. Pour in half the wine mixture and add 3 thyme sprigs. Place in the oven to roast for 20 minutes.

2 Meanwhile, use a draining spoon to discard the onions and garlic from the frying pan. Add the mushrooms, remaining onions and the sugar to the frying pan and sauté for about 7 minutes or until the mushrooms are browned. Cook the carrots in a pan of boiling water for 5–7 minutes or until they are just tender. Drain.

3 Add the carrots and sautéed vegetables to the roasting tin and pour in the remaining wine mixture. Roast until the fillet is cooked to your taste – about 25 minutes longer for medium. Transfer the fillet to a carving board and allow to rest for 10 minutes. Add the tomatoes to the vegetables in the roasting tin, cover and keep warm.

4 Meanwhile, cook the noodles according to the packet directions; drain. Arrange the noodles and vegetables on a platter. Slice the beef, add to the platter and garnish with the rest of the thyme sprigs. Serve with the skimmed pan juices.

preparation time **15 mins**

cooking time **45 mins**

serves **10**

PER SERVING

555 kcal

50g protein

17g total fat
7g saturated fat

137mg cholesterol

49g total carbohydrate
11g sugars

4g fibre

200mg sodium

HEALTH HINT

Cooking mushrooms breaks down their fibrous cell walls, making their nutrients more available to the body.

tender beef with oyster sauce

 Stir-fries are a simple way to incorporate a variety of meat, vegetables and grains in one dish. Here, thin slices of rump steak team with egg-fried rice and colourful red pepper and broccoli to make a delicious combination.

 Fb

preparation and cooking time **45 mins**

serves **4**

PER SERVING

520 kcal

31g protein

16g total fat
3g saturated fat

163mg cholesterol

65g total carbohydrate
10g sugars

4g fibre

724mg sodium

HEALTH HINT

Stir-frying keeps all the water-soluble vitamins and minerals from the vegetables in the dish rather than pouring them down the sink with the cooking water. It's also a very quick method of cooking, so there is minimal nutrient loss.

1 Cook the rice in a pan of boiling water for 10–12 minutes, or according to the packet instructions, until tender. Drain if necessary, return it to the pan, cover and keep hot.

2 Heat a wok or heavy frying pan until hot, add 1 tablespoon of the oil and swirl to coat the wok. Add the beef, garlic and ginger and stir-fry for 2 minutes or until the beef is browned. Remove from the wok with a draining spoon and set aside.

3 Heat the remaining oil in the wok until hot, then add the red onions, red pepper and broccoli. Stir-fry for 2 minutes or until the onions begin to colour. Return the beef and its juices to the wok, then add the oyster sauce and simmer for 1 minute.

4 At the same time as you are cooking the beef and vegetables, heat the oil for the egg-fried rice in another wok or frying pan and add the spring onions and petit pois. Stir-fry for 1 minute, then pour in the eggs and soy sauce and continue stirring until the eggs begin to scramble. Add the rice and stir well to mix, then leave to cook gently for 1 minute.

5 Spoon the rice into bowls, top with the beef mixture and garnish with coriander leaves. Serve immediately.

2 tablespoons sunflower oil

300g lean rump steak, trimmed of visible fat and cut across the grain into thin slices

1 garlic clove, thinly sliced

2.5cm piece fresh root ginger, cut into fine shreds

2 red onions, cut into wedges

1 large red pepper, deseeded and sliced

200g small broccoli florets

3 tablespoons oyster sauce

fresh coriander leaves to garnish

EGG-FRIED RICE

225g long-grain rice

1 tablespoon sunflower oil

4 spring onions, sliced diagonally

100g frozen petit pois

2 eggs, beaten

1 tablespoon reduced-sodium soy sauce

French beef casserole

Long, slow cooking gives this traditional casserole its inimitable flavour. The cooking liquid is reduced simply by removing the casserole lid, resulting in a wonderfully aromatic sauce that glazes the meat and vegetables.

1 Preheat the oven to 150°C (gas mark 2).

2 Heat the oil in a large flameproof casserole. Add the onion and cook over moderately high heat for about 5 minutes or until softened and beginning to brown.

3 Add the beef to the casserole and fry for 5 minutes, stirring frequently, until the cubes of beef are browned on all sides. Stir in the carrots, parsnips, mushrooms and garlic.

4 Pour in the red wine, then stir in the orange zest and juice, thyme, rosemary and bay leaf and season with pepper. Bring to the boil, then cover the casserole and transfer it to the oven. Cook for 1¼ hours.

5 Remove the lid and cook for a further 30 minutes, stirring once or twice. Stir in the broad beans and cook, uncovered, for another 30 minutes, again stirring once or twice.

6 Taste and add pepper if necessary, and stir in the chopped parsley. Warm the brandy in a small saucepan and pour it over the casserole. Immediately set the brandy alight and carry the casserole to the table while still flaming.

Variations You can easily vary the vegetables in this recipe. Small broccoli florets or shelled fresh or frozen peas can be added instead of the broad beans, and large carrots and parsnips, cut into equal-sized chunks, are alternatives to the baby vegetables. • If you prefer, omit the flaming with brandy. • For an everyday beef casserole, replace the wine with 750ml low-sodium beef stock (or stock made without salt) or with light ale.

2 tablespoons sunflower oil
1 large onion, sliced
450g lean stewing beef, cubed
250g baby carrots
250g baby parsnips
250g button mushrooms
1 garlic clove, finely chopped
1 bottle full-bodied red wine
grated zest and juice of 1 orange
1 sprig of fresh thyme
1 sprig of fresh rosemary
1 bay leaf
pepper to taste
200g shelled fresh or thawed frozen broad beans
2 tablespoons chopped fresh parsley
3 tablespoons brandy

Fb

preparation time **20 mins**
cooking time **2½ hours**
serves **4**

PER SERVING

390 kcal	
32g protein	
13g total fat	
4g saturated fat	
75mg cholesterol	
22g total carbohydrate	
13g sugars	
9g fibre	
113mg sodium	

HEALTH HINT

Recent research shows that, in moderation, red wine consumption may help protect the body against heart disease, and can reduce bad cholesterol levels.

spicy steak with garlic toasts

This is a delicious combination of juicy sliced steak, red pepper and sweetcorn salsa and a hefty hunk of grilled garlic toast, all totally heart-healthy. You can grill the steak and toasts or light a charcoal fire and barbecue them outdoors.

2 teaspoons ground cumin

1½ teaspoons mild chilli powder

¾ teaspoon dried oregano

½ teaspoon pepper

150ml spicy tomato-vegetable juice

3 tablespoons freshly squeezed lime juice

320g frozen sweetcorn, thawed

2 spring onions, thinly sliced

1 small red pepper, deseeded and diced

370g well-trimmed rump steak

1 ciabatta loaf, about 250g, halved horizontally, then halved crossways

1 garlic clove, halved

1 Stir together the cumin, chilli powder, oregano and pepper in a small bowl. Place the tomato-vegetable juice and lime juice in a measuring jug. Measure out 2½ teaspoons of the spice mixture and stir into the tomato juice mixture.

2 Combine the sweetcorn, spring onions, red pepper and 125ml of the tomato juice mixture in a medium bowl. Stir to combine. Keep the salsa chilled until serving time.

3 Preheat the grill. Rub the remaining spice mixture onto both sides of the steak. Grill the steak 8cm from the heat for about 4 minutes per side (the steak will be medium rare; grill for longer if you prefer it medium or well done). Remove the steak but leave the grill on. Allow the steak to rest for 10 minutes before thinly slicing across the grain, on the diagonal.

4 Grill the bread, cut-side up, until lightly toasted. Rub the toasted side with the cut garlic and the remaining tomato juice mixture. Grill for a further 1 minute or until lightly browned. Serve the steak with the sweetcorn salsa and the garlic toasts.

30

preparation time **10 mins** plus 10 mins resting

cooking time **10 mins**

serves **4**

PER SERVING

374 kcal

30g protein

8g total fat

2g saturated fat

54mg cholesterol

49g total carbohydrate

6g sugars

3.5g fibre

480mg sodium

HEALTH HINT

Garlic bread is usually soaked with butter, but these grilled toasts are fine without the fat because they're rubbed with garlic, then brushed with a pleasantly spicy tomato and lime mixture.

beef in beer

This hearty and satisfying Flemish casserole is an ideal dish for entertaining because it can be prepared ahead and then just reheated. Serve with mashed potatoes and steamed seasonal greens for a complete meal.

1 Preheat the oven to 180°C (gas mark 4). Heat 1 tablespoon of the oil in a flameproof casserole, add the beef and cook over moderately high heat for 4–5 minutes or until browned all over. Transfer the meat and its juices to a plate.

2 Add the remaining 1 tablespoon oil to the pan and reduce the heat to low, then add the onion, carrots, parsnip and garlic. Cook, stirring frequently, for 5 minutes. Return the beef and its juices to the pan together with the stout, stock, mixed herbs, vinegar, mustard and sugar. Stir well and bring to the boil. Cover the casserole and transfer to the oven. Cook for 2 hours or until the beef is tender.

3 Meanwhile, to make the garlic bread, cut the baguette into eight thick slices. Mix together the garlic, parsley, thyme and oil and spoon evenly over one side of each slice of bread.

4 Uncover the casserole and add pepper to season. Lay the slices of bread, oiled side up, in a circle around the top edge of the casserole, overlapping them slightly. Return the casserole to the oven to cook for 20–30 minutes or until the bread is golden and crisp. Serve hot.

Variation Use 12 whole shallots or baby onions in place of the large onion, carrots and parsnips, and a full-bodied red wine instead of the stout. Omit the vinegar, mustard and sugar and add 1 tablespoon redcurrant jelly instead, stirring it in with the pepper in step 4.

2 tablespoons extra virgin olive oil

450g lean braising steak, trimmed of visible fat and cut into 5cm cubes

1 large onion, cut into wedges

2 large carrots, thickly sliced on the diagonal

1 large parsnip, cut into cubes

1 large garlic clove, crushed

300ml stout

300ml low-sodium beef stock or stock made without salt

1 teaspoon dried mixed herbs

1 tablespoon red wine vinegar

1 tablespoon wholegrain mustard

1 teaspoon dark brown sugar

pepper to taste

GARLIC AND HERB BREAD

1 piece of traditional long French baguette, about 250g

1 large garlic clove, crushed

1 tablespoon chopped fresh parsley

1 tablespoon chopped fresh thyme

3 tablespoons extra virgin olive oil

Fb

preparation time **15 mins**
cooking time **2¾ hours**
serves **4**

PER SERVING

560 kcal

35g protein

23g total fat
5g saturated fat

71mg cholesterol

52g total carbohydrate
17g sugars

6g fibre

700mg sodium

HEALTH HINT

A casserole such as this makes a particularly healthy meal. Water-soluble vitamins – C and B complex – and minerals that seep from food during the cooking process are usually thrown away with the cooking water. In casseroles, more of the nutrients are retained in the gravy.

keema curry with cucumber raita

This mellow curry of minced beef has just a hint of chilli, so it's ideal for children who like to be a little adventurous with their food. Serve with steamed basmati rice and warm naan bread.

500g lean minced beef

1 onion, finely chopped

450g potatoes, peeled and diced

3 garlic cloves, chopped

2.5cm piece fresh root ginger, finely chopped

1 cinnamon stick, halved

1 teaspoon turmeric

1 teaspoon cumin seeds, roughly crushed

1 teaspoon coriander seeds, crushed

½ teaspoon crushed dried chillies

1 can (about 400g) chopped tomatoes

300ml low-sodium beef or lamb stock or stock made without salt

pepper to taste

150g baby spinach

fresh mint leaves to garnish

CUCUMBER RAITA

150g plain low-fat yoghurt

¼ cucumber, finely diced

4 teaspoons chopped fresh mint

1 Fry the beef and onion in a large saucepan for 5 minutes or until evenly browned, stirring to break up the meat. Add the potatoes, garlic, ginger, spices and chilli and fry for 2 minutes, stirring. Add the tomatoes with their juice and the stock and season with pepper. Bring to the boil, then cover and simmer for 20 minutes, stirring occasionally.

2 Meanwhile, to make the cucumber raita, mix the yoghurt, cucumber and mint together with a little pepper. Spoon into a small bowl and chill until required.

3 Stir the baby spinach into the curry and heat through for about 1 minute, then check the seasoning. Spoon the curry onto warmed plates and sprinkle with fresh mint leaves. Serve immediately, with the chilled cucumber raita.

Variations If you prefer, you can cook the curry in the oven. Brown the beef and onion in a flameproof casserole, then add the other ingredients and bring to the boil. Cover and cook in a preheated 180°C (gas mark 4) oven for 1 hour. Add the spinach and toss with the meat, then cover and return to the oven to cook for 10 minutes. • For a fruity curry, add 55g sultanas and 1 sliced dessert apple with the potatoes. Omit the spinach. Garnish the curry with 1 diced banana tossed with the juice of ½ lemon and 2 tablespoons chopped fresh coriander.

preparation time **15 mins**

cooking time **35 mins**

serves **4**

PER SERVING

369 kcal

35g protein

14g total fat
6g saturated fat

70mg cholesterol

30g total carbohydrate
10g sugars

4g fibre

388mg sodium

HEALTH HINT

A raita or sauce based on yoghurt is often served with curries to act as a cooling agent against the heat of the chillies and spices. Yoghurt is also extremely nutritious – it is a valuable source of calcium and it provides useful amounts of phosphorus and vitamins B_2 and B_{12}. In addition, live yoghurt provides beneficial bacteria that can help to maintain a healthy digestive tract.

Mediterranean stuffed vegetables

An array of colourful stuffed vegetables makes an appetising main dish, ideal for an informal help-yourself meal when entertaining guests. Serve with lots of crusty wholemeal bread and a mixed leaf salad.

1 Cook the rice in a pan of boiling water for 10–12 minutes, or according to the packet instructions, until tender. Drain.

2 Meanwhile, place the lamb and onion in a non-stick frying pan and fry until the lamb is lightly browned and cooked through and the onion softened. Place a sieve over a bowl and tip the meat and onions into it. The fat will drip through and can be discarded.

3 Cut each pepper in half lengthways and remove the core and seeds. Cut the tops off the tomatoes and hollow them out. Chop the tops and hollowed-out flesh and place in a bowl. Cut the courgettes in half lengthways and hollow out the centres to leave shells 5mm thick. Chop the removed courgette flesh and add it to the chopped tomatoes.

4 Preheat the oven to 180°C (gas mark 4). Heat the oil in the non-stick frying pan, add the garlic and chopped vegetables and cook, stirring, until softened. Add the spinach and cook until wilted. Remove from the heat. Stir in 2 tablespoons of the basil, the rice and lamb. Add the egg and pepper and mix well.

5 Spoon the stuffing into the vegetable shells. Arrange the peppers and courgettes in a single layer in a large roasting tin. Cover with foil or a lid and roast for 15 minutes. Add the tomatoes and roast for a further 15 minutes or until the vegetables are almost tender. Uncover the vegetables and continue roasting for 15–20 minutes or until they are tender and the tops are lightly browned. Serve either warm or cool, sprinkled with the remaining basil.

100g long-grain rice
250g lean minced lamb
1 onion, chopped
4 peppers of mixed colours
4 beefsteak tomatoes, ripe but firm
2 large courgettes, about 225g each
1 tablespoon extra virgin olive oil
3 garlic cloves, coarsely chopped
170g baby spinach leaves
4 tablespoons shredded fresh basil
1 egg, lightly beaten
pepper to taste

Kc **Fb**

preparation time **45 mins**
cooking time **45 mins**
serves **4**

PER SERVING

324 kcal

21g protein

15g total fat
5g saturated fat

106mg cholesterol

27g total carbohydrate

18g sugars

7g fibre

150mg sodium

HEALTH HINT

The Mediterranean-style vegetables used in this dish are high in phytochemicals and antioxidant vitamins. Among these is beta carotene from the peppers, courgettes, tomatoes and spinach. The antioxidant properties of beta carotene help to protect cells from damage by free radicals that are produced in the body in response to stress.

lamb kebabs with fig rice

Marinating is the key to success for these tender, juicy kebabs. Serve with a leafy mixed salad, and a bowl of plain low-fat yoghurt mixed with grated cucumber and chopped fresh mint and flat-leaf parsley.

3 tablespoons extra virgin olive oil

grated zest and juice of ½ lemon

1 large garlic clove, crushed

1 tablespoon chopped fresh thyme

pepper to taste

400g lean lamb neck fillets, trimmed of visible fat and cut into 5mm cubes

8 shallots

1 aubergine, about 280g

2 courgettes, about 400g in total

1 lemon

FIG RICE

300g basmati rice, well rinsed

100g dried figs, chopped

25g toasted flaked almonds

1 tablespoon freshly squeezed lemon juice, or to taste

1 In a shallow dish whisk the oil with the lemon zest and juice, garlic, thyme and pepper to taste. Add the cubes of lamb and coat them in the mixture, then cover the dish with cling film. Leave to marinate in a cool place for 30 minutes, or in the fridge overnight.

2 Cut each shallot in half through the root. Cut the aubergine lengthways in half, then cut each half across into 8 slices. Cut each courgette into 8 slices and the lemon into 8 wedges.

3 When ready to cook, preheat the grill to high. Remove the lamb from the marinade with a draining spoon, shaking the marinade back into the dish. Place the vegetables in the marinade and turn them to moisten.

4 Thread the lamb and vegetables onto eight long metal skewers, placing the lemon wedges on the ends. Don't pack the ingredients too tightly together on the skewers or they will not cook thoroughly. Put the skewers under the grill, about 7.5cm away from the heat if possible, or reduce the heat of the grill to moderate. Cook for 6–8 minutes on each side.

5 Meanwhile, put the rice in a saucepan of cold water and bring to the boil. Cover and simmer gently for 10 minutes, or according to the packet instructions, until tender. Drain well and stir in the chopped figs, flaked almonds and pepper to taste. Add the lemon juice. Serve the fig rice on warmed plates, with the lamb kebabs placed on top.

Fb GI

preparation time **30 mins** plus 30 mins marinating

cooking time **15–20 mins**

serves **4**

PER SERVING

680 kcal

29g protein

27g total fat
8g saturated fat

74mg cholesterol

78g total carbohydrate
18g sugars

5g fibre

91mg sodium

HEALTH HINT

Dried figs are a good source of potassium, calcium and iron as well as fibre, both soluble and insoluble. Insoluble fibre helps to prevent constipation and bowel disorders.

shepherd's pie

In this version of a long-time family favourite, the minced lamb filling contains plenty of vegetables and red lentils, giving a rich flavour and texture. A generous serving of peas will make the meal even more nutritious.

(Fb)

preparation time **45 mins**
cooking time **20 mins**
serves **4**

PER SERVING

600 kcal

41g protein

25g total fat
7g saturated fat

94mg cholesterol

63g total carbohydrate
20g sugars

12g fibre

445mg sodium

HEALTH HINT

This well-balanced dish of lean meat, vegetables and pulses provides plenty of soluble fibre, mainly from the lentils but also from the parsnips, carrots and leeks. Soluble fibre controls levels of cholesterol and sugar in the blood.

1 Heat the oil in a large heavy saucepan. Add the lamb and cook over a high heat, stirring well with a wooden spoon to break up the meat, for about 5 minutes or until lightly browned. Push the meat to one side of the pan and add the onion. Reduce the heat to low and cook for 5 minutes, stirring occasionally, until the onion is softened and lightly browned.

2 Add the carrots, celery and leeks and stir well, then add the tomato purée, Worcestershire sauce, stock and lentils. Increase the heat and bring to the boil, stirring frequently. Partly cover with a lid, then reduce the heat to low and simmer for about 20 minutes, stirring occasionally.

3 While the meat mixture is cooking, preheat the oven to 200°C (gas mark 6) and prepare the topping. Place the potato and parsnip chunks in a saucepan and pour over boiling water to cover by 5cm. Bring back to the boil, then reduce the heat and cook for 15–20 minutes or until the potatoes and parsnips are very tender. Heat the milk in a small saucepan until hot.

4 Drain the potatoes and parsnips well and return them to the pan. Pour the hot milk over them, then mash until they are completely smooth. Beat in the margarine and add pepper.

5 Remove the meat mixture from the heat, add the chopped parsley and stir well. Spoon into a large ovenproof dish, about 2.5 litre capacity. Top with the mashed vegetables, spreading in an even layer. Bake for 20 minutes or until bubbling and lightly browned. Serve hot, garnished with parsley sprigs.

1 tablespoon extra virgin olive oil

500g lean minced lamb

1 large onion, finely chopped

3 carrots, finely chopped

3 celery sticks, thinly sliced

2 leeks, thinly sliced

1 tablespoon tomato purée

1 tablespoon Worcestershire sauce

350ml low-sodium lamb or beef stock or stock made without salt

100g split red lentils

3 tablespoons chopped fresh parsley

parsley sprigs to garnish

POTATO AND PARSNIP TOPPING

500g floury potatoes, peeled and cut into chunks

500g parsnips, cut into chunks

75ml semi-skimmed milk

30g margarine

pepper to taste

roast leg of lamb with beans

Lamb and flageolet beans are often combined in French country cooking because they complement each other so well. In this recipe flageolets are mixed with potatoes, and the lamb is flavoured with lemon, garlic and rosemary.

1 Drain and rinse the flageolets, then place them in a large saucepan and cover generously with cold water. Cover the pan and bring to the boil. Skim off any scum, then reduce the heat and add 2 of the garlic cloves and the bay leaf. Cook the beans, covered, over a low heat for about 1½ hours or until tender.

2 Meanwhile, preheat the oven to 180°C (gas mark 4). Untie the lamb if necessary, season the inside with pepper and sprinkle over the leaves from half of the rosemary sprigs. Place the lemon slices down the middle, then roll up the meat and tie it with string at 2.5cm intervals. Rub the outside of the joint with 1 teaspoon of the oil and season with pepper. Cut the remaining garlic cloves into slivers. With the tip of a knife, cut slits in the lamb and insert the garlic slivers and the remaining rosemary, broken into little sprigs.

3 Weigh the lamb and calculate the cooking time (see Cook's tip), then set it, rounded side up, on a rack in a shallow roasting tin. Put into the oven to roast.

4 About 30 minutes before the lamb is ready, cook the potatoes in boiling water for about 10 minutes or until just tender, then drain well. When the lamb is done, transfer it to a carving board, cover with foil and leave to rest. Drain off any fat from the roasting tin.

5 Heat the remaining oil in a large saucepan over a moderate heat. Add the shallots and cook for 2 minutes, then add the tomatoes and cook for 3–4 minutes. Drain the cooked beans and discard the bay leaf. Add the beans to the tomato mixture, then add the parsley. Cover and cook for 3–4 minutes, then gently stir in the potatoes. Season with pepper. Keep warm.

6 Put the green beans in a saucepan and barely cover with boiling water. Cook over a moderate heat for 3–4 minutes or until just tender. Drain well and keep warm.

7 To make the gravy, place the roasting tin on top of the cooker and pour in the wine and stock. Bring to the boil over a moderate heat, stirring and scraping the bottom of the tin to mix in any cooking residue, then boil for 1 minute. Keep warm.

8 Carve the lamb. Put the bean and potato mixture on a warmed serving platter and arrange the slices of lamb on top. Serve the gravy and green beans separately.

250g dried flageolet beans, soaked overnight in cold water

4 large garlic cloves, peeled

1 bay leaf

900g boneless lean leg of lamb, trimmed of visible fat

pepper to taste

4 small sprigs of fresh rosemary

½ lemon, thinly sliced

3 teaspoons olive oil

675g floury potatoes, peeled and cut into 2.5cm cubes

2 shallots, finely chopped

4 tomatoes, diced

4 tablespoons chopped fresh parsley

450g green beans

4 tablespoons red wine

300ml low-sodium lamb or beef stock or stock made without salt

Fb GI

preparation and cooking time **1¼–1¾ hours** plus overnight soaking

serves **6**

PER SERVING

514 kcal

53g protein

13g total fat
5g saturated fat

111mg cholesterol

51g total carbohydrate
11g sugars

8g fibre

227mg sodium

COOK'S TIP

For rare lamb, roast for 20 minutes per 450g plus an extra 20 minutes; for medium lamb roast for 25 minutes per 450g plus 25 minutes; and for well done lamb roast for 30 minutes per 450g plus 30 minutes. To check if the lamb is cooked to your taste by using a meat thermometer, rare will register 60°C, medium 70°C and well done 80°C.

Persian lamb couscous

Chunks of lean lamb are gently simmered with dates in a richly spiced gravy, then piled atop couscous and pistachio nuts, and sprinkled with pomegranate seeds. Serve this exotic dish for a special family meal for entertaining.

340g boneless lean leg of lamb, trimmed of visible fat and cut into cubes

1 tablespoon extra virgin olive oil

4 garlic cloves, finely chopped

2 tablespoons finely chopped fresh root ginger

2 onions, halved and thinly sliced

1 fresh red chilli, deseeded and thinly sliced

2 pinches of saffron threads

2 teaspoons ground coriander

2 teaspoons ground cumin

1 teaspoons ground cinnamon

1 teaspoon paprika

100g stoned dates, sliced

900ml low-sodium lamb stock or stock made without salt

pepper to taste

400g couscous

15g fresh coriander, chopped

25g pistachio nuts, roughly chopped

seeds of 1 small pomegranate to garnish

1 Heat a large non-stick saucepan and fry the cubes of lamb, in batches, until browned all over. Lift from the pan with a draining spoon and set aside.

2 Add the oil to the pan, then add the garlic, ginger, onions and chilli. Fry, stirring frequently, over a low heat for about 10 minutes.

3 Return the lamb to the pan, together with the saffron, ground coriander, cumin, cinnamon and paprika. Cook for about 30 seconds, stirring well, then add the dates and 600ml of the stock. Season with pepper. Cover and simmer gently for 1 hour or until the lamb is tender.

4 About 15 minutes before the lamb is ready, heat the remaining stock in another saucepan until boiling. Add the couscous and return to the boil. Remove from the heat, cover tightly and set aside for 10 minutes.

5 Fork the couscous through lightly to fluff up the grains, then toss in the coriander and pistachios. Pile onto a warmed large serving platter. Spoon the lamb on top of the couscous, sprinkle with the pomegranate seeds and serve immediately.

 Fb

preparation time **20 mins**
cooking time **1¼ hours**
serves **4**

PER SERVING

561 kcal

35g protein

15g total fat
4g saturated fat

64mg cholesterol

76g total carbohydrate
22g sugars

3g fibre

527mg sodium

HEALTH HINT

Pomegranate seeds make a very pretty garnish for sweet or savoury dishes, and they are deliciously sweet and tart all at once. In addition they contribute vitamin C and fibre, so all the more reason for using them often.

Irish stew

Traditional recipes for Irish stew use a tough, fatty cut of lamb and only potatoes, onions and herbs. This up-to-date version with lamb leg steaks is leaner, and more colourful with the addition of carrots.

1 Preheat the oven to 160°C (gas mark 3). In a large casserole, make layers of lamb, potatoes, onion and carrots, sprinkling each layer with parsley, thyme, chives and pepper. Finish with a layer of potatoes, then pour over the stock.

2 Cover the casserole with a tight-fitting lid and place in the oven to cook for about 2 hours or until both the meat and vegetables feel tender when tested with a skewer.

3 Increase the oven temperature to 200°C (gas mark 6). Remove the casserole lid and cook for a further 20 minutes or until the potatoes on top are golden brown and crisp. Serve hot, sprinkled with more thyme and parsley.

Variations Add 120g small button mushrooms, layering them in the casserole with the onion and carrots. • If you want the cooking liquid to be slightly thickened, sprinkle 1 tablespoon pearl barley between the first few layers along with the herbs. • For a real taste of Ireland, you can replace half of the stock with Guinness.

4 boneless lean lamb leg steaks, about 500g in total, trimmed of visible fat and each steak cut into 4 pieces

1kg floury potatoes, peeled and thickly sliced

1 large onion, sliced

500g carrots, thickly sliced

2 tablespoons chopped fresh parsley

1 teaspoon fresh thyme leaves

1 tablespoon snipped fresh chives

pepper to taste

450ml hot low-sodium lamb or vegetable stock or stock made without salt

chopped fresh thyme and parsley to garnish

preparation time **20 mins**

cooking time
2 hours 20 mins

serves **4**

PER SERVING

508 kcal

32g protein

19g total fat
8g saturated fat

95mg cholesterol

58g total carbohydrate
14g sugars

7g fibre

382mg sodium

HEALTH HINT

Carrots are not traditional in Irish stew, but they are well worth including, both for their colour and flavour and also their nutritional properties. They provide vitamins A and C as well as potassium.

sticky pork spare ribs

In this dish, pork spare ribs are simmered first to tenderise the meat and to remove some of the fat, before being roasted in a deliciously sticky orange and mustard glaze. Choose the meatiest ribs you can find.

12 meaty pork spare ribs, about
    1kg in total
3 tablespoons red wine vinegar
2 teaspoons sunflower oil
large strip of orange zest
150ml freshly squeezed orange juice
1 tablespoon tomato purée
2 tablespoons dark brown sugar
2 tablespoons Worcestershire sauce
1 tablespoon Dijon mustard
½–1 teaspoon chilli powder, to taste

1 Preheat the oven to 200°C (gas mark 6). Trim as much fat as possible off the spare ribs, then place them in a saucepan. Cover with cold water and add 2 tablespoons of the vinegar. Bring to the boil, then simmer for 20 minutes, skimming the fat from the surface from time to time.

2 Meanwhile, combine the remaining 1 tablespoon vinegar, the oil, orange zest and juice, tomato purée, brown sugar, Worcestershire sauce, mustard and chilli powder in a small pan and bring to the boil. Simmer for 4–5 minutes or until the mixture is slightly reduced.

3 Drain the spare ribs and arrange them in a single layer in a large roasting tin. Pour over the orange juice mixture and turn the ribs to coat them evenly. Loosely cover the ribs with foil and roast for 20 minutes.

4 Remove the foil and roast for a further 20–25 minutes, turning and basting occasionally, until the ribs are dark brown and sticky. Transfer to a large serving dish and serve warm.

 Kc

preparation time **30 mins**
cooking time **40–45 mins**
serves **4**

PER SERVING

222 kcal

27g protein

6g total fat
2g saturated fat

79mg cholesterol

13g total carbohydrate
13g sugars

0g fibre

301mg sodium

HEALTH HINT

Spare ribs are one of the fattier cuts of pork. Trimming off any visible fat, simmering in water and then roasting until crisp are clever ways to reduce their fat content.

pork medallions with peppers

This quick sauté makes an excellent dinner party dish, with its well-balanced sweet and sour elements coming from balsamic vinegar, oranges and olives. It is especially good – and extra nutritious – served with broccoli.

Fb GI

preparation time **25 mins**

cooking time **25 mins**

serves **4**

PER SERVING

550 kcal

27g protein

9g total fat
2g saturated fat

55mg cholesterol

90g total carbohydrate
19g sugars

4g fibre

165mg sodium

HEALTH HINT

Wild rice comes from North America. It is not a true rice, but the seeds of a wild aquatic grass. It is gluten-free, like the basmati rice it is mixed with here, and contains useful amounts of B vitamins, particularly niacin, as well as dietary fibre.

1 Place the rice in a saucepan and pour over the boiling water. Bring back to the boil, then reduce the heat to low. Cover and simmer for about 15 minutes, or according to the packet instructions, until the rice is tender and all the water has been absorbed.

2 Meanwhile, peel the oranges and cut them crossways into slices about 1cm thick. Stack the slices three or four at a time and cut into quarters. (If possible, use a chopping board with a well to catch the juices.) Set the orange slices and juice aside.

3 Heat the oil in a large non-stick frying pan over moderately high heat. Add the pork medallions and fry for 2–3 minutes on each side. Remove with a slotted spoon and set aside.

4 Reduce the heat to moderate and add the onion, pepper strips, carrot and garlic to the pan. Cover and cook, stirring frequently, for 5–6 minutes or until the vegetables start to soften. Add 2 tablespoons water, then the 100ml orange juice and balsamic vinegar. Stir well to mix. Cover and cook for 3–4 minutes or until the vegetables are tender.

5 Return the pork to the pan. Add the olives, orange slices and their juice and the basil leaves. Cook for 1 minute to reheat the pork, stirring well. Add pepper to taste.

6 To serve, divide the rice among four warmed plates and place the pork medallions and vegetables on top. Drizzle over any juices remaining in the pan and serve immediately.

350g mixed basmati and wild rice

600ml boiling water

2 oranges

1 tablespoon extra virgin olive oil

350g pork fillet (tenderloin), sliced across into medallions 1cm thick

1 large red onion, halved lengthways and thinly sliced into half rings

1 red pepper, deseeded and sliced into strips

1 yellow pepper, deseeded and sliced into strips

1 large carrot, grated

1 garlic clove, finely chopped

100ml freshly squeezed orange juice

3 tablespoons balsamic vinegar

35g chopped black olives

10g fresh basil leaves

pepper to taste

cassoulet

A warming combination of haricot beans, pork, spicy garlic sausage and lots of vegetables makes this classic dish from south-west France a real winner. In traditional fashion, it is finished with a breadcrumb crust.

150g dried haricot beans, soaked for at least 8 hours

1 tablespoon extra virgin olive oil

280g pork fillet (tenderloin), cut into 2.5cm dice

85g coarse-cut, dry-cured garlicky French sausage, diced

1 onion, chopped

2 celery sticks, chopped

2 carrots, thickly sliced

1 turnip, chopped

1 can (about 400g) chopped tomatoes

150ml dry white wine

400ml low-sodium pork or chicken stock or stock made without salt

1 tablespoon tomato purée

2 bay leaves

4 sprigs of fresh thyme

pepper to taste

BREADCRUMB CRUST

1 tablespoon extra virgin olive oil

85g fresh white breadcrumbs

15g parsley, chopped

1 Drain the soaked beans and rinse under cold running water. Put in a saucepan, cover with plenty of fresh water and bring to the boil. Boil rapidly for 10 minutes, then partly cover and simmer for 50–60 minutes or until tender. Drain and set aside.

2 Heat the oil in a large flameproof casserole, add the pork fillet and cook over moderately high heat for 5–6 minutes or until browned. Remove with a draining spoon and set aside. Add the sausage to the casserole and brown lightly. Remove with a draining spoon and set aside with the pork.

3 Add the onion, celery, carrots and turnip to the casserole and cook for 5 minutes, stirring occasionally, until softened and lightly browned.

4 Return the pork and sausage to the casserole. Add the beans, tomatoes with their juice, the wine, stock, tomato purée, bay leaves and thyme. Bring to the boil, then reduce the heat, cover and simmer for 1½ hours or until the meat and vegetables are very tender.

5 Just before serving, prepare the breadcrumb crust. Heat the olive oil in a frying pan, add the breadcrumbs and parsley and cook over moderate heat, stirring constantly, for 3–4 minutes or until the crumbs are lightly golden and quite dry.

6 Taste the cassoulet and season with pepper. Scatter the breadcrumb mixture evenly over the top of the cassoulet and serve immediately.

Fb **GI**

preparation time **1½ hours** plus 8 hours soaking

cooking time **1¾ hours**

serves **4**

PER SERVING

434 kcal

31g protein

14g total fat

3g saturated fat

57mg cholesterol

42g total carbohydrate

12g sugars

10g fibre

685mg sodium

HEALTH HINTS

Haricot beans can provide protein in casseroles and stews such as this one, which means the amount of meat used can be reduced.

Lean pork has a lower fat content than beef or lamb. It is a good source of zinc and also provides useful amounts of iron.

preparation and cooking
time **about 40 mins**

serves **2**

PER SERVING

372 kcal

26g protein

21g total fat
5g saturated fat

7mg cholesterol

21g total carbohydrate
8g sugars

9g fibre

471mg sodium

HEALTH HINT

Contrary to popular
belief, spinach is not a
particularly good source
of absorbable iron, but it
does have a lot of other
nutrients to offer. It is a
good source of vitamins
C and E, and it provides
useful amounts of the
B vitamins folate, niacin
and B$_6$. In addition, it
offers several cancer-
fighting phytochemicals.

spinach, ham and asparagus salad with rye croutons

 Here, pan-fried pieces of asparagus and Parma ham are combined with wilted baby spinach and crisp-baked croutons in a delicious warm salad for two. Serve with a side dish of new potatoes tossed with a little extra virgin olive oil.

1 Preheat the oven to 200°C (gas mark 6). Toss the bread cubes with 1 tablespoon of the olive oil, then spread out on a baking tray. Bake for about 5 minutes or until crisp.

2 Meanwhile, heat the remaining oil in a wok or frying pan. Add the asparagus, arranging it in a single layer, and cook over moderate heat for 5 minutes, without stirring. Turn the asparagus over, add the garlic and shallots, and cook for a further 3 minutes. Add the Parma ham and cook for 2 more minutes, stirring constantly.

3 Using a slotted spoon, remove the asparagus, ham and shallot mixture from the wok and put it in a bowl. Keep warm. Add the balsamic vinegar, lemon juice and honey to the wok and stir to mix with the cooking juices. Add the spinach and cook, stirring and turning, until just wilted.

4 Season the spinach with pepper, then divide between two plates. Arrange the asparagus mixture on top. Spoon on any cooking juices and scatter over the croutons and Parmesan.

55g crustless dark rye bread,
    cut into cubes

2 tablespoons extra virgin olive oil

250g asparagus spears,
    cut into short pieces

2 garlic cloves, thinly sliced

4 shallots, cut into wedges

85g Parma ham, trimmed of visible
    fat and torn into pieces

1 tablespoon balsamic vinegar

2 tablespoons freshly squeezed
    lemon juice

1 teaspoon clear honey

250g baby spinach leaves

pepper to taste

few shavings of Parmesan cheese,
    about 15g in total

toad-in-the-hole

Skinless sausages are simple to prepare, and you know what goes into them when you make your own. Here home-made pork sausages are cooked in a herby batter, then served with root vegetable mash and quick 'baked' beans.

300g lean minced pork

100g fresh breadcrumbs

1 leek, about 150g, finely chopped

55g dry-packed soft (mi-cuit) sun-dried tomatoes, chopped

2 tablespoons sunflower oil

pepper to taste

BATTER

125g plain flour

2 eggs

300ml semi-skimmed milk

2 tablespoons chopped fresh parsley

ROOT VEGETABLE MASH

225g carrots, cut into chunks

400g parsnips, cut into chunks

400g swede, cut into chunks

200g French beans, trimmed and sliced diagonally

BAKED BEANS

1 small red onion, finely chopped

1 garlic clove, crushed

3 tablespoons tomato purée

200ml low-sodium vegetable stock or stock made without salt

2 cans (about 400g each) cannellini beans, drained and rinsed

1 Preheat the oven to 220°C (gas mark 7). Combine the pork, breadcrumbs, leek and sun-dried tomatoes in a bowl and season with pepper. Mix well, then shape into eight sausages, each about 10 x 2.5cm. Place on a plate, cover and chill while you make the batter.

2 Sift the flour into a bowl. Make a well in the centre and add the eggs and half the milk. Whisk, gradually incorporating the flour to make a thick lump-free batter. Slowly whisk in the remaining milk, then whisk in the parsley.

3 Put the oil in a 30 x 25cm non-stick roasting tin and heat in the oven for 5 minutes. Add the sausages to the tin, spacing them out in one layer, and cook for 10 minutes. Remove the tin from the oven. Stir the batter well, then pour it over the sausages. Return the tin to the oven and cook for 30 minutes or until the batter is crisp and golden brown.

4 Meanwhile, for the mash, put the carrots, parsnips and swede in a saucepan and pour over boiling water to cover them by 5cm. Bring back to the boil, then simmer for 20 minutes or until the vegetables are very tender.

5 Combine all the ingredients for the baked beans in a large saucepan and bring to the boil. Cook for about 10 minutes or until thickened. Keep hot. At the same time, steam the French beans for about 3 minutes or until they are just tender.

6 Drain the root vegetables well. Return them to the pan and mash until they are completely smooth, then stir in the French beans and season with pepper. Serve the toad-in-the-hole hot, with the mashed root vegetables and baked beans alongside.

preparation and cooking time **1¼ hours**

serves **4**

PER SERVING

800 kcal
46g protein
25g total fat
5g saturated fat
170mg cholesterol
106g total carbohydrate
78g sugars
25g fibre
549mg sodium

COOK'S TIP

This is an excellent meal for growing children and teenagers because it contains such a variety of nutrients. The pork provides protein and zinc. The eggs provide protein, iron, zinc, selenium and vitamins A, B and E, while the milk provides protein, calcium, phosphorus and many of the B vitamins. Between them, the vegetables supply vitamins A, B, C and E.

pork nasi goreng

In this Indonesian-style recipe, rice is combined with stir-fried pork, vegetables, prawns and strips of omelette to make an excellent all-in-one supper dish. Serve with a green salad tossed in a dressing spiked with fresh ginger.

Fb

preparation and cooking time **55 mins**

serves **6**

PER SERVING

502 kcal

32g protein

9g total fat

2g saturated fat

162mg cholesterol

77g total carbohydrate

8g sugars

4g fibre

921mg sodium

HEALTH HINT

Both prawns and pork are useful sources of selenium, an important micronutrient (needed in very small amounts). Selenium works to protect the cardiovascular system.

1 Bring the stock to the boil in a large saucepan, add the rice and cook for 10–12 minutes or until the rice is just tender and most of the stock has been absorbed. Remove the pan from the heat, cover and set aside.

2 Heat a wok or large heavy-based frying pan until hot, then add the oil and swirl to coat the wok. Add the onion, garlic and carrots and stir-fry for 5 minutes or until the onion has softened.

3 Toss the pork into the wok and stir-fry for 3 minutes, then add the mushrooms and cook for 2 minutes. Add the chilli powder and turmeric and stir for a minute or two, then add the peas, ketchup and soy sauce.

4 Gradually add the cooked rice to the wok, tossing to mix, and stir-fry until all the ingredients are well blended and heated through. Toss in the spring onions and then the prawns. Remove from the heat and keep hot.

5 To make the omelette, beat the egg in a small bowl with the soy sauce and 1 tablespoon water. Heat the oil in an 18cm omelette pan, pour in the egg mixture and fry until just set. Tip the omelette out onto a board, roll it up and cut into strips.

6 To serve, spoon the pork and rice mixture into a warmed serving dish and arrange the omelette strips on top.

1.2 litres low-sodium chicken stock or stock made without salt

450g long-grain rice

2 tablespoons sunflower oil

1 onion, finely chopped

2 garlic cloves, crushed

3 carrots, finely diced

2 lean boneless pork leg steaks, about 340g in total, trimmed of visible fat and diced

150g button mushrooms, sliced

1 teaspoon mild chilli powder

$\frac{1}{2}$ teaspoon turmeric

150g frozen peas

3 tablespoons tomato ketchup

2 tablespoons reduced-sodium soy sauce

4 spring onions, thinly sliced or shredded

100g peeled cooked prawns

OMELETTE

1 large egg

dash of reduced-sodium soy sauce

1 teaspoon sunflower oil

Normandy pork with apples, celery and walnuts

Fresh and fruity, this casserole comes from northwestern France, where cider apples grow in profusion. A dish of rice is cooked in the oven at the same time, making this a very simple meal to prepare. Serve with green vegetables.

2 tablespoons sunflower oil

500g pork fillet (tenderloin), trimmed of visible fat and cut into cubes

8 celery sticks, cut across into 5cm lengths, leaves reserved and chopped

1 onion, roughly chopped

450ml cider or apple juice

1 bay leaf

pepper to taste

300g long-grain rice

900ml boiling low-sodium chicken stock or stock made without salt

3 crisp dessert apples, preferably red-skinned

100g broken walnuts

1 Preheat the oven to 160°C (gas mark 3). Heat the oil in a flameproof casserole, add the pork and fry, stirring frequently, for 5 minutes or until browned on all sides. Add the celery and onion and fry gently for about 10 minutes or until softened.

2 Pour in the cider or apple juice and add the bay leaf. Season with pepper. Bring to the boil, then cover the casserole tightly and transfer to the oven. Cook for 1¼ hours or until the cubes of pork are tender.

3 About 40 minutes before the pork is ready, place the rice in an ovenproof dish and pour over the boiling stock. Stir well, then cover and place in the oven to cook with the pork.

4 About 25 minutes before the end of the cooking time, quarter and core the apples but do not peel them. Slice the quarters thickly, then add to the pork and continue cooking.

5 Meanwhile, heat a small frying pan over moderate heat, add the walnuts and cook, stirring, until lightly toasted. When the pork is tender, stir in the walnuts. Garnish with the chopped celery leaves and serve hot, with the rice.

Variation Add 1 chopped garlic clove and 1 teaspoon chopped fresh root ginger to the onion and use freshly squeezed orange juice instead of the cider or apple juice. Replace the apple slices with the segments of 2 oranges, adding them 10 minutes before the end of the cooking time. Garnish the casserole with fine shreds of orange zest. Cook the rice in a mixture of orange juice and vegetable stock.

Fb

preparation time **15 mins**

cooking time **2 hours**

serves **4**

PER SERVING

734 kcal

37g protein

27g total fat
3g saturated fat

80mg cholesterol

91g total carbohydrate
17g sugars

4g fibre

585mg sodium

HEART SUPERFOOD

Some studies indicate that a small quantity of walnuts eaten regularly can help to reduce high blood cholesterol levels. Walnuts may also guard against cardiovascular disease and cancer because of the antioxidants they contain: selenium, zinc, copper and vitamin E.

stir-fried pork with Chinese greens

Stir-fries do not have to be complicated, with numerous ingredients, as this simple recipe shows. Here strips of pork fillet are marinated then stir-fried with green vegetables. Egg noodles make the perfect accompaniment.

30 · **Fb** · **GI**

preparation time **15 mins**
cooking time **6–7 mins**
serves **4**

PER SERVING

437 kcal

28g protein

14g total fat
2.5g saturated fat

52mg cholesterol

50g total carbohydrate
5g sugars

5g fibre

295mg sodium

HEALTH HINT

Pak choy, a variety of Chinese cabbage or greens, has broad white stalks topped with large, dark green leaves. Like other dark green, leafy vegetables, it is a particularly good source of folate, a B vitamin that may help to protect against heart disease.

300g pork fillet (tenderloin), trimmed of visible fat

3 tablespoons dry sherry

4 teaspoons toasted sesame oil

1 tablespoon reduced-sodium soy sauce

1 bunch of spring onions, about 170g

200g mange-tout

350g pak choy

250g medium Chinese egg noodles

1 tablespoon groundnut oil

1 Cut the pork across into 5mm slices, then cut each slice into 5mm strips. Place in a bowl with the sherry, 1 teaspoon of the sesame oil and the soy sauce. Toss to mix well, then set aside to marinate while preparing the vegetables.

2 Cut the spring onions across in half, then lengthways into shreds. Halve the mange-tout lengthways. Trim the pak choy and tear it into large bite-sized pieces.

3 Bring a large pan of water to the boil. Add the egg noodles and cook according to the packet instructions.

4 Meanwhile, heat a wok or large frying pan until hot, then add the oil. Add the pork, reserving the marinade, and stir-fry over high heat for 3 minutes or until the meat is lightly browned and tender. Remove from the wok and set aside.

5 Add the mange-tout to the wok and stir-fry for 30 seconds, then add the spring onions and pak choy and continue to stir-fry for 1 minute. Return the pork to the wok, together with the reserved marinade, and stir-fry all together for 1–2 minutes or until everything is piping hot. The pak choy should have wilted, but still be a bit crisp.

6 Drain the noodles well and toss with the remaining sesame oil. Spoon onto warmed serving plates. Divide the stir-fried pork and greens among the plates and serve.

cidered pork stew with herb dumplings

A spoonful of mustard peps up this simple, vegetable-rich pork stew. Fluffy dumplings served on top help to mop up every bit of the full-flavoured sauce, and turn the stew into a well-balanced meal in a bowl.

Fb

preparation time **30 mins**
cooking time **1¾ hours**
serves **4**

PER SERVING

510 kcal

34g protein

16g total fat
4g saturated fat

131mg cholesterol

56g total carbohydrate
10g sugars

5g fibre

562mg sodium

HEALTH HINT

Swede is a member of the cruciferous family of vegetables. It is rich in cancer-fighting phytochemicals and a useful source of vitamin C and beta carotene.

1 Heat the oil in a flameproof casserole and add the pork. Cook over high heat for 10 minutes or until browned, stirring frequently. Use a slotted spoon to transfer the meat to a plate.

2 Reduce the heat to moderate. Add the carrots, celery, leeks, bay leaves and sage and cook for 5 minutes, stirring often, until the leeks are softened. Pour in the cider and stock. Return the pork to the casserole with any juices and the mustard. Mix well.

3 Bring to the boil, then reduce the heat to low and cover. Simmer gently for 45 minutes. Stir in the potatoes and swede. Bring back to simmering point, cover again and cook over low heat for 30 minutes or until the pork and vegetables are cooked.

4 Meanwhile, for the dumplings, mix the breadcrumbs, flour, baking powder, chives and parsley in a bowl. Make a well in the centre and add the egg, milk and oil. Mix the liquids together, then gradually stir in the dry ingredients to make a dough.

5 Bring a pan of water to the boil. Dust your hands with flour, then divide the dumpling mixture into 12 portions and roll each one into a round dumpling. Add the dumplings to the water, adjust the heat so that they simmer gently and cook for about 10 minutes or until risen and firm.

6 Use a slotted spoon to lift the dumplings out of the water, shaking gently to drain them well, and arrange them on top of the casserole. Serve at once.

1 tablespoon extra virgin olive oil

450g lean boneless pork, cut into 2.5cm chunks

2 carrots, cut into 1cm cubes

2 celery sticks, sliced

2 leeks, sliced

2 bay leaves

2 tablespoons finely shredded fresh sage or 1 teaspoon dried sage

300ml dry cider

300ml low-sodium chicken stock or stock made without salt

1 tablespoon Dijon mustard

675g potatoes, peeled and cut into 1cm cubes

225g swede, cut into 1cm cubes

FRESH HERB DUMPLINGS

100g fresh wholemeal breadcrumbs

55g self-raising flour

½ teaspoon baking powder

3 tablespoons snipped fresh chives

3 tablespoons chopped fresh parsley

1 egg, lightly beaten

3 tablespoons semi-skimmed milk

1 tablespoon sunflower oil

Toulouse sausages with Puy lentils

This easy recipe turns just a few simple ingredients into the most satisfying and well-balanced midweek supper. Serve with thickly sliced crusty bread and a peppery rocket or watercress salad.

170g Puy lentils

750ml low-sodium chicken stock or stock made without salt

1 large onion, roughly chopped

600g potatoes, peeled and quartered

300g butternut squash, peeled, deseeded and chopped

4 Toulouse sausages, about 280g in total

1 can (about 400g) chopped tomatoes

3 tablespoons semi-skimmed milk

pepper to taste

TO SERVE

4 teaspoons balsamic vinegar

3 tablespoons chopped fresh flat-leaf parsley

1 Preheat the grill to moderate. Rinse the lentils and place them in a saucepan with 600ml of the stock and the chopped onion. Bring to the boil, then reduce the heat, cover and simmer for 25 minutes.

2 Meanwhile, cook the potatoes in a large saucepan of boiling water for 10 minutes. Add the butternut squash and continue cooking for 10 minutes or until both the squash and potatoes are tender.

3 While the lentils, potatoes and squash are cooking, grill the sausages for 15 minutes, turning them several times so they cook and brown evenly.

4 Slice the sausages thickly and add them to the lentils, together with the tomatoes and their juice. If the lentils have absorbed all the liquid, add the remaining stock. Cover and cook for a further 10 minutes.

5 Drain the potatoes and squash and mash them with the milk. Season with pepper. Spoon onto plates and top with the sausages and lentils. Drizzle over the vinegar and sprinkle with the chopped parsley. Serve immediately.

preparation and cooking time **about 1 hour**

serves **4**

PER SERVING
520 kcal
23g protein
18g total fat
7g saturated fat
23mg cholesterol
67g total carbohydrate
11g sugars
9g fibre
800mg sodium

HEART SUPERFOOD

Mashing the potatoes with butternut squash adds wonderful colour, plus beneficial nutrients – it is an excellent source of vitamin C and a useful source of vitamin E and beta-carotene.

preparation and cooking
time **40 mins**
serves **4**

PER SERVING

556 kcal

29g protein

12g total fat
3g saturated fat

277mg cholesterol

83g total carbohydrate
10g sugars

6g fibre

91mg sodium

HEALTH HINT

Oranges are justly famous
for their vitamin C content
(54mg per 100g). Vitamin
C is one of the 'water-
soluble' vitamins that
cannot be stored by the
body, so it is essential that
fruit and vegetables
containing vitamin C are
eaten every day. As
scientists have increasingly
recognised, this vitamin
helps to prevent a number
of degenerative diseases,
such as heart disease and
cancer, through its
powerful antioxidant
activity.

calf's liver with rigatoni and orange

Here's a pasta recipe that proves the simplest ideas are the best. Savour the delicate flavour of calf's liver and broccoli with a subtle hint of garlic and chilli and the sweet freshness of orange.

1 Use a citrus zester to take the zest off one of the oranges in short strips; set the strips aside. Peel and segment both oranges, working over a bowl to catch the juice. Set aside 12 of the best segments, then squeeze the rest into the bowl to get about 5 tablespoons juice.

2 Drop the pasta into a large saucepan of boiling water. When the water returns to the boil, cook for 10 minutes, then add the broccoli and cook for a further 2–3 minutes or until the pasta and broccoli are just tender.

3 While the pasta is cooking, heat 1 tablespoon of the oil in a frying pan large enough to take the liver in one layer. Sprinkle in the garlic and chilli and stir over a moderately high heat for 1 minute. Add the liver and toss for 1 minute or until browned. Add the Marsala or sherry and the orange zest and juice and cook for 1 more minute.

4 Drain the pasta and broccoli and return to the saucepan, off the heat. Remove the liver from the sauce and add to the pasta and broccoli together with the remaining oil and pepper to taste. Toss well.

5 Bring the sauce to the boil and boil to reduce by half. Stir in the balsamic vinegar and margarine to make the sauce glossy. Add the orange segments and warm through for 30 seconds, then spoon over the liver, pasta and broccoli and toss gently to combine. Sprinkle with the coriander seeds, if using, and serve immediately.

2 large oranges

400g rigatoni or other pasta shapes

250g broccoli, cut into 2.5cm pieces

2 tablespoons extra virgin olive oil

1 garlic clove, crushed

1 small fresh red chilli, deseeded and
finely chopped

300g calf's liver, trimmed and cut into
short strips 1cm wide

4 tablespoons Marsala or medium sherry
pepper to taste

1 teaspoon balsamic vinegar

2 teaspoons margarine

1 teaspoon crushed toasted coriander
seeds to garnish (optional)

venison steaks with pears

Venison has a deep, rich flavour, and steaks taken from the loin are very tender. Here they are cooked with pears and cranberries. A root vegetable rösti is the most delicious accompaniment.

4 venison steaks, about 140g each

coarsely ground black pepper

1 tablespoon extra virgin olive oil

2 shallots, finely chopped

1 garlic clove, crushed

3 tablespoons port

120ml low-sodium beef stock or stock made without salt

200g fresh or frozen cranberries

2 ripe but firm medium-sized pears, such as Conference or Comice, peeled, quartered and cored

1 tablespoon light muscovado sugar, or to taste

RÖSTI

1 small celeriac, about 350g

2 medium-sized sweet potatoes, about 400g in total

2 potatoes, about 400g in total

1 small swede, about 400g

pepper to taste

40g margarine

1 First make the rösti. Preheat the oven to 200°C (gas mark 6). Peel the celeriac, sweet potatoes, potatoes and swede and coarsely grate them, then squeeze out excess liquid. Place in a large bowl, season with pepper to taste and mix well.

2 Put half of the margarine into a large ovenproof frying pan, or a round or oval baking dish or tin about 25cm across. Heat in the oven for 3–4 minutes or until foaming, then remove and add the grated vegetables. Press down to make an even, compact cake. Dot with the remaining margarine, then cover with foil. Bake for 15 minutes. Remove the foil and bake for a further 20–25 minutes or until the top is lightly browned.

3 While the rösti is in the oven, pat the steaks dry, then season with coarsely ground black pepper. Heat the oil in a non-stick frying pan, add the steaks and fry over a moderately high heat for 3–4 minutes on each side. They will still be slightly rare in the centre. Lift out and keep warm.

4 Add the shallots and garlic to the pan and fry, stirring, for 1 minute. Add the port and boil, stirring well to deglaze the pan. Stir in the stock and cranberries and cook over a moderate heat for about 5 minutes or until the berries split and soften. Add the pears and heat gently for 2–3 minutes. Add the sugar and season with pepper.

5 Tip any juices from around the steaks into the sauce and stir gently to mix. Turn out the rösti and cut it into wedges like a cake. Serve the rösti, steaks and pears on warmed individual plates, with the sauce spooned over and around.

Fb

preparation and cooking time **about 1¼ hours**

serves **4**

PER SERVING

441 kcal

36g protein

15g total fat
3g saturated fat

70mg cholesterol

41g total carbohydrate
24g sugars

11g fibre

344mg sodium

HEALTH HINT

Cranberries are rich in vitamin C, which boosts the immune system, and they are renowned for helping to control urinary tract infections such as cystitis. Research suggests that they can help to protect against infections of the kidney and prostate as well as preventing kidney stones.

venison bangers and mash

Lean venison makes a good flavoursome sausage, perfect for this sophisticated version of a traditional favourite, here made with olive oil mash. Serve with broccoli florets or another seasonal green vegetable.

1 Heat the oil in a deep non-stick frying pan. Add the sausages and fry them over a moderate heat, turning occasionally, for about 10 minutes or until they are lightly browned all over.

2 Meanwhile, start cooking the potatoes for the mash. Place the potatoes in a saucepan and pour over boiling water to cover by 5cm. Bring back to the boil, then reduce the heat and cook for 15–20 minutes or until the potatoes are very tender.

3 Add the onions to the sausages and cook for a further 5 minutes or until they are golden and the sausages are nicely browned all over. Remove the sausages to a plate and set aside. Drain off the excess oil from the pan.

4 Add the garlic, mushrooms and red pepper to the onions in the pan and cook gently for a few minutes until softened. Pour in the stock and wine and add the jelly and 2 sprigs of thyme. Season with pepper. Mix the cornflour with 1 tablespoon cold water and stir into the liquid in the pan. Bring to the boil, stirring until lightly thickened, then reduce the heat. Return the sausages to the pan and simmer gently for 10 minutes.

5 Drain the potatoes, shaking the colander or sieve to remove any excess water, and return them to their pan. Heat the milk in a small saucepan until hot, pour over the potatoes and mash until smooth. Beat in the oil, parsley and pepper to taste.

6 To serve, divide the mash among warmed plates and top with the sausages, vegetables and sauce (discarding the thyme sprigs). Sprinkle with the leaves from the remaining thyme sprig and serve immediately.

1 tablespoon sunflower oil
8 large venison sausages, about 500g in total
170g baby onions, halved
1 large garlic clove, crushed
170g button mushrooms, halved
1 red pepper, deseeded and thinly sliced
200ml low-sodium beef stock or stock made without salt
150ml full-bodied red wine
1 tablespoon redcurrant or bramble jelly
3 sprigs of fresh thyme
pepper to taste
2 teaspoons cornflour

OLIVE OIL MASH
750g floury potatoes, peeled and cut into chunks
120ml semi-skimmed milk
2 teaspoons extra virgin olive oil
1 tablespoon chopped fresh parsley

Fb

preparation and cooking time **1½ hours**
serves **4**

PER SERVING

666 kcal
40g protein
33g total fat
11g saturated fat
70mg cholesterol
48g total carbohydrate
13g sugars
7g fibre
302mg sodium

HEALTH HINT

Venison sausages contain just over half the fat in traditional pork sausages (11 per cent fat compared with 20 per cent fat).

vegetable dishes & salads

broccoli and pearl barley salad

 Pearl barley, with its nutty flavour and firm texture, makes an interesting change from rice in a salad, and it blends beautifully with this mixture of vegetables, apricots and pumpkin seeds.

150g pearl barley

200g broccoli, cut into small florets

3 courgettes, thickly sliced

100g sugarsnap peas, halved

55g ready-to-eat dried apricots, thinly sliced

pepper to taste

30g pumpkin seeds

SPICY TOMATO DRESSING

3 tablespoons extra virgin olive oil

1 tablespoon tomato purée

juice of 1 lime

2 teaspoons ground cumin

dash of Tabasco sauce

1 garlic clove, crushed

2 tablespoons chopped fresh coriander or parsley (optional)

1 Rinse the barley in one or two changes of water – do this in a bowl, swirling the grains with your fingers and pouring off the cloudy water. Drain the barley in a sieve, then place it in a saucepan and pour in 750ml cold water. Bring to the boil. Reduce the heat and cover the pan. Simmer the barley very gently for about 30 minutes or until most of the water has been absorbed and the grains are tender but still firm. Drain the barley well.

2 While the barley is cooking, bring a second pan of water to the boil. Add the broccoli florets, courgettes and sugarsnap peas and bring back to the boil. Reduce the heat and simmer the vegetables for 3–4 minutes or until they are just tender but still crisp, then drain well and rinse briefly with cold water to refresh and stop the cooking.

3 Whisk all the dressing ingredients together in a large bowl. Stir in the apricots. Add the barley and vegetables as soon as they are cooked, and mix well to coat with the dressing. Season with pepper, then cover and cool until just warm.

4 Add the pumpkin seeds to the salad just before serving, warm or at room temperature. Soda bread or wholemeal bread are good accompaniments.

  Fb GI

preparation and cooking time **50 mins**

serves **4**

PER SERVING

315 kcal

10g protein

13g total fat
2g saturated fat

0mg cholesterol

42g total carbohydrate
9g sugars

4g fibre

19mg sodium

HEALTH HINT

Broccoli is an excellent source of beta carotene and vitamin C. It also provides the B vitamins B_6, folate and niacin.

vegetable and wholewheat pan-fry with teriyaki tofu

Here pre-cooked wholewheat grains are cooked in stock, then tossed with fresh ginger and oriental vegetables to make the perfect partner for Japanese-style marinated tofu. This is a delicious, nutritious dish made in minutes.

1 Pour the vegetable stock into a saucepan and bring to the boil. Add the wholewheat grains and simmer for 15–20 minutes or until they are tender and the stock has been absorbed.

2 Meanwhile, for the teriyaki tofu, mix together the garlic, ginger, soy sauce, mirin, sunflower oil, honey and five-spice powder in a bowl. Cut the tofu into bite-sized triangles and add to the bowl. Turn until all the pieces are coated in the mixture. Set aside to marinate while cooking the vegetables.

3 Heat the oil in a wok or large frying pan, add the garlic and ginger, and stir-fry for a few seconds. Add the red pepper and leek strips, and stir-fry for 3–4 minutes or until softened. Stir in the bean sprouts and stir-fry for 3 minutes.

4 Add the wholewheat grains to the wok. Hold a sieve over the wok and tip the tofu mixture into it, straining the marinade into the wok. Toss until the wholewheat grains and marinade are mixed with the vegetables. Gently toss in the tofu and cook for 1–2 minutes longer or until heated through. Serve immediately.

600ml low-sodium vegetable stock
200g pre-cooked wholewheat grains
2 garlic cloves, crushed
1 tablespoon finely grated fresh root ginger
2 tablespoons low-sodium soy sauce
1 tablespoon mirin
1 tablespoon sunflower oil
1 tablespoon clear honey
1 teaspoon Chinese five-spice powder
1 packet (about 285g) firm tofu
VEGETABLE PAN-FRY
2 tablespoons sunflower oil
2 garlic cloves, crushed
1 tablespoon finely grated fresh root ginger
1 large red pepper, deseeded and cut into long matchsticks
1 leek, cut into long matchsticks
250g bean sprouts

preparation and cooking time **30 mins**
serves **4**

PER SERVING

375 kcal	
16g protein	
13g total fat	
2g saturated fat	
0mg cholesterol	
50g total carbohydrate	
12g sugars	
6g fibre	
402mg sodium	

HEALTH HINTS

Wholewheat grains are low in fat and high in starchy carbohydrate. Because the whole of the grain is eaten, they are also a good source of dietary fibre.

Evidence suggests that including soya beans and products made from soya beans, such as tofu, in the diet regularly may help to reduce the risk of certain cancers and heart disease and help east symptoms of the menopause.

oaty red lentil gratin

Red lentils are mixed with chestnut mushrooms and celery to form the base of this hearty main dish. The Double Gloucester cheese and oat topping becomes lightly browned and crunchy during the few minutes in the oven.

2 tablespoons extra virgin olive oil

1 onion, chopped

2 celery sticks, chopped

200g chestnut mushrooms, sliced

250g split red lentils

600ml low-sodium vegetable stock or stock made without salt

100g rolled oats

100g Double Gloucester cheese, grated

pinch of cayenne pepper

pepper to taste

1 Heat the oil in a saucepan over a moderate heat, add the onion and celery and cook, stirring occasionally, for 5 minutes.

2 Add the sliced mushrooms and stir well to combine. Cook for about 5 minutes longer or until softened.

3 Stir in the lentils and add 500ml of the stock. Bring to the boil, then reduce the heat and cover the pan. Simmer for about 20 minutes or until the lentils are tender, adding the rest of the stock if the lentils appear to be drying out.

4 Preheat the oven to 220°C (gas mark 7). Mix the oats with the grated cheese and cayenne pepper. When the lentils are cooked, season with pepper. Transfer them to a shallow ovenproof dish and spread out evenly.

5 Spread the oat and cheese mixture over the top. Place the dish in the oven and bake for about 10 minutes or until the topping is crisp and golden brown. Serve hot.

 Fb GI

preparation time **45 min**

cooking time **10 mins**

serves **4**

PER SERVING

464 kcal

25g protein

17g total fat
7g saturated fat

24mg cholesterol

55g total carbohydrate
4g sugars

6g fibre

300mg sodium

HEALTH HINT

Lentils are one of the nutritional wonders – high in protein, starchy carbohydrate and fibre, but very low in sodium and fat.

potato and pumpkin gratin

For a layered gratin such as this, a mixture of roots and softer vegetables yields a well-textured result and provides a good mix of nutrients. It's satisfying enough to make a one-pot meal in itself.

450g small main-crop potatoes, halved
600g pumpkin
150ml dry cider
300ml boiling low-sodium vegetable stock or stock made without salt
1 small sprig of fresh rosemary
1 large red onion, halved and thinly sliced
pepper to taste
3 beefsteak tomatoes, thickly sliced
2 sprigs of fresh oregano, stalks discarded
225g Red Leicester cheese, grated
115g fresh white breadcrumbs

1 Preheat the oven to 180°C (gas mark 4). Put the potatoes in a medium-sized saucepan, cover with boiling water and bring back to the boil. Cook for 15 minutes or until they are just tender, then drain.

2 Meanwhile, prepare the pumpkin. Discard any seeds and fibres, then peel the flesh and cut it into 2.5cm cubes. Place in a saucepan and pour in the cider and stock. Add the rosemary sprig. Bring to the boil, then partly cover the pan and simmer for 15 minutes. Add the onion and continue to simmer for 10 minutes. Discard the rosemary and season with pepper.

3 Slice the potatoes and arrange half of them over the bottom of a 2 litre ovenproof dish. Lay half the tomato slices on the potatoes and scatter half the oregano leaves over them. Season with pepper and sprinkle with half of the cheese.

4 Spoon the cooked pumpkin on top, adding all the cooking liquid. Top with the remaining potatoes, tomatoes and oregano. Mix the remaining cheese with the breadcrumbs and sprinkle over the top of the vegetables.

5 Bake the vegetable gratin for 35–40 minutes or until the topping is crisp and golden brown. Serve piping hot.

Fb

preparation time **45 mins**
cooking time **35–40 mins**
serves **4**

PER SERVING

480 kcal	
22g protein	
20g total fat	
12g saturated fat	
54mg cholesterol	
53g total carbohydrate	
11g sugars	
5g fibre	
685mg sodium	

HEALTH HINT

Pumpkin contains soluble fibre, which may help reduce LDL ('bad') cholesterol by blocking its absorption into the body.

roasted vegetable and pasta bake

A hearty vegetarian dish packed with flavour, this selection of vegetables – butternut squash, asparagus and leeks – is roasted in garlicky olive oil, then tossed with chunky pasta shapes and a cheese sauce.

1 small butternut squash, peeled,
  deseeded and cut into 5cm cubes,
  about 450g peeled weight
2 red onions, cut into large chunks
2 garlic cloves, thinly sliced
2 tablespoons extra virgin olive oil
pepper to taste
2 large leeks, thickly sliced
170g asparagus spears,
  cut across in half
300g rigatoni or penne

CHEESE SAUCE
600ml semi-skimmed milk
3 tablespoons cornflour
75g reduced-fat mature
  Cheddar cheese, grated
2 teaspoons wholegrain mustard

1 Preheat the oven to 220°C (gas mark 7). Place the squash and onions in a roasting tin. Scatter over the garlic. Drizzle with the oil and season with pepper. Toss to coat the vegetables with oil, then place in the oven and roast for 15 minutes.

2 Remove the tin from the oven and add the leeks and asparagus. Toss gently to mix with the other vegetables, then return to the oven. Roast for a further 20 minutes or until all the vegetables are tender and beginning to brown.

3 Meanwhile, cook the pasta in a large saucepan of boiling water for 10–12 minutes, or according to the packet instructions.

4 Meanwhile, to make the sauce, measure 4 tablespoons milk into a jug, add the cornflour and stir to make a smooth paste. Heat the remaining milk in a saucepan until almost boiling. Stir the hot milk into the cornflour mixture, then return to the saucepan and heat gently, stirring, until the mixture boils and thickens. Simmer for 2 minutes. Remove the sauce from the heat and add two-thirds of the cheese and the mustard. Season with pepper.

5 Remove the vegetables from the oven. Drain the pasta well, then tip over the vegetables and stir to combine. Stir in the sauce. Sprinkle the remaining cheese over the top. Return to the oven and bake for 10–15 minutes or until golden and bubbling. Serve hot.

preparation and cooking
time **about 1¼ hours**

serves **4**

PER SERVING

528 kcal

24g protein

13g total fat
5g saturated fat

17mg cholesterol

83g total carbohydrate
19g sugars

7g fibre

248mg sodium

HEALTH HINT

The bright orange flesh of butternut squash is an indicator of its high beta carotene content. This squash is also a good source of vitamin C and a useful source of vitamin E.

baked aubergines with yoghurt

In this delicious dish, grilled slices of aubergine and courgette are layered with a rich tomato sauce and cumin-flavoured yoghurt, then baked. Thick slices of multigrain bread and a crisp green salad are perfect accompaniments.

1 Heat 1 tablespoon of the oil in a saucepan, add the onion and cook for about 8 minutes or until softened. Add the garlic and cook for a further minute, stirring. Stir in the chopped tomatoes with their juice, the tomato paste, wine and bay leaf. Cover and simmer gently for 10 minutes.

2 Uncover the pan and allow the sauce to bubble for a further 10 minutes or until thickened, stirring occasionally. Remove the bay leaf. Stir in the parsley and pepper.

3 While the sauce is simmering, preheat the grill to moderate. Lightly brush the aubergine and courgette slices with the remaining 2 tablespoons oil. Cook under the grill, in batches, for 3–4 minutes on each side or until browned and very tender.

4 Preheat the oven to 180°C (gas mark 4). Stir the cumin into half of the yoghurt. Arrange one-third of the aubergine slices, in one layer, in a large ovenproof dish with a capacity of about 2.5 litres. Spoon over half of the tomato sauce. Arrange half of the courgette slices on top, in one layer, then drizzle with half of the cumin-flavoured yoghurt. Repeat the layers, then finish with a layer of the remaining aubergine slices.

5 Mix the remaining 200g yoghurt with the beaten eggs and half of the Parmesan cheese. Spoon the yoghurt mixture over the top layer of aubergine, spreading to cover evenly. Sprinkle with the remaining Parmesan cheese.

6 Bake for 40–45 minutes or until the top is lightly browned and set, and the sauce is bubbling. Serve hot, in the baking dish.

3 tablespoons extra virgin olive oil
1 red onion, finely chopped
2 garlic cloves, finely chopped
1 can (about 400g) chopped tomatoes
2 teaspoons sun-dried tomato paste
6 tablespoons dry red wine
1 bay leaf
2 tablespoons chopped fresh parsley
pepper to taste
3 small aubergines, about 675g in total, cut into 1cm slices
3 courgettes, about 450g in total, thinly sliced
$\frac{1}{2}$ teaspoon ground cumin
400g plain low-fat yoghurt
2 eggs, beaten
30g Parmesan cheese, freshly grated

Cheshire and root vegetable bake

This country-style dish tops nutty-flavoured root vegetables with a crisp mixture of wholemeal bread cubes and Cheshire cheese. It makes a really satisfying meal on a chilly day. Serve piping hot, with a leafy green vegetable.

200g carrots, thinly sliced

250g parsnips, thinly sliced

300g celeriac, thinly sliced

400g potatoes, peeled and thinly sliced

3 tablespoons chopped fresh chives

½ teaspoon freshly grated nutmeg

pepper to taste

200ml semi-skimmed milk

75g fromage frais

4 tablespoons half-fat crème fraîche

2 thick slices of wholemeal bread, about 85g in total

15g margarine, melted

100g Cheshire cheese, finely grated

1 Preheat the oven to 180°C (gas mark 4). Layer the carrot, parsnip, celeriac and potato slices in a large, shallow ovenproof dish, sprinkling the chives, nutmeg and pepper to taste between the layers.

2 In a mixing bowl, lightly whisk together the milk, fromage frais and crème fraîche, then pour evenly over the vegetables. Cover the dish with foil and bake for 1–1½ hours or until the vegetables are tender.

3 Cut the bread into 5mm dice and toss with the melted margarine and grated cheese to mix evenly. Spoon the mixture in an even layer over the vegetables. Return to the oven, without the foil covering, and bake for 15–20 minutes or until the top is crisp and golden. Serve hot.

Variations For a slightly stronger onion flavour, replace the chives with a bunch of spring onions, chopped, or 1 thinly sliced leek. • Other British cheeses can be used in place of Cheshire, such as Wensleydale or Lancashire. Or use Emmenthal cheese. • To make a Cheddar and sweet potato bake, peel and thinly slice 600g sweet potatoes and layer in a large, shallow ovenproof dish with 200g thinly sliced celery and 1 thinly sliced onion, sprinkling the layers with 1 tablespoon chopped fresh thyme, 1 teaspoon caraway seeds and pepper to taste. Instead of crème fraîche, whisk 4 tablespoons reduced-fat single cream with the fromage frais and milk. For the topping, mix 85g fresh wholemeal breadcrumbs with 15g melted margarine and 100g grated Cheddar cheese.

preparation and cooking time **about 2 hours**

serves **4**

PER SERVING
400 kcal
16g protein
19g total fat
9g saturated fat
27mg cholesterol
44g total carbohydrate
14g sugars
9g fibre
404mg sodium

HEALTH HINTS

Cheshire cheese is believed to be one of the oldest of all English cheeses. It is available white or orangey-red (coloured with a vegetable dye). Nutritionally there is no difference between the two varieties.

Root vegetables are inexpensive and a good source of carbohydrate and fibre.

vegetable tart Provençale

Brimming with the sunny flavours typical of southern France, this delectable tart is perfect for lunch or supper. An easy-to-assemble, herb-scented crust is the perfect partner for heart-healthy fresh vegetables.

2 large onions, sliced

plain flour for dusting

2 sheets puff pastry, about 300g in total, thawed if frozen

2 courgettes

4 tomatoes, cut into 5mm slices

2 tablespoons freshly grated Parmesan cheese

1 Coat a large non-stick frying pan with cooking spray and set over moderately high heat. When hot, reduce the heat to moderately low and sauté the onions for about 20 minutes or until very soft and golden. Transfer to a plate.

2 Preheat the oven to 200°C (gas mark 6). Lightly sprinkle a work surface with flour and form the pastry into a 25 x 40cm rectangle or 33cm round. Fold in half and transfer to a 15 x 30cm flan tin or a 23cm round flan tin with a removable base. Trim the edges of the pastry.

3 Cut the courgettes on the diagonal into long slices 5mm thick. Lightly coat the frying pan again with cooking spray and set over moderate heat. Add the courgettes and sauté for 5–7 minutes or until golden.

4 Arrange the courgettes, tomatoes and onions in neat rows in the pastry case, overlapping them slightly. Sprinkle with the Parmesan cheese. Bake for about 20 minutes or until the pastry is golden and crisp. Serve the tart hot, warm or at room temperature.

preparation time **35 mins**

cooking time **20 mins**

serves **4**

PER SERVING

380 kcal
9g protein
24g total fat 11g saturated fat
7mg cholesterol
36g total carbohydrate 8g sugars
2g fibre
300mg sodium

HEART SUPERFOOD

Centuries ago, folk healers recommended onions as a heart tonic. Modern science supports this ancient practice. Studies indicate that flavonoids, compounds present in onions, may raise the levels of HDL ('good') cholesterol, thus protecting against the artery-clogging damage of LDL ('bad') cholesterol. These and onion's sulphur compounds can hinder the formation of blood clots, which may further help protect against heart attacks.

mange-tout with apples and ginger

 Slices of firm apple, briefly stir-fried, have the same crunch as water chestnuts, so they partner well with crisp fresh mange-tout.

1 Heat the oil in a non-stick wok or large non-stick frying pan over low heat. Add the ginger and garlic and cook for about 2 minutes or until tender.

2 Add the mange-tout and apples and cook, stirring frequently, for 7 minutes or until the mange-tout are just tender.

Variation For an unusual main-dish salad, fold the cooled mange-out and apple mixture into slightly chilled cooked rice along with cubes of cooked chicken breast or pork fillet (tenderloin).

2 teaspoons extra virgin olive oil

2 tablespoons finely slivered fresh
    root ginger

3 garlic cloves, finely chopped

500g mange-tout, strings removed

2 crisp red-skinned dessert apples,
    unpeeled, cut into
    thin wedges

lemony sugarsnap peas

 The very essence of early summer, emerald-green sugarsnaps are so tender you eat them pods and all. These sweetest of peas shine in a simple stir-fry accented with shallots, garlic and lemon zest.

1 Remove the strings from both sides of the sugarsnap peas.

2 Heat the oil in a non-stick wok or large non-stick frying pan over moderate heat. Add the shallots and garlic and stir-fry for 3 minutes or until the shallots are softened.

3 Add the peas and lemon zest and stir-fry for about 4 minutes or until the peas are just tender.

750g sugarsnap peas

2 teaspoons extra virgin olive oil

3 shallots, thinly sliced

1 garlic clove, finely chopped

1 tablespoon grated lemon zest

HEALTH HINT

Sugarsnap peas and other edible-podded peas (such as mange-tout) supply three times as much vitamin C as shelled peas.

braised baby vegetables

Slowly braising whole baby vegetables preserves and enriches their flavours, and reducing the cooking juices in the final stages of cooking creates a delicious dressing that makes an attractive glaze.

4 baby leeks, about 200g in total

250g baby parsnips

30g margarine

250g baby carrots

8 pickling onions or shallots

150ml low-sodium vegetable stock or stock made without salt

1 teaspoon sugar

1 bay leaf

pepper to taste

1 Trim the leeks and split them lengthways without cutting them completely in half. Open out and wash under running water to remove any dirt. Cut the parsnips in half lengthways.

2 Melt the margarine in a large saucepan or flameproof casserole. Add all the vegetables. Stir in the stock, sugar, bay leaf and pepper to taste. Bring to the boil, then cover and reduce the heat to the lowest setting.

3 Cook for 20–25 minutes or until the vegetables are barely tender. Remove the lid and boil the liquid for 2–3 minutes or until reduced to a thick syrup-like glaze.

4 Turn the vegetables in the glaze so they are coated all over, then discard the bay leaf and serve immediately.

preparation time **15 mins**

cooking time **25 mins**

serves **4**

PER SERVING

100 kcal

2g protein

5g total fat
1g saturated fat

0.5mg cholesterol

12.5g total carbohydrate
4.5g sugars

4g fibre

63mg sodium

HEALTH HINT

Unlike other vegetables, which are at their most nutritious when eaten raw, carrots have more nutritional value when cooked. This is because carrots have tough cell walls; cooking breaks down the cell membrane, making it easier for the body to absorb and convert the beta carotene in carrots into vitamin A.

three-vegetable mash

Here's a chef-worthy accompaniment you can do yourself. It's based on mashed white potato that's tinted and flavoured three different ways – with health-giving sweet potatoes, spinach and beetroot.

1 Preheat the oven to 190°C (gas mark 5). Wrap the sweet potato chunks in a large parcel of heavy-duty foil. Combine the white potatoes, garlic and 4 tablespoons water in a roasting tin, tossing to coat. Cover the pan with foil. Place the roasting tin and the sweet potato parcel in the oven and bake for about 45 minutes or until both types of potato are tender.

2 Transfer the white potatoes and garlic to a large bowl. Add the crème fraîche and coarsely mash with a potato masher. Divide the potato mixture among three medium bowls.

3 Add the spinach, lemon zest and marjoram to one bowl of potatoes and coarsely mash together.

4 Drain the beetroot, reserving 1 tablespoon liquid. Add the beetroot, reserved liquid, orange zest and coriander to another bowl of potatoes and coarsely mash together.

5 Add the sweet potato, ginger and cayenne pepper to the third bowl and coarsely mash together. Serve hot.

370g orange-fleshed sweet potatoes, peeled and cut into large chunks

1.25kg floury white potatoes, peeled and cut into large chunks

8 garlic cloves, peeled

125ml half-fat crème fraîche

300g frozen chopped spinach, thawed and drained

1 teaspoon grated lemon zest

½ teaspoon dried marjoram

1 can (about 450g) sliced beetroot

1 teaspoon grated orange zest

¼ teaspoon ground coriander

½ teaspoon ground ginger

¼ teaspoon cayenne pepper

preparation time **25 mins**

cooking time **45 mins**

serves **8**

PER SERVING

200 kcal

5g protein

3g total fat
1.5g saturated fat

0mg cholesterol

40g total carbohydrate
9g sugars

4g fibre

156mg sodium

HEALTH HINT

Beetroot is a good source of cholesterol-lowering fibre as well as phyto-chemicals, such as saponins, which show potential for reducing the risk of heart disease. Also high in folate, just 50g of beetroot provides about one-third of the daily requirement for this cardioprotective B vitamin.

char-grilled asparagus and peppers

 Here, spears of asparagus, spring onions and peppers are cooked in a ridged cast-iron grill pan, then mixed with oven-baked Parmesan croutons. If you haven't got a ridged grill pan, the vegetables can be sizzled under the grill.

500g asparagus spears, woody
   ends trimmed

2 large red peppers, halved
   and deseeded

225g spring onions

2 tablespoons extra virgin olive oil

shavings of Parmesan cheese, about
   15g in total, to garnish

PARMESAN CROUTONS

2 thick slices of bread, crusts
   removed, then diced

1 tablespoon extra virgin olive oil

pepper to taste

30g Parmesan cheese, freshly grated

LEMON AND BASIL DRESSING

2 tablespoons freshly squeezed
   lemon juice

2 tablespoons extra virgin olive oil

16 fresh basil leaves, torn into pieces

1 garlic clove, very finely chopped

1 Preheat the oven to 180°C (gas mark 4). Heat a ridged cast-iron grill pan. Place the asparagus, peppers and spring onions in a bowl, add the olive oil and toss to coat.

2 Arrange the asparagus and peppers in the hot grill pan, in one layer, and cook for 10 minutes or until tender, adding the spring onions after the asparagus and peppers have been cooking for a few minutes. Turn the vegetables frequently so they cook and colour evenly. (You may have to grill the vegetables in two batches, depending on the size of the pan.)

3 Meanwhile, to make the croutons, place the bread in a bowl with the oil and pepper to season and toss well. Spread out on a baking tray and bake for about 5 minutes. Sprinkle over the Parmesan cheese and bake for a further 5 minutes or until golden and crisp.

4 Whisk together the dressing ingredients in a salad bowl, adding pepper to taste. Roughly slice the grilled vegetables, add to the bowl and stir to coat with the dressing. Scatter the croutons over the top and garnish with a few shavings of Parmesan cheese. Serve while still warm.

 Kc — Fb

preparation and cooking
time **40 mins**

serves **4**

PER SERVING

296 kcal

12g protein

19g total fat

5g saturated fat

7mg cholesterol

20g total carbohydrate

11g sugars

5g fibre

173mg sodium

HEALTH HINT

Bread is an important part of a healthy diet as it is a very good source of starchy (complex) carbohydrate. It also contributes vitamins and minerals, particularly calcium, and dietary fibre.

orange-maple sweet potatoes

Try this method of cooking sweet potatoes – mashed and then finished with an orange-maple glaze – and you'll discover how subtly delicious they are. The dish can be prepared ahead, then reheated, covered, in a very low oven.

1 Preheat the oven to 230°C (gas mark 8). Place the sweet potatoes and garlic in a medium saucepan. Add enough water to cover and bring to the boil. Reduce the heat and cook for about 20 minutes or until the sweet potatoes are tender.

2 Drain the sweet potatoes and garlic, then transfer them to a medium bowl. Season with the pepper and add 2 teaspoons of the oil. With a potato masher, mash the sweet potatoes and garlic until almost smooth, but with some texture remaining.

3 Transfer to an ovenproof dish. Combine the remaining 2 teaspoons oil, the maple syrup and orange zest in a small saucepan and bring to the boil over low heat. Drizzle the mixture over the potatoes.

4 Bake the sweet potatoes for 25 minutes or until the top is lightly browned. Serve hot.

1kg orange-fleshed sweet potatoes, peeled and thickly sliced

6 garlic cloves, peeled and thinly sliced

½ teaspoon pepper

4 teaspoons extra virgin olive oil

3 tablespoons maple syrup

2 teaspoons grated orange zest

preparation time **30 mins**

cooking time **25 mins**

serves **6**

PER SERVING

183 kcal

2g protein

2.5g total fat
0.5g saturated fat

0mg cholesterol

40g total carbohydrate
11.6g sugars

4g fibre

67mg sodium

HEART SUPERFOOD

Sweet potatoes are a nutritional powerhouse because they're bursting with vitamins, minerals and fibre as well as beta carotene, which is the sweet potato's secret weapon against heart disease. So try to find ways of getting them into your diet on a regular basis – sliced and steamed, baked in their jackets or mashed.

breads
& pizzas

basic loaf

This recipe makes a very good basic loaf, but it is also infinitely flexible. You can make any number of breads, just by using different types of flour or adding herbs, nuts, cheese, olives, seeds, dried fruit and berries, or shape it into rolls.

340g white bread flour

340 g wholemeal bread flour, preferably stoneground, plus a little extra to dust

1 teaspoon salt

1 sachet (about 7g) easy-blend dried yeast

450ml tepid water

1 Sift the white and wholemeal flours into a large bowl, tipping in any bran left in the sieve. Add the salt. Stir in the dried yeast, then make a well in the centre and pour in the tepid water. Using your hands, gradually draw the flour into the water, mixing well to make a dough.

2 Gather the dough into a ball that feels firm and leaves the sides of the bowl clean; if necessary, add a little more flour or a little more water.

3 Turn the dough out onto a lightly floured work surface and knead for about 10 minutes or until smooth and elastic. Place the dough in a large, lightly greased bowl and cover with cling film. Leave to rise in a warm place for about 1 hour or until the dough has doubled in size.

4 Turn out the risen dough onto a floured work surface and knock it back with your knuckles. Gently knead the dough into a neat ball shape, then place it on a large greased baking tray. Cover with a damp tea-towel and leave to rise in a warm place for 1 hour or until doubled in size again.

5 Towards the end of the rising time, preheat the oven to 220°C (gas mark 7). Uncover the loaf and dust with a little wholemeal flour, then make four slashes across the top with a small serrated knife. Bake for 35 minutes or until the bread sounds hollow when tapped on the base.

6 Transfer the loaf to a wire rack and cool completely before slicing. It can be kept for up to 5 days.

 Fb

preparation time **25 mins**

rising time **2 hours**

cooking time **35 mins**

makes **1 large round loaf** (cuts into about 12 slices)

PER SLICE

180 kcal

6g protein

1g total fat
0g saturated fat

0mg cholesterol

40g total carbohydrate
1g sugars

3g fibre

165mg sodium

HEALTH HINT

Stoneground flour is milled by traditional methods, which keep the wheat grains cool and thus preserve almost all the nutrients in the whole grain.

quick wholemeal bread

With only one rising and no kneading, this bread couldn't be simpler to make. It is based on the famous 'Grant loaf', invented in the 1940s by Doris Grant. With its dense, moist texture, it is a filling bread that makes excellent toast.

Fb

preparation time **10 mins**

rising time **30 mins**

cooking time **30–40 mins**

makes **1 large loaf**
(cuts into about 14 slices)

PER SLICE

100 kcal

4g protein

1g total fat
0g saturated fat

0mg cholesterol

21g total carbohydrate
1g sugars

3g fibre

141mg sodium

HEALTH HINT

Yeast is particularly rich in folate and contains a number of other B vitamins.

1 Lightly grease a 900g loaf tin or line with baking parchment. Set aside in a warm place while you make the dough.

2 Sift the flour into a large mixing bowl, tipping in any bran left in the sieve. Add the salt. Stir in the yeast and make a well in the centre. Stir the sugar or honey into the tepid water, then pour into the well in the dry ingredients.

3 Mix together, then beat vigorously with your hand (or with a wooden spoon if you prefer) for about 2 minutes or until the dough comes away from the side of the bowl; it will be very soft and sticky.

4 Pour the dough into the prepared tin, cover with a damp tea-towel and leave in a warm place for about 30 minutes or until the dough has risen almost to the top of the tin.

5 Towards the end of the rising time, preheat the oven to 200°C (gas mark 6). Uncover the tin and dust the top of the loaf evenly with the white flour. Bake for 30–40 minutes or until well risen and brown. It should feel light and sound hollow when turned out of the tin and tapped on the base.

6 Transfer the loaf to a wire rack and, if necessary, return it to the oven for 5 minutes to crisp the sides and base. Leave on the wire rack to cool. It can be kept for up to 5 days.

450g wholemeal bread flour, preferably stoneground

1 teaspoon salt

1 sachet (about 7g) easy-blend dried yeast

1 teaspoon light muscovado sugar or clear honey

450ml tepid water

1 tablespoon plain white flour to dust

light rye bread

Rye flour is lower in gluten than wheat, so it produces a close-textured, moist loaf. Caraway seeds are a traditional seasoning, complementing the nutty rye flavour to make an excellent bread that goes well with soft cheeses.

300g rye flour
100g white bread flour
½ teaspoon salt
1 teaspoon caster sugar
1 sachet (about 7g) easy-blend dried yeast
2 teaspoons caraway seeds
2 tablespoons extra virgin olive oil
200ml tepid water

1 Sift the rye and white flours into a bowl. Add the salt and sugar, then stir in the yeast and caraway seeds. Stir the olive oil into the water, then pour this over the flour mixture. Mix the ingredients together with a wooden spoon at first, then with your hand, to make a stiff but sticky and slightly grainy dough.

2 Turn the dough out onto a floured work surface and knead for about 10 minutes or until smooth. The dough should be very firm. Shape it into an oval loaf about 18cm long and place it on a greased baking tray. Cover loosely with cling film and leave to rise in a warm place for about 1 hour or until almost doubled in size. It will be slightly cracked on top.

3 Towards the end of the rising time, preheat the oven to 200°C (gas mark 6). Uncover the loaf and bake for 40–45 minutes or until it is lightly browned and sounds hollow when tapped on the base.

4 Transfer to a wire rack and leave to cool. Once cold, place the loaf in a plastic bag and leave overnight (this allows the crust to soften). After this, the loaf can be kept for 2 days.

preparation time **20 mins**
rising time **1 hour**
cooking time **40–45 mins**
makes **1 small loaf**
(cuts into about
24 thin slices)

PER SLICE

65 kcal

1.5g protein

1g total fat
0g saturated fat

0mg cholesterol

13g total carbohydrate
0g sugars

1.5g fibre

41mg sodium

HEALTH HINT

Caraway seeds are said to stimulate the production of saliva and aid in the digestion of food.

multigrain seeded loaf

 Serve this nutty-textured loaf very fresh, cut into wedges. It's good with a hearty bowl of soup or cheese and pickles. The mix of kernels and seeds can be varied to your own taste, or you can use just one kind.

preparation time **30 mins**

rising time **2 hours**

cooking time **30–35 mins**

makes **1 round loaf**
(cuts into 8 wedges)

PER WEDGE

390 kcal

11g protein

11g total fat
1g saturated fat

0mg cholesterol

65g total carbohydrate
2g sugars

5g fibre

495mg sodium

HEALTH HINT

Pumpkin seeds are one of the richest vegetarian sources of zinc, a mineral that is essential for the functioning of the immune system. They are a good source of protein and unsaturated fat and a useful source of iron, magnesium and fibre.

1 Sift the white, wholemeal and buckwheat flours into a large bowl, tipping in any bran left in the sieve. Stir in the polenta, salt, yeast and sugar.

2 Mix together the sunflower and pumpkin seeds and linseeds. Set aside 1 tablespoon for the topping and stir the rest into the flour mixture.

3 Make a well in the dry ingredients and pour in the oil and most of the water. Work the dry ingredients into the liquid to make a soft dough, adding more water as needed. Turn out onto a lightly floured work surface and knead for 10 minutes or until smooth and elastic. Place in a large, lightly greased bowl and cover with a damp tea-towel. Leave in a warm place for 1½ hours or until doubled in size.

4 Turn the dough out onto a lightly floured surface and knock it back with your knuckles, then knead firmly for a few minutes. Shape into a 20cm round and place on a lightly greased baking tray. Cover with oiled cling film and set aside for 20–30 minutes or until well risen and springy to the touch.

5 Preheat the oven to 230°C (gas mark 8). Uncover the loaf and, using a sharp knife, cut deeply to mark into eight wedges. Brush with milk and sprinkle with the reserved seeds.

6 Bake for 15 minutes, then reduce the oven temperature to 200°C (gas mark 6). Bake for a further 15–20 minutes or until the loaf is golden brown and sounds hollow when tapped on the base. Allow to cool on a wire rack. This bread is best eaten on the day it is made.

300g white bread flour

200g wholemeal bread flour

100g buckwheat flour

75g polenta

2 teaspoons salt

1 sachet (about 7g) easy-blend
dried yeast

1 teaspoon light muscovado sugar

3 tablespoons sunflower seeds

2 tablespoons pumpkin seeds

2 tablespoons linseeds

2 tablespoons sunflower oil

450ml tepid water

a little semi-skimmed milk to glaze

sourdough bread

Instead of commercial yeast, delicious sourdough bread is made with a 'starter' that uses the yeasts that occur naturally in the atmosphere and on flour. Despite the time needed to 'grow' the starter, it is not a difficult bread to make.

STARTER

100g white bread flour, preferably unbleached organic flour

100ml tepid water, preferably spring water

TO 'FEED'

200–300g white bread flour, preferably unbleached organic flour

tepid water, preferably spring water

DOUGH

500g white bread flour, preferably unbleached organic flour

1 teaspoon salt

240ml tepid water, preferably spring water, or as needed

1 To make the starter, place the flour and tepid water in a bowl and stir together to make a sticky paste. Cover with a damp tea-towel (not cling film) and leave on the kitchen counter for 2 days, dampening the tea-towel again as needed to keep it moist. If after 2 days the mixture looks bubbly and has a milky smell, you can proceed to the first 'feed'. (It may take up to 4 days to reach this stage.) If there are patches of mould or the paste smells sour or bad, throw it away and begin again with a new batch of starter.

2 To 'feed' the starter, stir 100g flour and enough tepid water into the starter to make a soft, paste-like dough. Cover the bowl as before and leave for 24 hours or until the starter looks very active and bubbly.

3 Stir well, then discard half the starter. Stir another 100g flour and enough tepid water into the starter to make a soft, paste-like dough. Cover again and leave for 12 hours. If the starter looks very bubbly and lively, it is ready to use. If it seems only slightly bubbly, give it one more feed of 100g flour and tepid water and wait 6 hours.

4 To make the dough, place the flour and salt in a large bowl. Mix together and make a well in the centre. Weigh out 200g of the starter into a separate bowl and mix it with the tepid water, then pour it into the well in the flour. Gradually work the flour into the liquid mixture to make a soft dough. You may need to add a little more water as you work if the dough feels dry or crumbly, or more flour if it sticks to your hands or the bowl.

5 Turn the dough out onto a floured work surface and knead for about 10 minutes or until very pliable. Return it to the cleaned bowl, cover with a damp tea-towel and leave to rise in a warm place for 3–8 hours or until doubled in size. Rising time depends on the room temperature and on the strength of your starter. (A new starter will give a slower rise and less volume than one that is well established.)

6 Turn out the risen dough onto a floured work surface and knock it back with your knuckles to its original size. Shape the dough into a ball and set it in a basket or colander lined with a heavily floured linen tea-towel. Cover with a damp tea-towel and leave to rise for 2–6 hours or until doubled in size.

preparation time **40 mins** plus 4–6 days for the starter to develop
rising time **5–14 hours**

cooking time **35 mins**

makes **1 large round loaf** (cuts into about 20 slices)

PER SLICE

120 kcal

3g protein

0g total fat
0g saturated fat

0mg cholesterol

27g total carbohydrate
0.5g sugars

1g fibre

99mg sodium

HEALTH HINT

Sourdough starters can last for decades, and seem to be resistant to contamination. This may be due to an antibiotic action similar to that of the moulds in cheeses such as Stilton and Roquefort.

banana cinnamon muffins

These delicious, moist muffins with a crunchy sweet topping are not only low in fat, they contain bananas, oat bran, soya milk and soya flour – all beneficial for anyone eating for a healthy heart. Enjoy them warm with tea or coffee.

1 Preheat the oven to 180°C (gas mark 4). Line a 12-cup deep muffin tray with paper muffin cases.

2 Mix together 2 teaspoons of the oat bran, 1 teaspoon of the cinnamon and the demerara sugar, and set aside for the topping. Place the remaining oat bran in a bowl with the soya milk and leave to soak for 5 minutes.

3 Peel and roughly mash the bananas. Add the muscovado sugar, oil, vanilla extract and egg white, and beat well together.

4 Sift the plain and soya flours, baking powder and remaining cinnamon into a large bowl. Make a well in the centre and stir in the soaked oat bran and the banana mixture. Mix together lightly but thoroughly, just until smooth.

5 Spoon the mixture into the paper cases and sprinkle with the topping. Bake for 20–25 minutes or until well risen and golden brown. Lift the muffins out onto a wire rack to cool a little. Serve fresh, preferably still slightly warm from the oven. These muffins are best eaten on the day they are made.

55g oat bran
2 teaspoons ground cinnamon
1 tablespoon demerara sugar
200ml soya milk
3 bananas
125g light muscovado sugar
3 tablespoons sunflower oil
2 teaspoons pure vanilla extract
1 egg white
200g plain white flour
55g soya flour
1 tablespoon baking powder

preparation time **15 mins**
cooking time **20–25 mins**
makes **12 muffins**

PER MUFFIN

185 kcal

5g protein

5g total fat
0.5g saturated fat

0mg cholesterol

33g total carbohydrate
18g sugars

3g fibre

133mg sodium

HEART SUPERFOOD

Diets that are rich in soya protein are believed to help reduce high blood cholesterol levels. Several studies suggest that soya products may also help to reduce the risk of heart disease, certain cancers and osteoporosis, as well as alleviating some of the symptoms associated with the menopause.

malted sultana bread

This is a well-flavoured, pleasantly sweet bread with a moist texture and good keeping qualities. Slice it thickly and enjoy spread with a fruit purée or jam or soft fresh cheese at tea time.

1 Sift the wholemeal and white flours and the salt into a large bowl, tipping in any bran left in the sieve. Add the yeast and stir to mix, then make a well in the centre.

2 Stir the malt extract and honey into the tepid water and pour into the well in the flour. Gradually work the flour into the liquids to make a soft but not sticky dough. Mix in the sultanas.

3 Turn the dough out onto a lightly floured surface and knead for about 10 minutes or until very elastic. Place the dough in a greased bowl, cover with cling film and leave to rise in a warm place for 1 hour or until doubled in size. Meanwhile, grease a 450g loaf tin and line the bottom with baking parchment.

4 Turn the dough out onto the floured work surface again and knock it back with your knuckles. Press or roll out the dough into an oblong, then roll it up like a Swiss roll. Tuck the ends under and put it into the prepared tin. Cover with a damp tea-towel and leave to rise in a warm place for 1 hour or until it has doubled in size.

5 Towards the end of the rising time, preheat the oven to 190°C (gas mark 5). Uncover the loaf and bake for 35–40 minutes or until it sounds hollow when turned out of the tin and tapped on the base. Turn it out onto a wire rack and leave to cool. The bread can be kept for up to 4 days.

Variations For an attractive shiny finish, as soon as the bread comes out of the oven, brush the top with 2 teaspoons warmed clear honey. • For a malted apple and sultana bread, add 1 medium-sized dessert apple, cored and diced, and 50g lightly toasted and chopped almonds with the sultanas. • Slightly stale malted sultana bread makes an excellent bread pudding, and you don't need to add any extra dried fruit.

200g wholemeal bread flour, preferably stoneground
150g white bread flour
½ teaspoon salt
1 teaspoon easy-blend dried yeast
3 tablespoons malt extract
1 tablespoon clear honey
200ml tepid water
85g sultanas

---

preparation time **20 mins**

rising time **2 hours**

cooking time **35–40 mins**

makes **1 small loaf**
(cuts into about 16 slices)

PER SLICE

90 kcal

3g protein

0.4g total fat
0g saturated fat

0mg cholesterol

20g total carbohydrate
5g sugars

1.5g fibre

63mg sodium

HEALTH HINT

Malt extract is produced by soaking barley grains, then leaving them to germinate under controlled conditions so that the starch is converted into dextrin (a type of gum) and malt sugar (maltose). When added to baked goods, malt extract gives a distinctive taste and moist texture, and provides phosphorus and magnesium.

ricotta herb scones

*These savoury scones are made with soft cheese and plenty of fresh herbs –
ideally a mixture of flat-leaf parsley, chives, thyme and rosemary, although any
combination will do. The scones are nicest warm, with soup or salad.*

450g self-raising white flour
½ teaspoon salt
several grinds of black pepper
225g ricotta cheese
1 egg
3 tablespoons chopped mixed
    fresh herbs
240ml semi-skimmed milk, or more
    as needed, plus extra to glaze
1 tablespoon sesame seeds to sprinkle

1 Preheat the oven to 190°C (gas mark 5). Sift the flour into
a mixing bowl and stir in the salt and black pepper.

2 Place the ricotta, egg and herbs in another bowl and stir
well until smooth. Add to the flour and stir in with a round-
bladed knife. Work in the milk to make a slightly soft but not
sticky dough, adding a little more milk if needed.

3 Turn the dough out onto a lightly floured work surface and
knead gently for 1 minute or until smooth. Divide into eight
equal portions and shape each into a rough-looking ball.

4 Place the scones on a large greased baking tray, arranging
them so they do not touch. Brush lightly with milk to glaze,
then sprinkle with sesame seeds. Bake for 20–25 minutes or
until the scones are lightly browned and sound hollow when
they are tapped on the base.

5 Transfer to a wire rack to cool slightly, then eat warm or
allow to cool completely before serving. The scones can be
kept in an airtight container for 24 hours.

preparation time **20 mins**
cooking time **20–25 mins**
makes **8 scones**

PER SCONE

280 kcal

11g protein

7g total fat
3g saturated fat

46mg cholesterol

46g total carbohydrate
3g sugars

2g fibre

380mg sodium

HEALTH HINT

Herbs like parsley, chives,
rosemary, oregano, basil
and coriander add a
nutrition bonus to your
meals. They are fat-free
and rich in vitamins,
minerals, fibre and
hundreds of phyto-
chemicals, with virtually
no calories. Weight for
weight, parsley has almost
twice as much vitamin
C as oranges, and dill
has six times more beta
carotene than pumpkin.
However, we use the
herbs in much smaller
quantities than oranges
and pumpkin so the
nutritional benefits are
correspondingly small.

30

preparation time **10 mins**

cooking time **15–20 mins**

makes **6 scone wedges**

PER WEDGE

200 kcal	
4g protein	
6g total fat	
1g saturated fat	
4mg cholesterol	
35g total carbohydrate	
1g sugars	
1.5g fibre	
474mg sodium	

HEALTH HINT

Potatoes, while not particularly high in vitamin C, can contribute significant quantities of this essential nutrient to the diet if they are eaten regularly. Potatoes are also an excellent source of starchy carbohydrate. They provide fibre and potassium and are also low in fat.

potato scones

Served fresh from the oven while still warm, scones are a traditional favourite. Here, mashed potato is added to the mixture, which makes these savoury scones wonderfully moist. It's a great way of using up leftover potato.

1 Preheat the oven to 220°C (gas mark 7). Sift the flour, mustard powder, baking powder and salt into a large bowl. Add the margarine and rub in with your fingertips until the mixture resembles fine breadcrumbs.

2 Place the milk and mashed potato in another bowl and mix well. Add to the dry ingredients and stir with a fork, adding another 1–2 tablespoons milk, if needed, to make a soft dough.

3 Turn the dough out onto a floured work surface and knead lightly for a few seconds or until smooth, then roll out to a 15cm round about 2cm thick. Place on a greased baking tray. Using a sharp knife, cut deeply to mark into six wedges

4 Brush with milk or egg, then sprinkle with the oatmeal. Bake for 15–20 minutes or until well risen and golden brown.

5 Transfer to a wire rack and break into wedges. Serve warm or leave to cool. The scones can be kept in an airtight container for 3 days. They can be reheated to serve: set on a baking tray, cover with foil and warm in a low oven for about 5 minutes.

Variations Instead of oatmeal, dust the scones with a mixture of 2 teaspoons plain flour and a pinch of paprika before baking. • For potato and feta scones, instead of margarine, stir 75g feta cheese, finely crumbled, and 2 tablespoons snipped fresh chives into the dry ingredients.

225g self-raising white flour

¼ teaspoon mustard powder

1½ teaspoons baking powder

½ teaspoon salt

30g margarine

4 tablespoons semi-skimmed milk, or more as needed

170g cold mashed potato (without any milk or fat added)

semi-skimmed milk or beaten egg to glaze

2 teaspoons medium oatmeal to sprinkle

cinnamon raisin bread

This milk-enriched fruity loaf tastes good plain or can be served spread with a little honey or jam. It's also wonderful toasted for breakfast, when the gentle aroma of warm cinnamon makes a soothing start to the day.

450g wholemeal bread flour

1 teaspoon salt

2 teaspoons ground cinnamon

1 sachet (about 7g) easy-blend dried yeast

115g raisins

45g caster sugar

55g margarine

240ml semi-skimmed milk, plus 1 tablespoon to glaze

1 egg, lightly beaten

1 Grease and lightly flour a 900g loaf tin. Sift the flour, salt and cinnamon into a large mixing bowl, tipping in any bran left in the sieve. Stir in the yeast, raisins and sugar, and make a well in the centre.

2 Gently heat the margarine and 240ml milk in a small saucepan until the margarine has melted and the mixture is just tepid. Pour into the well in the dry ingredients and add the beaten egg. Mix together to make a soft dough.

3 Turn the dough out onto a lightly floured surface and knead for 10 minutes or until smooth and elastic. Shape the dough into an oblong, roll up and place in the prepared tin. Cover with oiled cling film or a clean tea-towel and leave to rise in a warm place for about 1 hour or until doubled in size.

4 Towards the end of the rising time, preheat the oven to 220°C (gas mark 7). Uncover the loaf and brush with the remaining milk to glaze. Bake for about 30 minutes or until the loaf sounds hollow when removed from the tin and tapped on the base. Cover the loaf with foil towards the end of the baking time if the top is browning too much.

5 Turn out onto a wire rack and leave to cool. The bread can be kept, wrapped in foil, for 2–3 days.

Fb

preparation time **20 mins**

rising time **1 hour**

cooking time **30 mins**

makes **1 large loaf**
(cuts into about 16 slices)

PER SLICE

156 kcal

5g protein

4g total fat
1g saturated fat

16mg cholesterol

27g total carbohydrate
3g sugars

3g fibre

164mg sodium

HEALTH HINT

Dried fruit, such as raisins, is a concentrated source of energy. Raisins are also a useful source of fibre and potassium.

preparation time **15 mins**
cooking time **10 mins**
serves **4**

PER SERVING

380 kcal

17g protein

12g total fat
1.5g saturated fat

6mg cholesterol

52g total carbohydrate
10g sugars

4g fibre

482mg sodium

HEALTH HINT

With its abundance of vegetables, this pizza provides a range of nutrients – especially vitamin C from the tomatoes – which promote the absorption of iron in the body. And the half-fat mozzarella supplies calcium, which helps prevent osteoporosis.

pepperoni pizza

Here's proof that you can enjoy a slice of pepperoni pizza and do your heart good. A few heart-smart substitutions and lots of vegetables make this much more healthy than a pizzeria's, and you get to savour the aroma as it bakes.

1 Preheat the oven to 220°C (gas mark 7). Line a 30cm pizza tray or a large baking tray with baking parchment.

2 Heat the olive oil in a large saucepan. Add the mushrooms, onion, garlic and oregano and fry over a moderate heat for about 7 minutes or until the mushrooms are golden brown. Stir in the tomatoes and sprinkle with the vinegar. Cover the pan, remove from the heat and leave to stand for 3 minutes.

3 Meanwhile, place the pizza base on the pizza tray. Spread over the pizza sauce. Top with the vegetable mixture, pepperoni and mozzarella, then sprinkle over the parsley.

4 Bake for about 10 minutes or until the crust is golden brown and crisp and the cheese is melted and bubbly. Remove from the oven and serve hot.

1 teaspoon extra virgin olive oil

140g button mushrooms, trimmed and sliced

1 large onion, cut into thin wedges

2 garlic cloves, crushed

2 teaspoons fresh oregano or 1 teaspoon dried oregano

4 plum tomatoes, sliced

2 teaspoons balsamic vinegar

1 ready-made thick pizza base, about 300g

175ml tomato-based pizza sauce

30g pepperoni (about 16 slices)

150g half-fat mozzarella cheese, grated

3 tablespoons chopped fresh parsley to sprinkle

tomato and basil galettes

Galette is the French term for a flat, round pastry or cake. The galettes here are made from wholemeal scone dough flavoured with a little Parmesan cheese. They make a delicious base for a tomato, basil and pine nut topping.

PARMESAN SCONE DOUGH
115g self-raising white flour
85g self-raising wholemeal flour
1 teaspoon baking powder
pinch of salt
30g cool margarine, diced
25g Parmesan cheese, freshly grated
120ml semi-skimmed milk

TOMATO AND BASIL TOPPING
3 teaspoons extra virgin olive oil
1 garlic clove, crushed
3 tablespoons sun-dried tomato paste
3 tablespoons shredded fresh basil
    leaves
3 large plum tomatoes, thinly sliced
30g pine nuts
fresh basil leaves to garnish

1 Preheat the oven to 220°C (gas mark 7). Sift the white and wholemeal flours, baking powder and salt into a bowl, tipping in the bran left in the sieve. Rub in the margarine until the mixture resembles fine breadcrumbs. Stir in the Parmesan. Make a well in the middle, pour in the milk and mix to make a fairly soft dough. Knead lightly until smooth.

2 Roll out the dough on a lightly floured surface to 5mm thickness. Cut out six rounds about 10cm in diameter. You will need to re-roll the trimmings to cut out the last round. Transfer the rounds to a non-stick baking sheet, spacing well apart. Mark the edges with a fork, if liked.

3 Brush the tops with 2 teaspoons of the olive oil. Mix the remaining oil with the garlic, tomato paste and basil, and spread thinly over the rounds, leaving a border of about 5mm clear. Arrange the tomato slices on top, overlapping them slightly and covering all of the basil topping.

4 Bake for 7 minutes, then scatter the pine nuts over the tomatoes. Return to the oven and bake for 3–5 minutes or until the galettes are risen and the edges are golden brown. Serve hot, garnished with basil leaves.

30 **Fb**

preparation time **20 mins**
cooking time **10–12 mins**
makes **6 galettes**

PER GALETTE

241 kcal

7g protein

12g total fat
3g saturated fat

19mg cholesterol

28g total carbohydrate
5g sugars

3g fibre

341mg sodium

HEALTH HINT

Wholemeal flour contains more B vitamins, iron, selenium and zinc than white flour, but used on its own makes heavy pastry and scone mixtures. Mixing wholemeal and white flours produces a lighter result.

tuna and tomato pizza

Add canned tuna to a good tomato sauce, spread it on a ready-made pizza base and you have a delicious, healthy pizza in no time at all. It makes a flavourful change from the usual cheese-laden pizzas.

1 Preheat the oven to 220°C (gas mark 7). Heat 1 teaspoon oil in a small saucepan. Add the onion and cook over a moderate heat for 4 minutes or until softened. Add the tomatoes and their juice, the oregano, sugar and pepper. Bring to the boil, then leave to bubble for 10 minutes, stirring occasionally.

2 Place the pizza bases on two baking trays. Spread half of the tomato purée over each base. Spoon the tomato mixture over the pizzas, then lay the tuna over the top. Add the capers and sliced olives, and drizzle over the remaining oil.

3 Bake the pizzas for 10 minutes or until the bases are golden brown and crisp. Garnish with the torn basil leaves and serve.

3 teaspoons extra virgin olive oil

1 onion, finely chopped

1 can (about 400g) chopped tomatoes

½ teaspoon dried oregano

good pinch of sugar

pepper to taste

2 ready-made thick pizza bases, about 230g each

2 tablespoons tomato purée

1 can (about 150g) tuna in water, drained and flaked into chunks

4 teaspoons capers

8 black olives, stoned and sliced

fresh basil leaves to garnish

preparation time **15 mins**
cooking time **10 mins**
serves **4**

PER SERVING

300 kcal

28g protein

9g total fat
3g saturated fat

40mg cholesterol

37g total carbohydrate
9g sugars

3g fibre

619mg sodium

HEALTH HINT

Canned tomatoes and tomato purée are healthy ingredients. They are both rich sources of the phytochemical lycopene (other good sources include pink grapefruit, watermelon and guava), which can help to protect against several types of cancer and heart disease.

desserts, cakes & biscuits

peach and berry cobbler

Bringing this luscious pudding to the table will put smiles on your family's faces. Full of sweet fruit and topped with pecan dumplings, it's sure to please. And don't worry if anyone asks for seconds – it's a low-fat treat.

1.5kg peaches, peeled, stoned and sliced

340g blackberries or raspberries

150g light soft brown sugar

1 tablespoon cornflour

2 tablespoons freshly squeezed lemon juice

250g self-raising white flour

45g pecan nuts, toasted and chopped

¼ teaspoon grated nutmeg

90g cold margarine

175ml plus 2 tablespoons semi-skimmed milk

2 tablespoons granulated sugar

1 Preheat the oven to 180°C (gas mark 4). Coat a 23 x 33cm ovenproof dish with cooking spray. Toss the peaches and blackberries or raspberries with 100g brown sugar, the cornflour and lemon juice in a large bowl. Turn into the dish and bake for 30 minutes.

2 Meanwhile, combine the flour, pecan nuts, remaining brown sugar and nutmeg in a large bowl. Rub in the margarine until the mixture resembles very coarse crumbs. Add 175ml milk and stir with a fork to make a thick batter-like dough.

3 Drop the dough on top of the fruit, spacing evenly, to make 12 dumplings. Lightly brush the dumplings with the remaining milk and sprinkle with granulated sugar.

4 Bake for 25–30 minutes or until a skewer inserted in the centre of a dumpling comes out with moist crumbs sticking to it. Serve warm or at room temperature.

 Fb

preparation time **1 hour**

cooking time **25–30 mins**

serves **12**

PER SERVING

270 kcal

4g protein

10g total fat
2g saturated fat

1mg cholesterol

45g total carbohydrate
27g sugars

3g fibre

137mg sodium

COOK'S TIP

If you don't have any self-raising flour, you can substitute plain flour sifted with 1 tablespoon baking powder. When fresh berries are not available, use 1.25kg frozen blackberries or raspberries.

steamed kumquat honey pudding

A pleasingly light yet traditional pudding for wintry days, this offers all the pleasure of a steamed pudding without the unhealthy saturated fat of suet. Layers of sliced kumquats add a deliciously tangy citrus flavour.

preparation time **15 mins**
cooking time **1¾ hours**
serves **6**

PER SERVING

330 kcal

10g protein

9g total fat
2g saturated fat

122mg cholesterol

56g total carbohydrate
29g sugars

2g fibre

402mg sodium

HEALTH HINT

Milk provides calcium and phosphorus – both important for strong bones and teeth – as well as protein and many B vitamins.

1 Place the honey in the bottom of a 900ml pudding basin and turn it so that the honey coats the bottom half. Set aside.

2 Place the breadcrumbs in a large mixing bowl. Stir in the sugar, flour and baking powder. Add the egg, milk and margarine and mix together to form a stiff cake-like mixture.

3 Place one-quarter of the pudding mixture in the basin and arrange half the kumquat slices on top. Add half the remaining mixture and top with the remaining kumquats. Finish with the pudding mixture. Press down lightly to smooth the surface.

4 Bring a steamer or deep saucepan of water to the boil. Cover the pudding basin with aluminium foil and tie string round the rim. Use more string to make a handle. Place the basin in the steamer; the water should come halfway up the basin. Cover and steam for 1¾ hours, adding water as necessary.

5 About 20 minutes before serving, make the custard. Put the eggs, sugar and 3 tablespoons milk in a bowl and beat. Place the remaining milk in a saucepan and heat until bubbles appear around the edge. Pour the milk over the egg mixture, stirring, then strain it all back into the saucepan. Cook over low heat, stirring constantly, until the custard thickens enough to coat the spoon thinly. Do not allow to boil. Stir in the vanilla extract.

6 When the pudding is cooked, carefully remove the basin from the steamer. Remove the foil, place a plate over the top of the basin and invert it. Serve the pudding hot with the custard.

2 tablespoons clear honey
150g fresh fine white breadcrumbs
100g demerara sugar
50g self-raising white flour
1 teaspoon baking powder
1 egg, beaten
2 tablespoons semi-skimmed milk
30g margarine
225g kumquats, sliced (with skin)

CUSTARD
2 eggs
1 tablespoon sugar
300ml semi-skimmed milk
1 teaspoon pure vanilla extract

sticky date and walnut pudding

On a chilly winter day, nothing could be more welcoming than a pudding full of dates and toasted walnuts. It is easy to make and has a lovely moist texture. A tangy pineapple and marmalade sauce makes a perfect accompaniment.

170g dried pitted dates, chopped

3 tablespoons semi-skimmed milk

85g margarine

85g light muscovado sugar

2 eggs, lightly beaten

115g self-raising white flour

¼ teaspoon ground cinnamon

½ teaspoon ground ginger

50g walnuts, toasted and
  roughly chopped

PINEAPPLE AND MARMALADE SAUCE

1 can (about 400g) pineapple pieces
  in natural juice, finely chopped

1 teaspoon arrowroot

4 tablespoons fine-cut orange
  marmalade

1 Preheat the oven to 180°C (gas mark 4). Lightly grease a 900ml pudding basin and line the bottom with a disc of greaseproof paper.

2 Place the dates in a bowl and pour over 2 tablespoons milk. Stir to coat, then leave to soak.

3 Place the margarine, sugar, eggs and remaining milk in a bowl. Sift over the flour, cinnamon and ginger, and beat with an electric mixer until smooth. Fold in the dates and walnuts.

4 Spoon the mixture into the pudding basin. Set the basin in a baking tin and pour in boiling water to come 1cm up the sides of the basin. Cover the tin and basin with a tent of foil. Bake for about 1 hour or until the pudding is lightly risen and a skewer comes out clean. If not, bake for a further 10 minutes.

5 Meanwhile, make the sauce. Drain the pineapple, reserving 150ml of the juice. Blend the arrowroot with a little of the juice in a small saucepan, then stir in the remaining juice. Bring to the boil and simmer for 1 minute or until thickened and clear. Stir the pineapple and marmalade into the sauce and simmer for a further 2–3 minutes, stirring occasionally.

6 Turn the pudding onto a serving plate. Spoon over a little sauce and serve with the remaining sauce in a bowl.

preparation time **25 mins**

cooking time **1 hour**

serves **8**

PER SERVING

340 kcal

5g protein

15g total fat
3g saturated fat

60mg cholesterol

49g total carbohydrate
36g sugars

1.5g fibre

153mg sodium

HEART SUPERFOOD

Walnuts have a high unsaturated fat content, particularly as linoleic acid. Some studies have suggested that regularly including a small quantity of walnuts in the diet can help to reduce high blood cholesterol levels and reduce the risk of heart attacks.

apricot and rum brioche pudding

This glamorous version of bread and butter pudding is based on brioche and custard spiked with rum or brandy for a seductive flavour. Sultanas, dried apricots and apricot conserve provide lots of sweetness, so no sugar is needed.

1 Spread the brioche slices with the conserve. (If the conserve is a little thick, warm it gently so that it can be spread easily.) Cut the slices in half diagonally or into squares.

2 Arrange the pieces of brioche in a lightly greased 1.2 litre ovenproof dish, scattering the sultanas and dried apricots between the layers.

3 Place the eggs in a mixing bowl. Add the milk, vanilla extract and rum or brandy, and whisk together until well combined. Pour the mixture over the brioche, then gently press the brioche down into the liquid. Leave to soak for 20 minutes.

4 Preheat the oven to 180°C (gas mark 4). If desired, pull up the edges of some of the brioche slices to make a peaked effect. Bake the pudding for 30–35 minutes or until it is just firm to the touch. Serve immediately.

Variation If preferred, you can omit the brandy or rum and add another teaspoon pure vanilla extract.

8 medium-sized slices of brioche loaf, about 200g in total
4 tablespoons apricot conserve
50g sultanas
100g ready-to-eat dried apricots, chopped
2 eggs
450ml semi-skimmed milk
1 teaspoon pure vanilla extract
1 tablespoon dark rum or brandy

preparation time **15 mins** plus 20 mins soaking

cooking time **35 mins**

serves **4**

PER SERVING

354 kcal

13g protein

9.5g total fat
3.5g saturated fat

125mg cholesterol

55.5g total carbohydrate
30g sugars

3g fibre

380mg sodium

HEALTH HINT

Dried apricots are a useful source of fibre and also contain some beta carotene, iron and potassium. Regularly using dried apricots in recipes and enjoying them as a snack will help to boost your intake of these essential nutrients.

cinnamon banana caramels

Any fruit – fresh, canned or frozen – can be used to make this instant version of crème brûlée. The fruit is topped with Greek-style yoghurt – lower in fat than cream – then with demerara sugar and grilled to a rich caramel topping.

4 bananas
¼ teaspoon ground cinnamon
300g Greek-style yoghurt
4 tablespoons demerara sugar

1 Preheat the grill. Peel the bananas and cut each one into about 16 slices. Divide the slices among four 250ml ramekins and sprinkle with the ground cinnamon. Divide the yoghurt between the ramekins, spooning it over the banana slices to cover them completely. Sprinkle 1 tablespoon sugar evenly over each dessert.

2 Place the ramekins on a baking tray and place them under the grill. Cook for about 1 minute or until the sugar melts into the yoghurt – keep watching to make sure that it does not burn. Remove from the grill and leave to cool for a few minutes before serving.

Variations Instead of yoghurt, use low-fat soft cheese, thick fromage frais or half-fat crème fraîche. • Try chopped peaches or nectarines, or a mixture of summer fruits, prepared the same way. Plums, rhubarb, cherries and raspberries can also be used, but these fruits are best if they are lightly stewed in a minimum amount of water until tender, then cooled, before the yoghurt topping goes on.

 30 GI

preparation time **8 mins**
cooking time **1 min**
serves **4**

PER SERVING

240 kcal

6g protein

7g total fat
4g saturated fat

12mg cholesterol

40g total carbohydrate
38g sugars

1g fibre

51mg sodium

HEALTH HINT

Bananas are great energy providers and one of the best fruit sources of potassium, a mineral we need in order to keep a stable balance of water in our bodies. Apart from carbohydrate, bananas also provide fibre plus useful amounts of vitamins B_6 and C, magnesium and copper.

very fruity Christmas pudding

Lighter than the traditional Christmas pudding, this is packed with fruit that has been soaked in sherry or brandy and orange juice so it's extra juicy. Served with brandy sauce, it won't leave you feeling uncomfortably full.

preparation time **45 mins**
cooking time **3 hours**
plus 1½ hours
serves **10**

PER SERVING

470 kcal	
9g protein	
15g total fat	
3g saturated fat	
52mg cholesterol	
75g total carbohydrate	
53g sugars	
2g fibre	
250mg sodium	

COOK'S TIP

The brandy-laced sauce, made with semi-skimmed milk and cornflour, is a low-fat alternative to cream or brandy butter.

1 Place all the dried fruit in a bowl. Add the orange zest and juice and sherry or brandy, and set aside to soak.

2 Grease a 1.4 litre pudding basin and place a disc of greaseproof paper on the bottom.

3 Beat together the margarine and sugar until light and fluffy, then gradually beat in the eggs. Stir in the apple, carrot, almonds and soaked fruits. Sift over the flour and mixed spice, add the breadcrumbs and mix together.

4 Spoon the mixture into the pudding basin and smooth the top. Lay a doubled sheet of greaseproof paper and then of aluminium foil on top. Fold to make a pleat in the centre, then smooth down round the basin. Tie securely with string.

5 Bring a steamer or deep pan of water to the boil. Place the basin inside and steam for 3 hours, adding water as needed.

6 Remove the basin and take off the foil and paper. Cover with a tea-towel and cool completely. Wrap in fresh greaseproof paper and foil. Store in a cool, dark place for up to 3 months.

7 On the day of serving, steam the pudding for a further 1½ hours. To make the sauce, blend the cornflour with 6 tbsp milk. Heat the remaining milk until almost boiling, then pour over the cornflour mixture, stirring. Return to the pan and stir over moderate heat until thickened. Simmer for a further 1–2 minutes, still stirring. Add the sugar and brandy and stir to dissolve. Taste for sweetness, adding a little more sugar if necessary. Turn out the pudding onto a serving plate. Serve with the hot brandy sauce in a sauceboat or jug.

85g currants
85g raisins
85g sultanas
85g dried pitted dates, chopped
85g dried apricots, chopped
75g dried cranberries
grated zest and juice of
   1 large orange
3 tablespoons sherry or brandy
115g margarine
115g dark muscovado sugar
2 eggs, beaten
1 dessert apple, peeled, cored
   and diced
1 large carrot, finely grated
30g flaked almonds, toasted
55g self-raising white flour
2 teaspoons ground mixed spice
100g fresh white breadcrumbs

BRANDY SAUCE

6 tbsp cornflour
900ml semi-skimmed milk
3 tablespoons caster sugar,
   or to taste
3 tablespoons brandy

upside-down pear pudding

This comforting pudding is perfect for a Sunday lunch on a chilly day. Pears and blackberries are topped with an orange-scented sponge mixture and baked, then the pudding is turned out upside-down, so the luscious fruit is on top.

2 tablespoons golden syrup
3 ripe pears
170g blackberries
115g margarine
115g light muscovado sugar
2 eggs, beaten
170g self-raising white flour
finely grated zest of 1 small orange
2 tablespoons semi-skimmed milk,
        or as needed
Greek-style yoghurt to serve (optional)

1 Preheat the oven to 180°C (gas mark 4). Grease a 20cm round, deep cake tin and line the bottom with a disc of greaseproof paper.

2 Heat the golden syrup gently in a small saucepan until it is runny, then pour it over the bottom of the tin. Peel, halve and core the pears. Arrange them, cut side down and in one layer, over the bottom of the tin. Scatter over the blackberries.

3 Place the margarine and sugar in a large bowl and beat until pale and fluffy. Gradually add the eggs and beat well. Fold in the flour, orange zest and 2 tablespoons milk with a large metal spoon to give a soft, dropping consistency. Add a little more milk if needed. Spoon the sponge mixture evenly over the fruit in the tin and level the surface.

4 Bake for 50–60 minutes or until risen and golden brown. If the pudding seems to be browning too much towards the end of the cooking time, cover loosely with aluminium foil.

5 Leave to cool in the tin for about 10 minutes, then place an inverted serving plate on top. Turn the tin and plate over, holding them firmly together, so the pudding falls out onto the plate. Serve warm, cut into wedges, with yoghurt, if liked.

Variations Use 6 canned pear halves in natural juice, well drained, instead of fresh pears, and substitute maple syrup for the golden syrup.
 Make an upside-down pineapple and blueberry pudding: replace the pears and blackberries with 4 canned pineapple rings in natural juice, well drained, and 170g fresh blueberries. • Or make an upside-down ginger and plum pudding: instead of pears and blackberries, arrange 6 halved plums on the bottom of the tin. For the sponge mixture, use 85g each of white and wholemeal self-raising flours. Omit the orange zest and add 1½ teaspoons ground ginger and 3–4 pieces preserved ginger in syrup, drained and finely chopped.

Fb

preparation time **25 mins**
cooking time **1 hour**
serves **6**

PER SERVING

252 kcal

6g protein

3g total fat
1g saturated fat

80mg cholesterol

55g total carbohydrate
32g sugars

3g fibre

150mg sodium

COOK'S TIP

Golden syrup is derived from molasses, the residual syrup from sugar milling. It is made up of the sugars sucrose, glucose and fructose, but because it contains more water and less sucrose than table sugar, it is not as sweet.

marbled winter fruit fool

Dried prunes and peaches have an intense, concentrated flavour and sweetness and, with the addition of a dash of peach schnapps or brandy, they make a really special fruit fool that is healthily modest in its fat content.

150g ready-to-eat dried peaches

150g ready-to-eat stoned prunes

2 tablespoons peach schnapps or brandy

200ml freshly squeezed orange juice, or as needed

150ml whipping cream

150g plain low-fat yoghurt

1 Cut 30g of the peaches and 30g of the prunes into small dice. Put into a bowl, pour over the schnapps or brandy and set aside to marinate.

2 Place the remaining peaches and prunes in two separate saucepans and pour 100ml orange juice into each. Bring to the boil, then reduce the heat and simmer gently for 10 minutes or until the fruit is tender. Purée the peaches and prunes separately in a blender or food processor until smooth, adding a little extra orange juice if needed.

3 Whip the cream in a mixing bowl until thick. Add the yoghurt and whip to mix with the cream.

4 Layer alternate spoonfuls of the peach and prune purées and cream mixture in four stemmed glasses, swirling slightly for a marbled effect. Spoon the marinated fruits on top.

30

preparation and cooking time **30 mins**

serves **4**

PER SERVING

320 kcal

5g protein

15.5g total fat
9g saturated fat

40mg cholesterol

40g total carbohydrate
40g sugars

4.5g fibre

45mg sodium

HEALTH HINT

Dried fruits are a concentrated source of many nutrients, including iron. The vitamin C in the orange juice aids the absorption of iron from the dried fruits.

lemon mousse with strawberries

Sampling this mousse is like spooning up sunshine; jewel-like layers of berries are an unexpected delight. We've lightened up the mousse by substituting gelatine and fat-free yogurt for the usual quantities of eggs and cream.

preparation and cooking time **20 mins**
plus 3 hours chilling
serves **8**

PER SERVING

131 kcal

3g protein

3g total fat
1g saturated fat

30mg cholesterol

25g total carbohydrate
24g sugars

0.5g fibre

39mg sodium

HEALTH HINT

Although the vitamin C in the lemon juice is diminished somewhat by being heated, one serving still provides a useful amount of this antioxidant vitamin.

COOK'S TIP

When you're squeezing lemons for lemonade or other recipes, take a moment to grate the zest before you cut the lemons. Wrap the zest tightly in cling film and freeze it until needed.

1 Hull the strawberries and slice thickly.

2 Sprinkle the gelatine over 4 tablespoons cold water in a small bowl. Allow to stand for 5 minutes to soften.

3 Place another 4 tablespoons water, the sugar, lemon zest, lemon juice, oil and egg in a medium saucepan and whisk together until well combined. Cook over a low heat, whisking constantly, for about 5 minutes or until the mixture is hot. Whisk in the softened gelatine and cook, whisking constantly, until the gelatine has dissolved.

4 Remove from the heat, transfer to a medium bowl and cool to room temperature, whisking occasionally. Whisk in the yoghurt. Alternately layer the strawberries and lemon mousse in eight dessert bowls. Chill for about 3 hours or until set.

340g strawberries
1 tablespoon powdered gelatine
150g caster sugar
2 teaspoons grated lemon zest
125ml freshly squeezed lemon juice
1 tablespoon extra light olive oil
1 large egg
325g fat-free plain yoghurt

cherry and pistachio rice pots with cherry compote

This is a delightful rice pudding, made wonderfully creamy with fromage frais and full of texture and flavour from the addition of dried cherries and pistachio nuts. It's served in individual pots with a fresh cherry compote.

RICE PUDDING

45g pudding rice
2 tablespoons light muscovado sugar
450ml semi-skimmed milk
25g dried cherries, halved
30g pistachio nuts, chopped
few drops of pure vanilla extract
250g fromage frais

CHERRY COMPOTE

2 tablespoons redcurrant jelly
25g golden caster sugar
350g fresh cherries, stoned
75ml fruity red wine, such as
    Beaujolais

1 Put the rice in a medium-sized saucepan with the sugar and milk. Stir, then bring to the boil. Reduce the heat and simmer for 20–25 minutes, stirring occasionally, until the rice is cooked and the mixture creamy.

2 Remove the pan from the heat and stir in the cherries, pistachio nuts and vanilla extract. Cool for 15 minutes, then stir in the fromage frais. Spoon into four 170ml little pots or ramekins and set aside.

3 To make the compote, put the redcurrant jelly and caster sugar in a frying pan or wide saucepan and heat over a low heat, stirring, until the sugar has dissolved. Add the cherries and cook gently for 3–4 minutes or until the cherry juices start to run. Pour in the wine, bring just to a simmer and simmer for 1–2 minutes or until the cherries are tender. Serve the compote warm or cold with the rice pots.

GI

preparation and cooking time **40 mins**
plus 15 mins cooling

serves **4**

PER SERVING

359 kcal
11g protein
10.5g total fat 4g saturated fat
12mg cholesterol
56g total carbohydrate 46g sugars
1g fibre
78mg sodium

HEALTH HINT

Though white rice has less dietary fibre than brown rice, some of the starchy carbohydrate in the white rice is resistant to digestion and seems to aid digestion in a similar way to fibre.

Kc GI

preparation time **20 mins**
plus 15 mins cooling

serves **4**

PER SERVING

317 kcal

7g protein

20g total fat
11g saturated fat

43mg cholesterol

26g total carbohydrate
14g sugars

4g fibre

33mg sodium

HEALTH HINT

Since ancient times honey
has been used as a food,
a sweetener and a
preservative. Honey is
sweeter than sugar due to
its fructose content, and it
is lower in calories on a
weight for weight basis
because it has a higher
water content.

raspberry cranachan

 This traditional Scottish dessert is quick and easy to put together, and the nutritious combination of cream, fromage frais, oatmeal and fresh fruit makes a superb sweet course for a special occasion meal.

1 Preheat the grill to high. Line the rack in the grill pan with foil and spread the oatmeal over the foil. Toast under the grill for about 3 minutes, stirring once or twice, until the oatmeal is golden. Set aside to cool for about 15 minutes.

2 Put the cream and fromage frais in a bowl and whip together until thick. Stir in the honey and whisky. Fold in 4 tablespoons of the toasted oatmeal.

3 Reserve a few raspberries for the decoration. Layer the remaining raspberries with the cream mixture in four glasses or dessert dishes, starting with raspberries and ending with a layer of the cream mixture.

4 Decorate each dessert with a sprinkling of the remaining toasted oatmeal and the reserved raspberries. Serve immediately (or refrigerate for up to 1 hour before serving).

5 tablespoons medium oatmeal
150ml whipping cream
150g fromage frais
2 tablespoons clear honey
2 tablespoons whisky
400g raspberries

double raspberry sorbet

Go ahead raspberry lovers, take a bite. This velvety smooth sorbet and rich sauce give you a double dose of your favourite fruit – and you can make it from frozen berries any time of year.

200g sugar
1.5kg frozen raspberries, slightly thawed
1 tablespoon freshly squeezed lemon juice

1 Place the sugar and 250ml water in a medium saucepan. Bring to the boil, stirring until the sugar dissolves. Simmer gently for 5 minutes, then remove from the heat.

2 Place the raspberries and lemon juice in a food processor or blender and process until smooth. Press through a nylon sieve into a large bowl; discard the seeds in the sieve. Stir in the sugar syrup. Cover and chill for about 1 hour.

3 Reserve 125ml to use as the sauce. Pour the remainder into an ice-cream machine. Freeze according to the manufacturer's instructions, then transfer to a large freezerproof container, cover and freeze until ready to serve. If you do not have an ice-cream machine, pour the raspberry mixture into a chilled shallow tin and freeze for about 1½ hours or until slushy, stirring every 30 minutes. Place in a food processor and process until smooth. Transfer to a large freezerproof container, cover and freeze for about 4 hours or until firm.

4 Remove from the freezer 10 minutes before serving. Divide the sorbet among eight dessert dishes and drizzle 1 tablespoon of the sauce over each.

preparation time **35 mins** plus freezing
serves **8**

PER SERVING

145 kcal

2g protein

0.5g total fat
0g saturated fat

0mg cholesterol

35g total carbohydrate
33g sugars

0.5g fibre

6mg sodium

HEALTH HINT

75g of fresh raspberries contains no fat, 20 kcal, about 10 per cent of the fibre you need every day, and about half of the vitamin C. Raspberries are also high in pectin, the soluble fibre that helps control blood cholesterol levels, and contain ellagic acid, a phytochemical that is thought to neutralise carcinogens.

Pimm's melon cup

This fruit salad is inspired by the classic summer drink. A mixture of melon, berries, pear and cucumber is marinated in Pimm's and then served in the melon shells. A decoration of pretty borage flowers is a traditional finish.

1 Cut the melons in half horizontally and scoop out the seeds. Using a melon baller or a small spoon, scoop out the flesh and place it in a large bowl. Reserve the melon shells.

2 Add the strawberries, pear and cucumber to the melon in the bowl. Reserve some slices of star fruit for decoration and chop the rest. Add to the bowl. Sprinkle the Pimm's over the fruit. Add the mint and stir gently. Cover with cling film and place in the refrigerator to marinate for 20 minutes.

3 Smooth the inside of the melon shells with a spoon. Pile the fruit mixture into the shells and decorate with the reserved slices of carambola and the borage flowers, if using.

Variation Turn this into a fruit and vegetable salad using just 1 melon, the strawberries and cucumber plus an apple instead of the pear and 100g seedless green grapes. Omit the Pimm's. Make a bed of salad leaves, including some watercress and chopped spring onion, on each plate and pile the fruit on top. Add a scoop of plain cottage cheese and sprinkle with chopped fresh mint and toasted pine nuts.

1 small Ogen melon

1 small cantaloupe or Charentais melon

200g strawberries, hulled and sliced

1 pear, cut into 2.5cm chunks

¼ cucumber, cut into 1cm dice

1 star fruit, cut into 5mm slices

6 tbsp Pimm's

2 tablespoons shredded fresh mint or lemon balm leaves

borage flowers to decorate (optional)

preparation time **25 mins** plus 20 mins marinating

serves **4**

PER SERVING

101 kcal

1.5g protein

0g total fat
0g saturated fat

0mg cholesterol

12g total carbohydrate
12g sugars

2g fibre

54mg sodium

HEALTH HINT

Moderate alcohol consumption is now associated with a lower risk of death from coronary heart disease. Moderate means avoiding binges and taking no more than three to four units a day for men and two to three units a day for women, with at least one alcohol-free day a week.

kiwi-berry cheesecake tart

Unlike many cheesecakes that are high in fat and calories, this tempting baked cheesecake tart, piled high with strawberries and kiwi fruit, uses a low-fat soft cheese for the filling and a crushed amaretti biscuit base made without butter.

1 Preheat the oven to 160°C (gas mark 3). Grease a 20cm springform tin and line the bottom with greaseproof paper. Sprinkle the amaretti biscuit crumbs evenly over the paper lining on the bottom and set aside.

2 Put the curd cheese, egg yolks, caster sugar, orange zest and cream in a blender or food processor. Blend until smooth and well mixed, then pour the mixture into a bowl. (Alternatively, beat the ingredients together with an electric mixer.) Sift the flour over the surface and fold it in.

3 In a separate clean, grease-free bowl, whisk the egg whites until stiff. Gently fold them into the cheese mixture. Pour into the tin, without disturbing the biscuit crumbs, and gently level the surface with a palette knife.

4 Bake for 1¼ hours or until slightly risen, lightly set and golden brown. Turn off the oven and leave the tart inside for 15 minutes, then remove and set aside to cool completely. If you like, chill before serving.

5 Remove the cheesecake tart from the tin and place it on a serving plate. Pile the strawberries and kiwi over the top and dust with the icing sugar. Cut into slices to serve.

Variations Use the finely grated zest of 1 small pink grapefruit or 1 lime in place of the orange zest. • Instead of amaretti, sprinkle 140g crushed digestive or oaty biscuits over the bottom of the tin. • Top the cheesecake tart with a mixture of sliced peaches or nectarines and blueberries. • For a raspberry cheesecake tart, sprinkle 140g crushed ginger biscuits over the bottom of the cake tin. Make the cheesecake mixture as in the main recipe, but using ricotta cheese in place of curd cheese, light soft brown sugar in place of caster sugar and the finely grated zest of 1 lemon in place of the orange zest. After baking, decorate the top with 350g fresh raspberries and dust with sifted icing sugar.

115g amaretti biscuits, crushed
450g curd cheese
3 eggs, separated
115g caster sugar
finely grated zest of 1 small orange
150ml whipping cream
30g plain white flour
FRUIT TOPPING
300g strawberries, halved or sliced
2 kiwi fruit, peeled and sliced
1 tablespoon icing sugar, sifted

preparation time **30 mins**
cooking time **1¼ hours**
serves **10**

PER SERVING

287 kcal

8g protein

15g total fat
8g saturated fat

87mg cholesterol

31g total carbohydrate
19g sugars

1g fibre

177mg sodium

HEALTH HINTS

Curd cheese contains about half the amount of fat that is found in hard cheeses such as Cheddar.

Kiwi fruits are an excellent source of vitamin C – a single fruit supplies enough to meet the daily requirement for this vitamin.

lemon banana tart

A crisp, sweet shortcrust pastry case is filled with a layer of strawberry conserve and thickly sliced bananas, then topped with a light but luscious lemon and fromage frais mixture that sets as it bakes.

LEMON SHORTCRUST

115g plain white flour

55g margarine

25g icing sugar, sifted

grated zest of 1 lemon

1 egg yolk lightly beaten with
    1 tablespoon cold water

FILLING

4 tablespoons strawberry conserve

3 firm bananas

5 tablespoons lemon curd

250g fromage frais

2 eggs, lightly beaten

strawberries to decorate (optional)

1 Sift the flour into a bowl, rub in the margarine and stir in the sugar and lemon zest. Mix in the egg yolk and gather into a soft dough. Wrap in cling film and chill for 30 minutes.

2 Preheat the oven to 200°C (gas mark 6). Roll out the dough thinly and use to line a 23.5cm fluted, loose-bottomed flan tin. Prick the pastry case, line with greaseproof paper and beans, and bake blind for 10 minutes. Remove the paper and beans and bake for a further 5 minutes. Remove from the oven. Reduce the temperature to 180°C (gas mark 4).

3 Spread the conserve over the bottom of the warm tart case. Slice the bananas and arrange evenly over the conserve. Blend the lemon curd with a little of the fromage frais, then stir in the remainder, together with the beaten eggs. Pour over the bananas and spread out evenly.

4 Bake the tart for 30–35 minutes or until the filling is set and lightly browned. Leave in the tin on a wire rack to cool to room temperature before serving.

preparation time **45 mins** plus 30 mins chilling

cooking time **30–35 mins**

serves **8**

PER SERVING
260 kcal
6g protein
11g total fat
4g saturated fat
88mg cholesterol
36g total carbohydrate
21g sugars
1g fibre
90mg sodium

HEALTH HINTS

Bananas have a high potassium content. This mineral is essential for the proper functioning of nerves and muscles.

Fromage frais is creamy, yet is relatively low in fat. It provides useful amounts of protein, calcium and vitamin B_{12}.

citrus meringue pie

A modern twist on lemon meringue pie, this recipe uses lime and orange as well as lemon in the filling. The case is made with crushed biscuit crumbs held together with egg white, rather than melted butter, to reduce the fat content.

preparation and cooking
time **55 mins**
plus cooling

serves **8**

PER SERVING

207 kcal

4g protein

5g total fat
2g saturated fat

56mg cholesterol

40g total carbohydrate
26g sugars

0.5g fibre

114mg sodium

HEALTH HINT

Eggs are one of the few sources of vitamin D. It is found in the yolk and is not destroyed by cooking. The vitamin A and vitamin B content of eggs is also concentrated in the yolk rather than the white.

1 Preheat the oven to 180°C (gas mark 4). To make the case, place the biscuits in a plastic bag and crush with a rolling pin. Tip into a mixing bowl, add the egg white and stir to moisten.

2 Spoon the biscuit mixture into a lightly greased, non-stick 21.5cm sandwich tin. Using the back of a spoon, press the crumbs in a thin layer over the bottom and sides of the tin. Bake for 7–10 minutes or until firm. Leave to cool.

3 To make the filling, combine the zest and juice of the lemon and lime with the orange juice in a heatproof bowl. Stir in the cornflour to make a smooth paste. Bring 300ml water to the boil in a saucepan. Pour the water over the juice mixture, stirring constantly, then return to the pan. Bring to the boil over moderate heat, stirring. Reduce the heat and simmer, stirring frequently, for 1 minute or until thick and smooth.

4 Remove the pan from the heat and cool for a minute. Meanwhile, place the egg yolks and sugar in a small bowl and combine. Add a little of the hot citrus mixture and stir, then pour this into the remaining citrus mixture and stir until thoroughly combined. Pour into the prepared biscuit case.

5 To make the meringue topping, place the egg whites in a clean, grease-free bowl and whisk until stiff. Gradually add the sugar, whisking until stiff, glossy peaks form.

6 Spoon the meringue over the top of the citrus filling to cover evenly, swirling the meringue attractively. Bake for about 15 minutes or until the meringue is golden brown. Leave the pie to cool before serving.

BISCUIT CASE

150g plain biscuits such as Petit Beurre or Abernethy

1 egg white, whisked lightly to loosen

CITRUS FILLING

grated zest and juice of 1 large lemon

grated zest and juice of 1 large lime

juice of 1 large orange

45g cornflour

2 large egg yolks

75g caster sugar

MERINGUE TOPPING

3 large egg whites

85g caster sugar

cherry and almond strudel

Austria's famous melt-in-the-mouth pastry looks very impressive, but is surprisingly easy to make. Ground almonds and breadcrumbs absorb the juice from the cherries, so the layers of filo pastry bake wonderfully light and crisp.

3 sheets filo pastry, 30 x 50cm each

30g margarine, melted

15g flaked almonds

1 tablespoon icing sugar, sifted, to decorate

Greek-style yoghurt to serve (optional)

FRUIT FILLING

30g fresh white breadcrumbs

55g ground almonds

45g soft light brown sugar

finely grated zest of 1 orange

675g cherries, pitted and halved if large

1 Preheat the oven to 200°C (gas mark 6). Lightly grease a non-stick baking tray. To make the fruit filling, place the breadcrumbs, almonds, brown sugar and orange zest in a large bowl and stir together. Add the cherries and mix well.

2 Lay a sheet of filo pastry out on a clean tea-towel and brush lightly with melted margarine. Place a second sheet of filo on top and brush with margarine. Repeat with the third sheet.

3 Spoon the fruit filling evenly over the pastry, leaving a 2.5cm margin clear around the edges. Fold in the edges along the short sides.

4 With the help of the tea-towel, roll up from a long side to make a thick sausage shape. Transfer to the prepared tray, placing the seam underneath and curving the strudel slightly to fit, if necessary. Brush with the remaining margarine, then scatter over the flaked almonds.

5 Bake for 20 minutes or until the pastry and almonds are golden brown. Dust with the icing sugar and serve hot or warm, with a little Greek-style yoghurt, if liked.

preparation time **30 mins**

cooking time **20 mins**

serves **6**

PER SERVING
225 kcal
4.5g protein
11g total fat
1.5g saturated fat
0mg cholesterol
29g total carbohydrate
21g sugars
2g fibre
75mg sodium

HEART SUPERFOOD

Almonds are a good source of vitamin E and calcium.

fruit and pistachio baklava

Here is an updated version of the traditional Greek pastries, made with a filling of dates, dried mango and pistachio nuts. Although this baklava uses less fat and honey than usual, it is most definitely a special sweet snack.

Kc

preparation time **40 mins**
cooking time **20–25 mins**
makes **20 squares**

PER SQUARE

133 kcal

2.5g protein

6g total fat
1g saturated fat

5mg cholesterol

16g total carbohydrate
9g sugars

0.5g fibre

23mg sodium

HEALTH HINT

The nutrients in fresh fruit are concentrated when they are dried, so they are much higher in minerals, dietary fibre and some vitamins such as beta carotene. Most of their vitamin C, however, is lost after drying, but they nevertheless remain nutritious cooking ingredients.

1 Gently heat the margarine and oil in a small saucepan until melted and blended. Remove the pan from the heat and set aside. Mix together the mango, dates, pistachios, cinnamon and half of the honey in a bowl. Set aside.

2 Preheat the oven to 220°C (gas mark 7). Lightly grease a shallow 18 x 28cm cake tin with some of the oil mixture.

3 Place one sheet of filo pastry in the bottom of the tin, allowing the pastry to come up the sides if necessary, and brush sparingly with the oil mixture. Layer four more sheets of filo in the tin, brushing each one lightly with the oil mixture. Spread with one-third of the fruit and honey mixture.

4 Repeat the layering of filo sheets and fruit mixture twice. Top with the remaining five sheets of filo, brushing each one with the oil mixture. Trim the edges of the pastry to fit the tin.

5 Mark the surface of the pastry into 20 squares. Bake for 5 minutes. Reduce the oven to 180°C (gas mark 4) and bake for a further 10–15 minutes or until crisp and golden brown.

6 Meanwhile, gently warm the remaining honey with the orange juice in a small saucepan until blended, stirring.

7 Remove the cake tin from the oven and pour the honey and orange mixture evenly over the cooked baklava. Leave it to cool in the tin. When cold, cut into the marked squares for serving.

55g margarine
2 tablespoons sunflower oil
85g dried mango, finely chopped
85g dried pitted dates, finely chopped
115g pistachio nuts, finely chopped
1½ teaspoons ground cinnamon
8 tablespoons clear honey
20 sheets filo pastry, about 18 x 30cm each
4 tablespoons freshly squeezed orange juice

hazelnut meringue cake

Simply add candles to turn this light but gooey meringue into a birthday cake. As it has a pastry cream and fresh raspberry filling, it's much lower in fat and calories than conventional celebration cakes.

65g hazelnuts
4 egg whites
225g caster sugar
225g fresh raspberries
icing sugar, sifted, to decorate

VANILLA PASTRY CREAM
300ml semi-skimmed milk, plus
    2 tablespoons extra
    if needed
1 vanilla pod, slit open lengthways
3 egg yolks
30g caster sugar
15g plain white flour
15g cornflour

1 Preheat the grill, then toast the hazelnuts until golden. Leave to cool. Roughly chop a few and set aside for decoration. Finely chop or grind the remaining hazelnuts in a food processor or blender.

2 Preheat the oven to 140ºC (gas mark 1). Line two baking trays with baking parchment and draw a 20cm circle on each piece of paper.

3 Place the egg whites in a large bowl and whisk until they form stiff peaks. Gradually add the caster sugar a tablespoon at a time, then continue to whisk for 1–2 minutes or until the meringue is very thick and glossy. Fold in the hazelnuts.

4 Divide the meringue mixture between the baking trays and spread evenly within the drawn circles. Bake for 40 minutes, then turn the baking trays around in the oven so that the meringues colour evenly. Bake for another 35 minutes or until the meringues are set and can be removed easily from the paper. Loosen them from the paper, then leave to cool completely on the baking trays.

5 While the meringues are cooling, make the pastry cream. Pour 300ml milk into a medium saucepan and bring to the boil. Add the vanilla pod, then remove from the heat and leave to infuse for 30 minutes.

6 Place the egg yolks and sugar in a medium bowl and beat with a whisk for 2–3 minutes or until pale. Sift in the flour and cornflour and whisk to combine. Remove the vanilla pod from the milk and scrape the seeds into the milk with a sharp knife; discard the pod. Bring the milk just to the boil, then gradually stir it into the egg yolk mixture.

7 Pour the mixture back into the saucepan and bring to the boil, stirring constantly with a wooden spoon or whisk. When thick, simmer gently for 1 minute, still stirring constantly. Remove from the heat. Cover the surface of the pastry cream with wet greaseproof paper and leave to cool. (Both the meringues and pastry cream can be made a day in advance; store the meringues in an airtight container and the pastry cream in a covered bowl in the refrigerator.)

8 Assemble the cake no more than 1 hour before serving. Place one of the meringues on a serving plate, flat side facing

preparation time **40 mins** plus 30 mins infusing
cooking time **1¼ hours**
serves **6**

PER SERVING

330 kcal

8g protein

10g total fat
2g saturated fat

119mg cholesterol

53g total carbohydrate
49g sugars

2g fibre

70mg sodium

HEART SUPERFOOD

Hazelnuts have excellent levels of copper and magnesium and also provide vitamins B_1 and B_6, folate, potassium, phosphorus and zinc. Hazelnuts offer decent amounts of fibre (3g per 50g nuts) too. They do contain fat, but it is mainly unsaturated fat.

upwards, and spread over the pastry cream. If the cream is too thick to spread, beat in the extra milk. Sprinkle with two-thirds of the raspberries, then top with the second meringue. Decorate with the remaining raspberries, the reserved toasted hazelnuts and a light dusting of icing sugar. Cut into thick slices with a sharp knife to serve.

Variations To make mini meringues, use ground hazelnuts or pistachio nuts in the meringue mixture and shape it into ovals with two spoons, placing them on baking trays lined with baking parchment. Bake for 50–60 minutes. Dip the base of each meringue in melted chocolate and sandwich pairs together with a mixture of 150g Greek-style yoghurt or fromage frais and 150ml whipping cream, whipped until thick. • For a chocolate and chestnut meringue cake, melt 90g good-quality dark chocolate in a bowl set over a saucepan of hot water. Spread it over the flat side of one meringue and leave to set. Mix 1 can (about 240g) sweetened chestnut purée with 200g fromage frais and spread over the chocolate. Top with the other meringue, and decorate with chocolate curls.

iced fairy cakes

Fairy cakes are easy to prepare and always popular with children. Using ricotta cheese in the topping makes a lighter, fresher alternative to the more usual glacé icing. The cakes are best iced shortly before serving.

125g margarine
125g caster sugar
2 eggs
100g self-raising white flour
30g self-raising wholemeal flour
½ teaspoon baking powder
finely grated zest of ½ orange
30g ready-to-eat dried apricots, thinly sliced, to decorate

ORANGE RICOTTA ICING
250g ricotta cheese
55g icing sugar
finely grated zest of ½ orange

1 Preheat the oven to 180°C (gas mark 4). Line a 12-cup and a 6-cup patty tin or shallow bun tin with paper cake cases.

2 Place the margarine, sugar and eggs in a large bowl. Sift the white and wholemeal flours and the baking powder into the bowl, tipping in any bran left in the sieve. Add the orange zest and beat for 2 minutes or until smooth and creamy.

3 Spoon the mixture into the paper cake cases. Bake for about 20 minutes or until just firm to the touch. Transfer to a wire rack to cool. (The cakes can be stored in an airtight container for up to 2 days before being iced.)

4 To make the icing, place the ricotta in a bowl and sift over the icing sugar. Add the orange zest and beat with a wooden spoon until well mixed.

5 Spread a little icing over the top of each cake and decorate with a couple of dried apricot slices. Serve the cakes as soon as possible after icing.

preparation time **20 mins**
cooking time **20 mins**
makes **18 cakes**

PER CAKE

150 kcal

3g protein

8g total fat
2.5g saturated fat

33mg cholesterol

17g total carbohydrate
11g sugars

0.5g fibre

108mg sodium

HEALTH HINT

Dried apricots are one of the richest fruit sources of iron, and they provide soluble fibre.

COOK'S TIP

Using a mixture of wholemeal flour and plain flour increases the fibre content of these cakes without making them too heavy.

raspberry and passionfruit sponge roll

This light, almost fat-free sponge, rolled up around a raspberry and passion-fruit filling, makes a very pretty dessert. It's ideal for late summer, when raspberries are particularly sweet. Serve with homemade custard, if liked.

30 Kc

preparation time **20 mins**
cooking time **10–12 mins**
serves **8**

PER SERVING

170 kcal

5.5g protein

3g total fat
1g saturated fat

102mg cholesterol

32.5g total carbohydrate
21.5g sugars

2g fibre

41mg sodium

HEALTH HINT

With 14 per cent fibre, passionfruit offers one of the highest fibre counts of any fruit. In addition, it supplies moderate amounts of vitamins B_2 and C and the minerals potassium, magnesium and zinc. One passionfruit gives you all this for only 35 kcal!

1 To make the fruit filling, place half the raspberries and the icing sugar in a bowl and crush lightly with a fork. Stir in the passionfruit pulp. Set aside.

2 Preheat the oven to 200°C (gas mark 6). Grease a 23 x 33cm Swiss roll tin and line the bottom with baking parchment.

3 Put the eggs and sugar in a large bowl and beat with an electric mixer until the mixture is very thick and pale, and leaves a trail on the surface when the beaters are lifted out. Sift half the flour over the mixture and gently fold in with a large metal spoon. Sift over the remaining flour and fold in, together with the tepid water.

4 Pour the mixture into the prepared tin and shake gently to spread it evenly into the corners. Bake for 10–12 minutes or until the sponge is well risen and pale golden, and springs back when pressed lightly.

5 Turn out onto a sheet of baking parchment that is slightly larger than the sponge. Peel off the lining paper. Remove the crusty edges of the sponge with a sharp knife and make a score mark 2.5cm in from one of the shorter edges. (This will make the sponge easier to roll up.)

6 Spread the fruit filling over the hot sponge, leaving a 1cm border all round. Scatter over the remaining raspberries. Carefully roll up the sponge, starting from the edge with the score mark. Place the roll, seam-side down, on a plate.

7 Serve warm or cold, cut into slices. Decorate each serving with a few extra raspberries and a sprig of mint.

FRUIT FILLING
350g raspberries
25g icing sugar, sifted
pulp from 4 passionfruits

WHISKED SPONGE
3 large eggs
115g caster sugar
115g plain white flour
1 tablespoon tepid water

TO DECORATE
24 raspberries, about 100g in total
sprigs of fresh mint

gingerbread

This delicious, lightly spiced gingerbread is hard to resist. Enjoy a slice with a cup of tea or try it for dessert, with custard or half-fat crème fraîche plus, perhaps, a spoonful of fresh apple compote.

115g light muscovado sugar
85g margarine
170g molasses
85g plain white flour
85g plain wholemeal flour
55g rye flour
1 teaspoon bicarbonate of soda
1 tablespoon ground ginger
1 teaspoon ground mixed spice
2 eggs, lightly beaten
150ml semi-skimmed milk

1 Preheat the oven to 160°C (gas mark 3). Lightly grease a 900g loaf tin and line the bottom with baking parchment.

2 Place the sugar, margarine and molasses in a medium saucepan and heat gently until melted and well blended, stirring occasionally. Remove from the heat and cool slightly.

3 Sift the white, wholemeal and rye flours, bicarbonate of soda, ginger and mixed spice into a large bowl, tipping in any bran left in the sieve. Make a well in the centre and pour in the melted mixture, together with the eggs and milk. Beat together until smooth (the mixture will be very runny). Pour into the tin.

4 Bake for 1¼–1½ hours or until risen, firm to the touch and nicely browned. Leave the cake to cool in the tin for a few minutes, then turn it out onto a wire rack to cool completely. Gingerbread can be kept, wrapped in foil or in an airtight container, for up to 1 week.

preparation time **20 mins**
cooking time **1½ hours**
serves **10**

PER SERVING

253 kcal

5g protein

9g total fat
2g saturated fat

48mg cholesterol

41g total carbohydrate
23g sugars

1.5g fibre

250mg sodium

HEALTH HINT

Compared with wheat flour, rye flour has much less gluten, which explains why rye breads such as pumpernickel tend to have a heavier texture. Rye flour contains high quantities of pentosans (long-chain sugars), which have a high water-binding capacity. Baked goods made with rye flour retain moisture, which means they swell in the stomach, giving a sensation of fullness.

carrot cake with light soft cheese icing

Go ahead, take another bite. This cake is delicious, and really good for you because it provides beta carotene, which helps protect your heart. The icing is rich and sweet, yet lower in fat than the traditional topping.

1 Preheat the oven to 180°C (gas mark 4). Coat a 25cm fluted ring tin with cooking spray. Dust the tin with a little flour, tapping out any excess.

2 Place the flour, mixed spice and bicarbonate of soda in a large bowl and stir together. Make a well in the centre. Place the buttermilk, oil, sugar, eggs and vanilla extract in a bowl and whisk until blended and frothy. Pour into the well in the dry ingredients and stir just until combined. Fold in the carrots.

3 Pour the mixture into the prepared tin and level the surface. Lightly tap the tin to break up any large air bubbles. Bake for about 50 minutes or until a skewer inserted in the centre comes out clean. Leave the cake to cool in the tin for 10 minutes, then turn it out onto a wire rack to cool completely.

4 To make the icing, place the vanilla extract, soft cheese and buttermilk in a medium bowl and beat until softened. Gradually beat in the icing sugar and continue beating just until the icing is smooth. Place the cake on a serving plate and cover with the icing, letting some drip down the sides. Keep the cake in the refrigerator until ready to serve.

450g self-raising white flour
1½ tablespoons ground mixed spice
1½ teaspoons bicarbonate of soda
500ml buttermilk
125ml vegetable oil
300g caster sugar
3 large eggs
2 teaspoons pure vanilla extract
8 carrots, finely grated

LIGHT SOFT CHEESE ICING
2 teaspoons pure vanilla extract
250g low-fat soft cheese,
    at room temperature
1 tablespoon buttermilk
250g icing sugar, sifted

---

preparation time **20 mins**
cooking time **50 mins**
serves **16**

PER SERVING

363 kcal

7g protein

11g total fat
3g saturated fat

70mg cholesterol

63g total carbohydrate
40g sugars

2g fibre

260mg sodium

HEALTH HINT

Cooking carrots, as in this recipe, breaks down the cellular walls that hold the heart-healthy beta carotene, thus increasing the availability of this vital nutrient to the body.

COOK'S TIP

This heart-smart cake recipe uses about one-third the oil of the traditional recipe, fewer eggs and buttermilk for extra moistness.

Spanish orange and almond cake

Made with whole oranges – simmered until very tender and then finely chopped – and ground almonds, this classic Spanish cake has a moist, light texture and a wonderful fresh flavour.

1 Place the chopped oranges in a small saucepan. Add 1 tablespoon water, then cover the pan and simmer gently for 30 minutes or until the oranges are soft and all the excess liquid has evaporated. Leave to cool.

2 Preheat the oven to 180°C (gas mark 4). Line the bottom and sides of a 23cm springform cake tin with baking parchment. Finely chop the oranges in a food processor or blender, or with a sharp knife.

3 Place the egg whites in a large bowl and whisk until they form stiff peaks. Gradually add half the caster sugar, then whisk for a further 1 minute.

4 Place the egg yolks and the remaining caster sugar in another bowl and whisk for 2–3 minutes or until pale and quite thick. Add the oranges and beat to combine well. Carefully fold in the ground almonds with a large metal spoon.

5 Stir in three spoonfuls of the egg whites to loosen the mixture, then gently fold in the remaining whites. Transfer the mixture to the tin and level the surface. Sprinkle with the flaked almonds.

6 Bake for 50–55 minutes or until the cake is golden and a skewer inserted in the centre comes out clean. Check the cake after 20 minutes and again at 30 minutes, and cover lightly with aluminium foil if it is browning too quickly.

7 Leave the cake to cool in the tin, then turn it out, peel away the lining paper and transfer to a serving plate. Dust with icing sugar before serving. The cake can be kept in an airtight container for up to 2 days.

Variations Instead of ground almonds alone, use a mixture of 100g each ground almonds and semolina or instant polenta. Because this cake will be a little drier, drizzle over 2–3 tablespoons Grand Marnier, Amaretto liqueur or freshly squeezed orange juice rather than dusting with icing sugar. This cake is delicious served with a mixture of 150ml whipping cream, whipped, and 150g fromage frais. • For a St Clement's cake, substitute a lemon for one of the oranges, and decorate the top with thin strips of crystallised citrus peel instead of flaked almonds.

2 oranges, about 280g, scrubbed and roughly chopped (with skin), pips discarded
5 eggs, separated
200g caster sugar
225g ground almonds
2 tablespoons flaked almonds
icing sugar, sifted, to decorate

---

preparation time **1 hour**
cooking time **55 mins**
serves **10**

PER SERVING

290 kcal

9g protein

17g total fat
2g saturated fat

116mg cholesterol

25g total carbohydrate
25g sugars

2g fibre

49mg sodium

HEALTH HINT

Using whole oranges boosts the fibre and vitamin C content of this cake. Studies have shown a connection between a regular intake of vitamin C and the maintenance of intellectual function in elderly people. Also, this cake is suitable for those on gluten-free or wheat-free diets as it is made without flour.

blueberry cheesecake

 Compared with most cheesecakes, this version isn't particularly high in fat, as it uses cottage and curd cheeses instead of the traditional full-fat soft cheese, and is lightened by folding in whisked egg whites before baking.

115g digestive biscuits
2 tablespoons jumbo oats
55g margarine, melted
200g cottage cheese
200g curd cheese
4 tablespoons fromage frais
1 egg
2 eggs, separated
1 tablespoon cornflour
finely grated zest of 1 large lemon
115g icing sugar, sifted
140g blueberries

TO DECORATE
55g blueberries
fresh mint leaves
1 tablespoon icing sugar, sifted

1 Preheat the oven to 180°C (gas mark 4). Line the bottom of a 21cm springform cake tin with baking parchment.

2 Place the biscuits in a plastic bag and crush with a rolling pin. Tip into a bowl, add the oats and margarine, and mix.

3 Spread this mixture evenly over the bottom and just up the sides of the prepared tin, pressing down firmly, and set aside.

4 Place the cottage cheese in a food processor or blender and blend until smooth. Add the curd cheese, fromage frais, whole egg, egg yolks, cornflour and lemon zest. Blend briefly until evenly mixed. Tip the mixture into a bowl.

5 Whisk the 2 egg whites in another bowl to form soft peaks. Slowly add the icing sugar and whisk until thick and glossy. Gently fold half the egg whites into the cheese mixture. Fold in the blueberries, then the remaining whites.

6 Pour the mixture into the tin and bake for 30 minutes. Cover loosely with foil and reduce the heat to 160°C (gas mark 3). Bake for a further 1 hour or until the cheesecake feels just set in the centre. Turn off the oven and leave the cheesecake inside for 30 minutes, with the door slightly ajar.

7 Transfer the cheesecake to a wire rack to cool completely, then chill until ready to serve. Remove it from the tin, peel off the lining paper and place it on a serving plate. Decorate with blueberries and a few mint leaves, and dust with icing sugar.

preparation time **25 mins** plus cooling and chilling
cooking time **1½ hours**
serves **8**

PER SERVING

393 kcal

9g protein

25g total fat
12g saturated fat

114mg cholesterol

32g total carbohydrate
21g sugars

1g fibre

336mg sodium

HEALTH HINT

Blueberries are a good source of vitamin C and, like cranberries, they contain compounds that have been shown to inhibit the bacteria that can cause urinary tract infections. Studies have suggested that these compounds may also help to protect against cataracts and glaucoma.

frosted chocolate ring cake

 Chocolate cake is always popular. This updated version is enriched with a sweet prune purée and topped with a creamy Italian-style frosting. Serve it at tea-time or for dessert – it's perfect with some fresh berries on the side.

1 Place the prunes in a bowl and pour over the boiling water. Cover and set aside to soak for 30 minutes.

2 Preheat the oven to 180°C (gas mark 4). Grease a 20cm ring tin that is 900ml in capacity.

3 Beat the margarine until soft and light, then gradually beat in the sugar. Purée the prunes with their soaking liquid in a blender, then add to the margarine mixture with the vanilla extract, beating until well mixed. Gradually beat in the eggs.

4 Sift the white flour, wholemeal flour, baking powder and cocoa powder over the mixture, tipping in any bran left in the sieve. Fold in the dry ingredients until evenly combined. The mixture should have a soft dropping consistency, so add a little water if necessary. Transfer to the tin and spread out evenly.

5 Bake for about 25 minutes or until well risen, slightly cracked on top and firm to the touch. Leave in the tin for 10 minutes, then run a knife around the inside of the tin to loosen the cake and turn it out onto a wire rack to cool. (The cake can be kept in an airtight tin for 3 days, before adding the topping.)

6 To make the ricotta frosting, press the ricotta through a sieve into a bowl. Add the vanilla extract and icing sugar, and beat until smooth.

7 Place the cake on a serving plate and spoon the ricotta frosting evenly around the top. Use a knife to swirl the frosting slightly, taking it a short way down the side of the cake. Place a little cocoa powder in a tea strainer or small sieve and dust it over the frosting. Serve as soon as possible.

140g stoned ready-to-eat prunes
150ml boiling water
55g margarine, at room temperature
140g light muscovado sugar
1 teaspoon pure vanilla extract
2 eggs, beaten
100g self-raising white flour
100g self-raising wholemeal flour
1 teaspoon baking powder
4 tablespoons cocoa powder, plus extra to dust

RICOTTA FROSTING
250g ricotta cheese
$\frac{1}{2}$ teaspoon pure vanilla extract
1 tablespoon icing sugar, or to taste, sifted

Fb

preparation time **25 mins** plus 30 mins soaking

cooking time **25 mins**

serves **10**

PER SERVING

262 kcal

8g protein

10g total fat
4g saturated fat

59mg cholesterol

37g total carbohydrate
21g sugars

3g fibre

223mg sodium

HEART SUPERFOOD

Prunes have a lot to offer nutritionally, being a good source of fibre, as well as providing several vitamins, minerals and phytochemicals. Made into a purée, they can replace some of the fat and sugar in cakes such as this one.

glazed mango sponge

In this unusual upside-down cake, juicy slices of mango are topped with a simple, light sponge mixture flavoured with lime zest and coconut. After baking, the cake finished by caramelising under a hot grill.

1 ripe mango
170g caster sugar
2 eggs, lightly beaten
115g plain low-fat yoghurt
120ml sunflower oil
finely grated zest of 1 lime
170g plain white flour
1½ teaspoons baking powder
30g desiccated coconut
2 tablespoons icing sugar, sifted

1 Preheat the oven to 180°C (gas mark 4). Grease a loose-bottomed 18cm square, deep cake tin, or a 20cm round deep cake tin, and line the bottom with baking parchment.

2 Peel the mango. Cut the flesh away from the stone and cut it into thin slices. Arrange over the bottom of the cake tin.

3 Put the caster sugar, eggs, yoghurt, oil and lime zest into a large bowl and stir until smooth and well mixed. Sift over the flour and baking powder and fold in with the coconut.

4 Spoon the mixture into the tin, over the sliced mango, and level the top. Bake for 50 minutes or until golden brown and firm to the touch, covering with foil after 30 minutes if the cake begins to brown too much.

5 Leave the cake in the tin for about 15 minutes. Meanwhile, preheat the grill to high. Turn out the cake onto the rack of a grill pan, mango-side up, and peel off the lining paper. Thickly dust with the icing sugar and place under the grill for 3–4 minutes or until the sugar has melted and is golden. Leave to cool on the rack.

6 Transfer the cake to a plate for serving. It can be covered with cling film and kept in the fridge for 2–3 days.

preparation time **20 mins**
cooking time **55 mins**
serves **8**

PER SERVING

335 kcal

5g protein

15g total fat
4g saturated fat

58mg cholesterol

48g total carbohydrate
31g sugars

2g fibre

122mg sodium

HEALTH HINT

Mangoes are rich in several carotenoid compounds, including beta carotene and vitamin C.

banana cake

Quick and easy to prepare, this cake makes a healthy snack for hungry children or a handy addition to lunchboxes. And it's a great way to use up bananas that have been sitting in the fruit bowl for too long.

1 Preheat the oven to 180°C (gas mark 4). Grease an 18cm round, deep cake tin and line the bottom with baking parchment. Peel the bananas, then mash with a fork.

2 Sift the flour and baking powder into a large bowl and stir in the sugar. Mix together the oil, milk and eggs in a separate bowl and add to the flour mixture. Stir in the sultanas and mashed bananas, then pour the mixture into the tin.

3 Bake for 50–55 minutes or until the cake is well risen and a skewer inserted in the centre comes out clean. Leave to cool for 15 minutes, then loosen the edge of the cake with a knife and turn it out onto a wire rack to cool completely. The cake can be kept in an airtight container for up to 4 days.

Variations You can substitute other dried fruit for the sultanas, such as dried cranberries, chopped dried figs or apricots, or a mix of chopped exotic dried fruit such as mango and papaya.

2 large, ripe bananas, about 400g in total
250g self-raising white flour
1 teaspoon baking powder
50g light muscovado sugar
6 tablespoons sunflower oil
6 tablespoons semi-skimmed milk
2 eggs
115g sultanas

preparation time **10 mins**
cooking time **55 mins**
serves **8**

PER SERVING

310 kcal

6g protein

10g total fat
2g saturated fat

56mg cholesterol

50g total carbohydrate
26g sugars

2g fibre

200mg sodium

HEALTH HINT

This cake is much lower in sugar than a conventional banana cake. Using sunflower oil instead of butter makes it low in saturated fat, too.

fudgy chocolate brownies

Most people's ideal brownie is moist in the centre, with a deep chocolate flavour. This recipe uses chocolate and cocoa powder to give plenty of chocolate flavour, and muscovado sugar for the desired fudgy texture.

85g good-quality dark chocolate
    (at least 70% cocoa solids)

100g margarine

125g caster sugar

100g light muscovado sugar

1 teaspoon pure vanilla extract

2 whole eggs and 1 egg yolk, at room
    temperature, beaten together

100g plain white flour

3 tablespoons cocoa powder

1 Preheat the oven to 180°C (gas mark 4). Grease a shallow 18cm square cake tin. Line the bottom with baking parchment.

2 Break up the chocolate and place it in a large heatproof bowl with the margarine. Set the bowl over a saucepan of simmering water, making sure the water is not touching the base of the bowl. Leave to melt, then remove from the heat and stir the mixture until smooth. Set aside to cool.

3 Stir in the caster sugar, muscovado sugar and vanilla extract. Gradually beat in the eggs. Sift over the flour and cocoa powder, and stir until evenly blended. Do not overmix.

4 Pour the mixture into the tin. Bake for about 30 minutes or until risen but still slightly soft in the middle – a skewer inserted in the centre should come out with a few moist crumbs sticking to it. The surface will look cracked. It is important not to overcook or the brownies will be dry.

5 Leave in the tin for 5 minutes, then turn out onto a wire rack and leave to cool. When cold, peel off the lining paper and cut into 16 squares. If possible, wrap the brownies in foil and leave until the next day before eating. They can be kept like this for 3–4 days.

preparation time **15 mins**
cooking time **30 mins**
makes **16 brownies**

PER BROWNIE

173 kcal

2.5g protein

8g total fat
3g saturated fat

60mg cholesterol

23g total carbohydrate
17g sugars

0.5g fibre

93mg sodium

HEALTH HINT

These are a healthier version of a traditionally high-fat favourite. The fat content is reduced by substituting cocoa powder for some of the chocolate. Cocoa powder contains five times as much iron as chocolate.

chocolate-nut meringue biscuits

Here's an astounding achievement: chocolate-nut biscuits with less than one gram of fat each! The secret is meringue. These biscuits contain no butter or margarine and no egg yolks, yet they're tender and rich tasting.

1 Preheat the oven to 150°C (gas mark 2). Line two baking trays with baking parchment. Toast the walnuts in a small pan, stirring frequently, for about 7 minutes or until crisp and fragrant. Allow to cool, then chop coarsely.

2 Sift 60g icing sugar with the cocoa powder and cinnamon.

3 Place the egg whites in a large, grease-free bowl and whisk until stiff peaks form. Gently fold in the cocoa mixture with a large metal spoon. Gently fold in the walnuts.

4 Drop generous teaspoonfuls of the mixture onto the baking trays, spacing them 2cm apart. Bake for about 20 minutes or until set. Remove and cool on a wire rack. Dust with the remaining icing sugar just before serving.

45g walnut halves
60g plus 2 tablespoons icing sugar
1 tablespoon cocoa powder
¼ teaspoon ground cinnamon
2 large egg whites

preparation time **20 mins**
cooking time **20 mins**
makes **36 biscuits**

PER BISCUIT

20 kcal

0.5g protein

1g total fat
0g saturated fat

0mg cholesterol

3g total carbohydrate
2.5g sugars

0g fibre

9mg sodium

HEART SUPERFOOD

Despite their relatively high calorie count, walnuts and other nuts eaten in small amounts every day can help keep cholesterol levels low.

COOK'S TIP

Meringues are sensitive to humidity (they will absorb moisture and become sticky), so bake these biscuits on a fairly dry day. Place them in an airtight tin once they've cooled completely.

chocolate chunk and nut cookies

These American-style cookies are simply irresistible while still warm, when the chocolate chunks are soft and melting. Macadamia nuts add a crunchy texture. Like the chocolate, the nuts should be in fairly large pieces.

115g margarine

85g light muscovado sugar

½ teaspoon pure vanilla extract

1 egg, beaten

85g self-raising white flour

55g plain wholemeal flour

20g cocoa powder

¼ teaspoon baking powder

115g good-quality dark chocolate (at least 70% cocoa solids), roughly chopped

55g macadamia nuts, roughly chopped

3 tablespoons semi-skimmed milk

1 Preheat the oven to 190°C (gas mark 5). Line two baking trays with baking parchment. Place the margarine, sugar and vanilla extract in a large bowl and beat until light and fluffy. Add the egg and beat well.

2 Sift the white and wholemeal flours, cocoa powder and baking powder over the creamed mixture, tipping in any bran left in the sieve, and stir to combine thoroughly. Add the chocolate, nuts and milk, and mix together.

3 Place tablespoonfuls of the mixture on the baking trays, arranging them well apart so they have space to spread during baking. Flatten slightly with the back of a fork, then bake for about 15 minutes or until soft and springy.

4 Leave the cookies to cool slightly on the baking trays, then transfer to a wire rack. Serve them while still slightly warm or leave until cold. They can be kept in an airtight container for up to 5 days.

Variations Use walnuts or pecan nuts instead of macadamia nuts.
• For cherry and almond cookies, replace the cocoa powder with plain white flour and substitute 55g dried sour cherries and 55g flaked almonds for the chocolate chunks and macadamia nuts. If you want a pronounced almond flavour, use ¼ teaspoon almond extract instead of vanilla.

preparation time **20 mins**

cooking time **15 mins**

makes **12 cookies**

PER COOKIE

234 kcal

3g protein

15g total fat
4g saturated fat

20mg cholesterol

22g total carbohydrate
13g sugars

1g fibre

130mg sodium

HEALTH HINT

Plain chocolate is a good source of copper and provides useful amounts of iron. The scientific name of the cocoa bean tree is *Theobroma cacao*, which means 'food of the gods'. Casanova was reputed to drink hot chocolate before his nightly conquests – in fact, he was said to prefer chocolate to champagne.

oatmeal and raisin cookies

Both children and adults will love these crisp, melt-in-the-mouth cookies. They are a wholesome treat, packed with oatmeal and raisins for extra flavour and nutrients. It's worth making a double batch and freezing some.

85g margarine
115g light muscovado sugar
1 egg, beaten
115g self-raising white flour
55g medium oatmeal
170g raisins

1 Preheat the oven to 180°C (gas mark 4). Put the margarine and sugar in a bowl and beat until pale and fluffy. Gradually beat in the egg. Sift over the flour, then add the oatmeal and raisins and fold in with a large metal spoon.

2 Drop heaped teaspoonfuls of the mixture onto three greased baking trays, leaving enough space around each spoonful to allow it to spread during baking.

3 Bake for 10–15 minutes or until golden brown. Cool slightly on the baking trays, then transfer to a wire rack and leave to cool completely. These cookies can be kept in an airtight container for 3–4 days or frozen for 2 months.

Variation For a warmer flavour, you can sift in 1–1½ teaspoons ground mixed spice, cinnamon or ginger with the flour.

30

preparation time **15 mins**
cooking time **10–15 mins**
makes **18 cookies**

PER COOKIE

124 kcal

2g protein

5g total fat
1g saturated fat

13mg cholesterol

20g total carbohydrate
13g sugars

0.5g fibre

67mg sodium

HEART SUPERFOOD

Oatmeal is an excellent source of soluble fibre, which can help to reduce high blood cholesterol levels, thereby reducing the risk of heart disease. Soluble fibre also helps to slow the absorption of carbohydrate into the bloodstream, resulting in a gentler rise and fall in blood sugar levels.

preparation time **15 mins** plus 30 mins chilling

cooking time **12 mins**

makes **25 biscuits**

PER BISCUIT

60 kcal

1g protein

2g total fat
0.5g saturated fat

0mg cholesterol

9g total carbohydrate
4g sugars

0.5g fibre

62mg sodium

HEALTH HINT

Muscovado sugar is an unrefined sugar produced from raw sugar cane. Dark muscovado retains more molasses, a by-product of the sugar-making process, than light muscovado and other lighter unrefined sugars, and thus slightly more of the minerals in molasses.

digestive biscuits

These crunchy, golden biscuits are full of nutty, slightly sweet flavours. They are sliced from a long piece of dough, which you can make ahead and store in the refrigerator or freezer. So you can bake the biscuits all at once or in batches.

1 Sift the flour, baking powder and bicarbonate of soda into a mixing bowl, tipping in any bran left in the sieve. Add the oatmeal, bran and sugar, and mix well to combine.

2 Add the margarine and rub it in with your fingertips until the mixture resembles breadcrumbs. Add 3 tablespoons milk and stir in well so the mixture forms a soft dough. If the mixture is a little dry, add the remaining 1 tablespoon milk.

3 Turn the dough out onto a sheet of cling film and shape it into a log about 25cm long. Wrap the film around the dough and roll it gently back and forth to make a smooth shape. Twist the ends of the film together to seal. Chill the dough for about 30 minutes. (It can be kept for up to 4 days in the refrigerator.)

4 Preheat the oven to 190°C (gas mark 5). Unwrap the dough and, using a very sharp knife, cut it across into slices 1cm thick. Use greaseproof paper to line a baking tray and place the slices on it. Bake for about 12 minutes or until lightly browned.

5 Transfer the biscuits to a wire rack and leave to cool completely. They can be kept in an airtight tin for up to 5 days.

150g plain wholemeal flour

1 teaspoon baking powder

½ teaspoon bicarbonate of soda

30g medium oatmeal

20g bran

100g dark muscovado sugar

50g margarine

4 tablespoons semi-skimmed milk, or as needed

index

a

alcohol 22, 24
almonds
    cherry and almond strudel 292
    lamb kebabs with fig rice 200
    Spanish orange and almond cake 301
    turkey biryani with cucumber raita 98
    turkey empanadas 150
    very fruity Christmas pudding 279
anchovies 16
    creamy tomato and crab soup 61
    salade niçoise 115
    spaghetti with puttanesca sauce 89
    summer chicken and pasta salad 146
apples 15
    chicken with apples and Calvados 165
    fennel, apple and herring salad 113
    fresh fruit muesli 35
    heringsalat 136
    mange-tout with apples and ginger 247
    Normandy pork with apples, celery and
        walnuts 212
    turkey burgers with tropical
        fruit salsa 151
apricots 15
    apricot lamb with minted couscous 107
    apricot and rum brioche pudding 277
    broccoli and pearl barley salad 222
    fresh fruit muesli 35
    Middle Eastern lentil salad 223
    very fruity Christmas pudding 279
artichoke hearts: puttanesca pizzinis 67
asparagus
    char-grilled asparagus and peppers 250
    cheesy rice with asparagus 97
    chicken with asparagus and pepper 160
    Parma-ham wrapped lemon sole 128
    risotto primavera 101
    roasted vegetable and pasta bake 238
    seafood lasagne 131
    spinach, ham and asparagus salad with
        rye croutons 209
    summer chicken and pasta salad 146
aubergines
    baked aubergines with yoghurt 239
    herb-infused vegetable lasagne 83
    lamb kebabs with fig rice 200
    rustic grilled vegetable and rigatoni
        salad 224
    tagliatelle with meatballs 82

avocados 12, 13, 25
    avocado and chicken club sandwich 50
    smoked trout and pasta salad 116

b

bacon 16
    butter beans and bacon on toast with
        red leaf salad 44
    herbed French toast with mushrooms 43
    potato and courgette tortilla 47
    tagliatelle with meatballs 82
bagels 261
    herbed cheese bagels 65
    hot turkey and Stilton bagels 177
baked beans 210
bamboo shoots: Oriental meatball broth 58
bananas 15
    American buttermilk pancakes 37
    banana cake 305
    banana cinnamon muffins 263
    caramelised banana crumpets 42
    cinnamon banana caramels 278
    coronation chicken 145
    lemon banana tart 290
basil
    angel hair pasta with basil and walnut
        pesto 88
    citrus-grilled chicken with melon salsa
        166
    fish steaks en papillote 118
    lemon and basil dressing 250
    marinated duck and kasha salad 172
    Mediterranean stuffed vegetables 199
    pasta and chicken salad with basil 90
    rustic grilled vegetable and rigatoni
        salad 224
    sun-dried tomato and basil crostini 64
    tagliatelle with meatballs 82
    tomato and basil galettes 270
    tomato and basil sauce 171
bean sprouts
    Chinese sea bass with noodles 126
    noodle and omelette salad 225
    Oriental prawn tartlets 71
    scallops with noodles and ginger 137
    sweet and sour chicken pancakes 148
    tamarind and cashew stir-fry 234
    vegetable and wholewheat pan-fry with
        teriyaki tofu 235
béchamel sauce 80

beef
    Argentinian char-grilled steak with
        crisp potatoes 184
    beef in beer 193
    beef salade niçoise 180
    French beef casserole 191
    grilled steak with mustard-glazed
        potatoes 181
    keema curry with cucumber raita 194
    pepper steak with leek mash 182
    roast fillet of beef in red wine 188
    seared sirloin steak with soba 185
    spaghetti bolognese 92
    spicy steak with garlic toasts 192
    stir-fried beef with fine noodles 95
    Sunday special roast beef 186-7
    tagliatelle with meatballs 82
    tender beef with oyster sauce 189
beetroot
    three-vegetable mash 249
    vegetable crisps with peanut dip 66
biscuits
    chocolate chunk and nut cookies 308
    chocolate-nut meringue biscuits 307
    digestive biscuits 311
    oatmeal and raisin cookies 310
black beans: spicy black bean dip 63
blackberries
    blackberry and lemon scones 38
    peach and berry cobbler 274
    upside-down pear pudding 280
blood pressure 11, 17, 20
blueberry cheesecake 302
borlotti beans
    spicy chicken tostadas 153
    Tuscan mixed bean soup 60
brandy sauce 279
bread 14, 15, 19, 22
    avocado and chicken club sandwich 50
    bagels 261
    basic loaf 254
    cinnamon raisin bread 268
    focaccia 260
    garlic and herb bread 193
    garlic toasts 192
    herbed cheese bagels 65
    herbed French toast with mushrooms 43
    light rye bread 256
    malted sultana bread 265
    multigrain seeded loaf 257
    Parmesan croutons 250
    quick wholemeal loaf 255
    roasted vegetable baguettines 51

sesame prawn and crab toasts 69
sourdough bread 258-9
spiced pumpkin teabread 262
sun-dried tomato and basil crostini 64
tomato crostini 57
tomato and ham bruschettas 41
tuna provençale baguette 111
broad beans
    beef salade niçoise 180
    French beef casserole 191
    summer chicken and pasta salad 146
broccoli
    broccoli and cauliflower with tagliatelle
        and blue cheese 230
    broccoli and pearl barley salad 222
    calf's liver with rigatoni and orange 217
    Middle Eastern lentil salad 223
    noodle and omelette salad 225
    prawn and vegetable stir-fry 139
    rice with prawns and dill dressing 102
    spinach and onion soup with crostini 57
    tender beef with oyster sauce 189
buckwheat (kasha): marinated duck and
    kasha salad 172
bulghur wheat
    bulghur and herb pilaf 118
    fresh fruit muesli 35
butter beans and bacon on toast with red
    leaf salad 44
buttermilk
    American buttermilk pancakes 37
    blackberry and lemon scones 38
butternut squash
    roasted vegetable and pasta bake 238
    squash and chickpea stew 231
    Toulouse sausages with Puy lentils 216

C

cabbage
    chicken and potato curry 161
    Greek salad 195
    noodle-stuffed Thai omelette 33
    stir-fried vegetable curry 233
cakes
    banana cake 305
    carrot cake with light soft cheese
        icing 299
    frosted chocolate ring cake 303
    fudgy chocolate brownies 306
    glazed mango sponge 304
    hazelnut meringue cake 294-5
    iced fairy cakes 296
    Spanish orange and almond cake 301
    see also biscuits; scones
calories and kilocalories 18, 25
cannellini beans: baked beans 210

capers
    puttanesca pizzinis 67
    rustic grilled vegetable and rigatoni
        salad 224
    salmon cakes with creamy tomato-garlic
        sauce 77
    smoked trout and pasta salad 116
    spaghetti with puttanesca sauce 89
    tuna and tomato pizza 271
carbohydrates 14, 22
carrots
    apricot lamb with minted couscous 107
    beef in beer 193
    braised baby vegetables 248
    carrot cake with light soft cheese
        icing 299
    cassoulet 208
    Cheshire and root vegetable bake 240
    Chinese sea bass with noodles 126
    cidered pork stew with herb
        dumplings 215
    country vegetable soup with pesto 54
    fish steaks en papillote 118
    French beef casserole 191
    fruity vegetable muffins 39
    ham and celeriac pittas 49
    Irish stew 205
    lamb and barley soup 62
    lamb chops teriyaki-style 198
    noodle and omelette salad 225
    noodle-stuffed Thai omelette 33
    one-pot Japanese chicken 168
    Oriental chicken and pasta salad 91
    Oriental prawn tartlets 71
    pork nasi goreng 211
    roast fillet of beef in red wine 188
    root vegetable mash 210
    shepherd's pie 201
    spaghetti bolognese 92
    spicy peanut salad 75
    stir-fried vegetable curry 233
    trio of warm seafood salad 114
    Tuscan mixed bean soup 60
    veggie burgers 232
cauliflower
    broccoli and cauliflower with tagliatelle
        and blue cheese 230
    cauliflower with herbed crumbs 245
    stir-fried vegetable curry 233
celeriac
    Cheshire and root vegetable bake 240
    ham and celeriac pittas 49
    rösti 218
celery
    apricot lamb with minted couscous 107
    Cajun-spiced barley 106
    cassoulet 208

chicken cacciatore 158
cidered pork stew with herb
    dumplings 215
coronation chicken 145
country vegetable soup with pesto 54
couscous Casablanca 229
golden-roasted chicken with old-
    fashioned stuffing 170
Normandy pork with apples, celery and
    walnuts 212
oaty red lentil gratin 236
Oriental chicken and pasta salad 91
red pepper pick-me-up 28
shepherd's pie 201
spaghetti bolognese 92
trio of warm seafood salad 114
Tuscan mixed bean soup 60
cereals 14, 15, 19, 20, 22
cheese 12, 16, 23, 24
    blueberry cheesecake 302
    broccoli and cauliflower with tagliatelle
        and blue cheese 230
    butter beans and bacon on toast with
        red leaf salad 44
    carrot cake with light soft cheese
        icing 299
    cheese sauce 31
    cheesy rice with asparagus 97
    Cheshire and root vegetable bake 240
    chickpea and feta parcels 243
    egg white omelette with spinach,
        tomato and Cheddar 32
    eggs Florentine 31
    fruity pasta salad 227
    goat's cheese and cranberry tartlets 72
    herb-infused vegetable lasagne 83
    herbed cheese bagels 65
    herbed polenta with Gorgonzola 104
    hot turkey and Stilton bagels 177
    kiwi-berry cheesecake tart 289
    leek and Parma ham pizza muffins 48
    macaroni and mushroom cheese 86
    Middle Eastern lentil salad 223
    oaty red lentil gratin 236
    pepperoni pizza 269
    potato cakes with baked tomatoes 46
    potato and pumpkin gratin 237
    puttanesca pizzinis 67
    rice croquettes with mozzarella 70
    roasted vegetable baguettines 51
    roasted vegetable and pasta bake 238
    turkey burgers with tropical fruit
        salsa 151
    see also Parmesan cheese; ricotta cheese
cherries
    cherry and almond strudel 292
    cherry and pistachio rice pots with cherry
        compote 284

chicken 19, 24
   avocado and chicken club sandwich 50
   chicken with apples and Calvados 165
   chicken with asparagus and pepper 160
   chicken breasts with roasted garlic and
      tomato sauce 155
   chicken cacciatore 158
   chicken fajitas with tomato salsa 154
   chicken with lemongrass 156
   chicken and potato curry 161
   chicken and ricotta cannelloni 96
   chicken and rosemary cobbler 149
   chicken satay salad 144
   chicken and yellow pepper loaf 171
   citrus-grilled chicken with melon salsa
      166
   coronation chicken 145
   dim sum with dipping sauce 74
   golden-roasted chicken with old-
      fashioned stuffing 170
   Hungarian-style chicken meatballs 164
   one-pot Japanese chicken 168
   Oriental chicken and pasta salad 91
   pasta and chicken salad with basil 90
   southeast Asian chicken salad 142
   spicy chicken satay 73
   spicy chicken tostadas 153
   summer chicken and pasta salad 146
   sweet and sour chicken pancakes 148
   teriyaki grilled poussin 167
   Tex-Mex chicken pie 163
chicken livers
   chicken liver and raspberry salad 143
   spaghetti bolognese 92
chickpeas
   chickpea and feta parcels 243
   couscous Casablanca 229
   squash and chickpea stew 231
   Tuscan mixed bean soup 60
chicory: heringsalat 136
chillies
   Cajun-spiced barley 106
   calf's liver with rigatoni and orange 217
   chickpea and feta parcels 243
   citrus-grilled chicken with melon salsa
      166
   Indian lamb with spiced lentils 196
   Indian-style fish parcels 120
   Persian lamb couscous 204
   puttanesca pizzinis 67
   spicy black bean dip 63
   stir-fried beef with fine noodles 95
   teriyaki grilled poussin 167
   Tex-Mex chicken pie 163
   tomato salsa 154
   turkey biryani with cucumber raita 98
   turkey empanadas 150
chimichurri sauce 184

Chinese leaves
   chicken satay salad 144
   fish steaks en papillote 118
   one-pot Japanese chicken 168
   scallops with noodles and ginger 137
   teriyaki-glazed prawn salad 135
chocolate
   chocolate chunk and nut cookies 308
   chocolate-nut meringue biscuits 307
   frosted chocolate ring cake 303
   fudgy chocolate brownies 306
cholesterol 11, 12, 13, 14, 18, 20,
   21, 22, 23, 25
chorizo: smoked fish paella 134
Christmas pudding 279
coconut
   chicken with lemongrass 156
   chicken satay salad 144
   glazed mango sponge 304
   Indian-style fish parcels 120
   spicy chicken satay 73
   stir-fried vegetable curry 233
   Thai green curry with monkfish 130
coronary heart disease (CHD) 10
courgettes
   baked aubergines with yoghurt 239
   broccoli and pearl barley salad 222
   chicken with lemongrass 156
   chicken and yellow pepper loaf 171
   coronation chicken 145
   country vegetable soup with pesto 54
   couscous Casablanca 229
   fruity vegetable muffins 39
   Indian-style fish parcels 120
   lamb kebabs with fig rice 200
   marinated duck and kasha salad 172
   Mediterranean stuffed vegetables 199
   mushroom ravioli in herb jus 84-5
   potato and courgette tortilla 47
   risotto primavera 101
   roasted vegetable baguettines 51
   rustic grilled vegetable and rigatoni
      salad 224
   seafood lasagne 131
   spicy chicken satay 73
   sweet and sour chicken pancakes 148
   teriyaki-glazed prawn salad 135
   vegetable tart Provençale 242
   veggie burgers 232
couscous
   apricot lamb with minted couscous 107
   couscous Casablanca 229
   fennel, apple and herring salad 113
   Persian lamb couscous 204
crab
   creamy tomato and crab soup 61
   sesame prawn and crab toasts 69
cranberries

fruity pasta salad 227
   goat's cheese and cranberry tartlets 72
   venison steaks with pears 218
   very fruity Christmas pudding 279
cucumbers
   baked trout with cucumber sauce 121
   chunky gazpacho with garlic croutons 56
   citrus-grilled chicken with melon salsa
      166
   cucumber and mint salad 117
   cucumber raita 98, 194
   fennel, apple and herring salad 113
   Greek salad 195
   herbed cheese bagels 65
   Japanese sushi rolls 110
   new potato salad 246
   Oriental chicken and pasta salad 91
   Pimm's melon cup 287
   roasted tomato salad 93
   spicy peanut salad 75
curries
   chicken and potato curry 161, 162
   coronation chicken 145
   keema curry with cucumber raita 194
   stir-fried vegetable curry 233
   Thai green curry with monkfish 130
custard 275

d

dates
   fruit and pistachio baklava 293
   Persian lamb couscous 204
   sticky date and walnut pudding 276
   very fruity Christmas pudding 279
desserts
   apricot and rum brioche pudding 277
   blueberry cheesecake 302
   cherry and almond strudel 292
   cherry and pistachio rice pots with cherry
      compote 284
   cinnamon banana caramels 278
   citrus meringue pie 291
   double raspberry sorbet 286
   fruit and pistachio baklava 293
   kiwi-berry cheesecake tart 289
   lemon banana tart 290
   lemon mousse with strawberries 283
   marbled winter fruit fool 282
   peach and berry cobbler 274
   raspberry cranachan 285
   raspberry and passionfruit sponge
      roll 297
   steamed kumquat honey pudding 275
   sticky date and walnut pudding 276
   upside-down pear pudding 280

very fruity Christmas pudding 279
diabetes 11
dim sum with dipping sauce 74
dips
    spicy black bean dip 63
    vegetable crisps with peanut dip 66
dressings
    anchovy dressing 115
    creamy peanut dressing 142
    curry dressing 145
    dill and mustard dressing 113
    garlic and herb dressing 81
    horseradish and caraway dressing 136
    lemon and basil dressing 250
    lemon and coriander dressing 223
    mustard vinaigrette 180
    rice vinegar dressing 225
    spicy peanut dressing 144
    spicy tomato dressing 222
drinks
    citrus wake-up 28
    red pepper pick-me-up 28
duck
    duck and wild mushroom risotto 175
    marinated duck and kasha salad 172
dumplings
    cidered pork stew with herb
        dumplings 215
    pork pot-sticker dumplings with crisp
        and spicy peanut salad 75

e

eggs
    American buttermilk pancakes 37
    egg white omelette with spinach,
        tomato and Cheddar 32
    egg-fried rice 189
    eggs Benedict 30
    eggs Florentine 31
    goat's cheese and cranberry tartlets 72
    herbed French toast with mushrooms 43
    noodle and omelette salad 225
    noodle-stuffed Thai omelette 33
    potato and courgette tortilla 47
    salade niçoise 115
exercise 11, 17, 18

f

fairy cakes, iced 296
fats 12-13, 19, 21, 22, 23, 25
fennel
    fennel, apple and herring salad 113
    fish steaks en papillote 118
    mackerel with gooseberry sauce 124

roasted tomato salad 93
    salade niçoise 115
    seafood lasagne 131
fibre 25
figs
    fresh fruit muesli 35
    lamb kebabs with fig rice 200
fish and seafood 19, 20
    fish steaks en papillote 118
    Indian-style fish parcels 120
    pesto fish cakes 138
    Thai fish cakes with dipping sauce 117
    see also individual varieties
flageolet beans: roast leg of lamb
    with beans 203
flapjacks, orange and sesame 36
focaccia 260
French beans see green beans, French beans
fruit 14, 19
    see also individual fruit

g

garlic 20
    chicken breasts with roasted garlic and
        tomato sauce 155
    garlic and herb bread 193
    garlic and herb dressing 81
    garlic toasts 192
ginger
    chicken with lemongrass 156
    chicken satay salad 144
    Chinese sea bass with noodles 126
    fried rice with tofu and vegetables 99
    gingerbread 298
    Indian lamb with spiced lentils 196
    Indian-style fish parcels 120
    mange-tout with apples and ginger 247
    Oriental meatball broth 58
    Oriental prawn tartlets 71
    Persian lamb couscous 204
    pork pot-sticker dumplings with crisp
        and spicy peanut salad 75
    prawn and vegetable stir-fry 139
    scallops with noodles and ginger 137
    spicy chicken satay 73
    stir-fried vegetable curry 233
    tender beef with oyster sauce 189
    teriyaki swordfish kebabs 129
    Thai fish cakes with dipping sauce 117
    turkey biryani with cucumber raita 98
    vegetable and wholewheat pan-fry with
        teriyaki tofu 235
glycaemic index (GI) 14-15, 20, 25
gooseberries: mackerel with
    gooseberry sauce 124
grapefruit: citrus wake-up 28

green beans, French beans
    beef salade niçoise 180
    chicken with lemongrass 156
    fruity pasta salad 227
    marinated duck and kasha salad 172
    roast leg of lamb with beans 203
    root vegetable mash 210
    salade niçoise 115
    smoked fish paella 134
    see also runner beans

h

haddock
    seafood and mushroom pie 125
    smoked fish paella 134
halibut: trio of warm seafood salad 114
ham
    avocado and chicken club sandwich 50
    eggs Benedict 30
    fruity pasta salad 227
    ham and celeriac pittas 49
    leek and Parma ham pizza muffins 48
    Parma-ham wrapped lemon sole 128
    spaghetti carbonara with roasted
        tomato salad 93
    spinach, ham and asparagus salad with
        rye croutons 209
    teriyaki-glazed prawn salad 135
    tomato and ham bruschettas 41
haricot beans: cassoulet 208
healthy diet 19-24
herrings
    fennel, apple and herring salad 113
    heringsalat 136
homocysteine 11
honey
    American buttermilk pancakes 37
    caramelised banana crumpets 42
    fried rice with tofu and vegetables 99
    fruit and pistachio baklava 293
    grilled steak with mustard-glazed
        potatoes 181
    lamb chops teriyaki-style 198
    lime and honey dipping sauce 117
    malted sultana bread 265
    raspberry cranachan 285
    skate with citrus-honey sauce 122
    spiced pumpkin teabread 262
    steamed kumquat honey pudding 275
    sweet and sour chicken pancakes 148
    teriyaki grilled poussin 167
    vegetable and wholewheat pan-fry with
        teriyaki tofu 235

i–k

Irish stew 205
kidney beans
    Tex-Mex chicken pie 163
    Tuscan mixed bean soup 60
kipper and sweetcorn chowder 55
kiwi fruit
    exotic fruit salad 29
    kiwi-berry cheesecake tart 289
kumquats: steamed kumquat
    honey pudding 275

l

lamb
    apricot lamb with minted couscous 107
    Indian lamb with spiced lentils 196
    Irish stew 205
    lamb and barley soup 62
    lamb chops teriyaki-style 198
    lamb kebabs with fig rice 200
    lamb kebabs with Greek salad 195
    Mediterranean stuffed vegetables 199
    Persian lamb couscous 204
    roast leg of lamb with beans 203
    shepherd's pie 201
leeks
    braised baby vegetables 248
    chicken and ricotta cannelloni 96
    cidered pork stew with herb dumplings 215
    eggs Florentine 31
    kipper and sweetcorn chowder 55
    leek and Parma ham pizza muffins 48
    pepper steak with leek mash 182
    potato cakes with baked tomatoes 46
    roasted vegetable and pasta bake 238
    shepherd's pie 201
    toad-in-the-hole 210
    turkey, pasta and leek crisp 173
    vegetable and wholewheat pan-fry with teriyaki tofu 235
lemongrass
    chicken with lemongrass 156
    stir-fried beef with fine noodles 95
    Thai fish cakes with dipping sauce 117
    Thai green curry with monkfish 130
lemons
    baked trout with cucumber sauce 121
    blackberry and lemon scones 38
    citrus meringue pie 291
    citrus wake-up 28
    lemon banana tart 290
    lemon and basil dressing 250

    lemon and coriander dressing 223
    lemon mousse with strawberries 283
    lemony sugarsnap peas 247
    ponzu sauce 168
lentils
    Indian lamb with spiced lentils 196
    Middle Eastern lentil salad 223
    oaty red lentil gratin 236
    shepherd's pie 201
    Toulouse sausages with Puy lentils 216
limes
    chicken with lemongrass 156
    chicken satay salad 144
    Chinese sea bass with noodles 126
    citrus meringue pie 291
    citrus wake-up 28
    citrus-grilled chicken with melon salsa 166
    lime and honey dipping sauce 117
    ponzu sauce 168
    spicy steak with garlic toasts 192
    teriyaki swordfish kebabs 129
    Thai green curry with monkfish 130
linseeds 20-1
liver
    calf's liver with rigatoni and orange 217
    see also chicken livers
lychees: southeast Asian chicken salad 142

m

mackerel with gooseberry sauce 124
mange-tout
    chicken satay salad 144
    mange-tout with apples and ginger 247
    mushroom ravioli in herb jus 84-5
    one-pot Japanese chicken 168
    Oriental meatball broth 58
    Oriental prawn tartlets 71
    pasta and chicken salad with basil 90
    prawn and vegetable stir-fry 139
    rice with prawns and dill dressing 102
    southeast Asian chicken salad 142
    stir-fried beef with fine noodles 95
    stir-fried pork with Chinese greens 214
    teriyaki swordfish kebabs 129
mangoes
    coronation chicken 145
    exotic fruit salad 29
    fruit and pistachio baklava 293
    glazed mango sponge 304
    turkey burgers with tropical fruit salsa 151
maple syrup: orange-maple sweet potatoes 251
meatballs
    Hungarian-style chicken meatballs 164

    rice and pork meatballs 58
    tagliatelle with meatballs 82
melons
    citrus-grilled chicken with melon salsa 166
    Pimm's melon cup 287
monkfish
    seafood paella 103
    Thai green curry with monkfish 130
muesli, fresh fruit 35
muffins
    banana cinnamon muffins 263
    eggs Benedict 30
    fruity vegetable muffins 39
    leek and Parma ham pizza muffins 48
mung beans: stir-fried vegetable curry 233
mushrooms
    apricot lamb with minted couscous 107
    chicken cacciatore 158
    chicken and rosemary cobbler 149
    dim sum with dipping sauce 74
    duck and wild mushroom risotto 175
    French beef casserole 191
    herb-infused vegetable lasagne 83
    herbed French toast with mushrooms 43
    Hungarian-style chicken meatballs 164
    macaroni and mushroom cheese 86
    mushroom ravioli in herb jus 84-5
    noodle-stuffed Thai omelette 33
    oaty red lentil gratin 236
    one-pot Japanese chicken 168
    Oriental meatball broth 58
    pepperoni pizza 269
    pork nasi goreng 211
    roast fillet of beef in red wine 188
    rustic grilled vegetable and rigatoni salad 224
    salmon koulibiac 132
    scallops with noodles and ginger 137
    seafood and mushroom pie 125
    seared sirloin steak with soba 185
    stir-fried beef with fine noodles 95
    turkey escalopes with chestnut mushrooms and Madeira 176
    venison bangers and mash 219
mussels
    seafood paella 103
    trio of warm seafood salad 114
mustard
    barbecued prawns with mustard sauce 136
    dill and mustard dressing 113
    grilled steak with mustard-glazed potatoes 181
    mustard vinaigrette 180
    sticky pork spare ribs 206

n

nectarines
  muesli, fresh fruit 35
  waffles with glazed nectarines 40
noodles
  Chinese sea bass with noodles 126
  lamb chops teriyaki-style 198
  noodle and omelette salad 225
  noodle-stuffed Thai omelette 33
  one-pot Japanese chicken 168
  scallops with noodles and ginger 137
  seared sirloin steak with soba 185
  stir-fried beef with fine noodles 95
  stir-fried pork with Chinese greens 214
  tamarind and cashew stir-fry 234
  teriyaki swordfish kebabs 129
nuts 12, 13, 15, 19, 21, 25
  cherry and pistachio rice pots with cherry
    compote 284
  chocolate chunk and nut cookies 308
  coronation chicken 145
  fennel, apple and herring salad 113
  fresh fruit muesli 35
  fruit and pistachio baklava 293
  hazelnut meringue cake 294-5
  Parma-ham wrapped lemon sole 128
  peach and berry cobbler 274
  Persian lamb couscous 204
  tamarind and cashew stir-fry 234
  see also almonds; peanuts; walnuts

o

oats, oatmeal 20, 22
  blueberry cheesecake 302
  digestive biscuits 311
  fresh fruit muesli 35
  goat's cheese and cranberry tartlets 72
  oatmeal and raisin cookies 310
  oaty red lentil gratin 236
  orange and sesame flapjacks 36
  raspberry cranachan 285
oils 12, 13, 22
olives
  beef salade niçoise 180
  chicken and rosemary cobbler 149
  ham and celeriac pittas 49
  marinated duck and kasha salad 172
  pasta and chicken salad with basil 90
  pork medallions with peppers 207
  puttanesca pizzinis 67
  salade niçoise 115
  spaghetti with puttanesca sauce 89
  tuna provençale baguette 111
  tuna and tomato pizza 271

oranges
  baked trout with cucumber sauce 121
  calf's liver with rigatoni and orange 217
  citrus meringue pie 291
  citrus wake-up 28
  iced fairy cakes 296
  kiwi-berry cheesecake tart 289
  marbled winter fruit fool 282
  orange and sesame flapjacks 36
  orange-maple sweet potatoes 251
  pork medallions with peppers 207
  skate with citrus-honey sauce 122
  smoked trout and pasta salad 116
  southeast Asian chicken salad 142
  Spanish orange and almond cake 301
  sticky pork spare ribs 206
  teriyaki-glazed prawn salad 135

p

pak choy
  fish steaks en papillote 118
  noodle and omelette salad 225
  Oriental prawn tartlets 71
  stir-fried pork with Chinese greens 214
  tamarind and cashew stir-fry 234
pancakes
  American buttermilk pancakes 37
  sweet and sour chicken pancakes 148
papayas: exotic fruit salad 29
Parmesan cheese
  crispy lace potatoes 244
  Parmesan croutons 250
  tomato and basil galettes 270
  vegetable tart Provençale 242
parsnips
  beef in beer 193
  braised baby vegetables 248
  Cheshire and root vegetable bake 240
  French beef casserole 191
  root vegetable mash 210
  shepherd's pie 201
  stir-fried vegetable curry 233
passionfruits
  fresh fruit muesli 35
  raspberry and passionfruit sponge
    roll 297
pasta 14, 15, 19
  angel hair pasta with basil and walnut
    pesto 88
  broccoli and cauliflower with tagliatelle
    and blue cheese 230
  calf's liver with rigatoni and orange 217
  chicken and ricotta cannelloni 96
  fruity pasta salad 227
  herb-infused vegetable lasagne 83
  linguine with no-cook sauce 88

  macaroni and mushroom cheese 86
  mushroom ravioli in herb jus 84-5
  pasta and chicken salad with basil 90
  pumpkin, ricotta and sage gnocchi 87
  roasted vegetable and pasta bake 238
  rustic grilled vegetable and rigatoni
    salad 224
  seafood lasagne 131
  seafood and mushroom pie 125
  smoked trout and pasta salad 116
  spaghetti bolognese 92
  spaghetti carbonara with roasted
    tomato salad 93
  spaghetti with puttanesca sauce 89
  summer chicken and pasta salad 146
  tagliatelle with meatballs 82
  turkey, pasta and leek crisp 173
peaches
  marbled winter fruit fool 282
  muesli, fresh fruit 35
  peach and berry cobbler 274
peanuts
  chicken satay salad 144
  southeast Asian chicken salad 142
  spicy chicken satay 73
  spicy peanut salad 75
  vegetable crisps with peanut dip 66
  veggie burgers 232
pearl barley
  broccoli and pearl barley salad 222
  Cajun-spiced barley 106
  lamb and barley soup 62
pears
  fruity pasta salad 227
  upside-down pear pudding 280
  venison steaks with pears 218
peas
  cheesy rice with asparagus 97
  chicken and potato curry 161
  chicken and ricotta cannelloni 96
  egg-fried rice 189
  macaroni and mushroom cheese 86
  pork nasi goreng 211
  risotto primavera 101
  seafood lasagne 131
  seafood paella 103
  smoked fish paella 134
  stir-fried vegetable curry 233
  see also mange-tout; sugarsnap peas
peppers
  Cajun-spiced barley 106
  char-grilled asparagus and peppers 250
  chicken with asparagus and pepper 160
  chicken fajitas with tomato salsa 154
  chicken and potato curry 161
  chicken and rosemary cobbler 149
  chicken and yellow pepper loaf 171

chunky gazpacho with garlic croutons 56
green coriander rice 100
Hungarian-style chicken meatballs 164
lamb chops teriyaki-style 198
macaroni and mushroom cheese 86
Mediterranean stuffed vegetables 199
Middle Eastern lentil salad 223
noodle and omelette salad 225
noodle-stuffed Thai omelette 33
Oriental chicken and pasta salad 91
pork medallions with peppers 207
prawn and vegetable stir-fry 139
red pepper pick-me-up 28
rice with prawns and dill dressing 102
risotto primavera 101
roasted vegetable baguettines 51
rustic grilled vegetable and rigatoni
    salad 224
salade niçoise 115
seafood paella 103
sesame prawn and crab toasts 69
smoked trout and pasta salad 116
spicy chicken satay 73
spicy chicken tostadas 153
spicy steak with garlic toasts 192
summer chicken and pasta salad 146
tamarind and cashew stir-fry 234
tender beef with oyster sauce 189
teriyaki swordfish kebabs 129
Tex-Mex chicken pie 163
Thai green curry with monkfish 130
tuna provençale baguette 111
turkey and spinach roulades 159
vegetable and wholewheat pan-fry with
    teriyaki tofu 235
venison bangers and mash 219
pesto
    angel hair pasta with basil and walnut
        pesto 88
    country vegetable soup with pesto 54
    pesto fish cakes 138
    pesto sauce 81
    tomato and ham bruschettas 41
Pimm's melon cup 287
pineapples
    fruity pasta salad 227
    pineapple and marmalade sauce 276
    turkey burgers with tropical fruit
        salsa 151
pizzas
    pepperoni pizza 269
    puttanesca pizzinis 67
    tuna and tomato pizza 271
plums: southeast Asian chicken salad 142
polenta: herbed polenta with
    Gorgonzola 104
pork
    cassoulet 208

cidered pork stew with herb dumplings
    215
Normandy pork with apples, celery and
    walnuts 212
pork medallions with peppers 207
pork nasi goreng 211
pork pot-sticker dumplings with crisp
    and spicy peanut salad 75
rice and pork meatballs 58
sticky pork spare ribs 206
stir-fried pork with Chinese greens 214
toad-in-the-hole 210
portion sizes 18
potatoes 14, 15, 19
    Argentinian char-grilled steak with crisp
        potatoes 184
    baked trout with cucumber sauce 121
    beef salade niçoise 180
    Cheshire and root vegetable bake 240
    chicken and potato curry 161
    chickpea and feta parcels 243
    cidered pork stew with herb dumplings
        215
    creamy tomato and crab soup 61
    crispy lace potatoes 244
    grilled steak with mustard-glazed
        potatoes 181
    heringsalat 136
    Hungarian-style chicken meatballs 164
    Indian-style fish parcels 120
    Irish stew 205
    keema curry with cucumber raita 194
    kipper and sweetcorn chowder 55
    mackerel with gooseberry sauce 124
    new potato salad 246
    olive oil mash 219
    pepper steak with leek mash 182
    pesto fish cakes 138
    potato cakes with baked tomatoes 46
    potato and courgette tortilla 47
    potato and pumpkin gratin 237
    potato scones 267
    roast salmon strips with potato salad 76
    rösti 218
    salade niçoise 115
    seafood and mushroom pie 125
    shepherd's pie 201
    skate with citrus-honey sauce 122
    stir-fried vegetable curry 233
    Thai fish cakes with dipping sauce 117
    Thai green curry with monkfish 130
    three-vegetable mash 249
    Toulouse sausages with Puy lentils 216
    turkey empanadas 150
    vegetable crisps with peanut dip 66
prawns
    barbecued prawns with mustard
        sauce 136

Oriental prawn tartlets 71
pork nasi goreng 211
prawn and vegetable stir-fry 139
rice with prawns and dill dressing 102
seafood lasagne 131
seafood and mushroom pie 125
sesame prawn and crab toasts 69
teriyaki-glazed prawn salad 135
prunes
    frosted chocolate ring cake 303
    marbled winter fruit fool 282
pulses 14, 19
    see also individual varieties
pumpkin
    couscous Casablanca 229
    potato and pumpkin gratin 237
    pumpkin, ricotta and sage gnocchi 87
    spiced pumpkin teabread 262

r

raisins and sultanas
    apricot and rum brioche pudding 277
    banana cake 305
    chickpea and feta parcels 243
    cinnamon raisin bread 268
    coronation chicken 145
    couscous Casablanca 229
    fruity vegetable muffins 39
    malted sultana bread 265
    oatmeal and raisin cookies 310
    spiced pumpkin teabread 262
    squash and chickpea stew 231
    turkey biryani with cucumber raita 98
    turkey empanadas 150
    very fruity Christmas pudding 279
raspberries
    chicken liver and raspberry salad 143
    double raspberry sorbet 286
    hazelnut meringue cake 294-5
    peach and berry cobbler 274
    raspberry cranachan 285
    raspberry and passionfruit sponge
        roll 297
rice 14, 15, 19
    cheesy rice with asparagus 97
    cherry and pistachio rice pots with cherry
        compote 284
    chicken satay salad 144
    coronation chicken 145
    duck and wild mushroom risotto 175
    egg-fried rice 189
    fried rice with tofu and vegetables 99
    green coriander rice 100
    Japanese sushi rolls 110
    lamb kebabs with fig rice 200
    Mediterranean stuffed vegetables 199